BRITISH WARSHIP DESIGN

SELECTED PAPERS ON
BRITISH WARSHIP DESIGN
IN WORLD WAR II

from
the Transactions of the
Royal Institution of Naval Architects

by R Baker, W J Holt, J Lenaghan,
A J Sims and A W Watson

Foreword by Admiral Sir Anthony Griffin,
President of the RINA

CONWAY

MARITIME PRESS

© The Royal Institution of Naval Architects 1947 and 1983
This edition first published 1983 by
Conway Maritime Press Ltd,
24 Bride Lane, Fleet Street,
London EC4Y 8DR

ISBN 0 85177 284 6

New layout and jacket design by Dave Mills

Printed and bound in the United Kingdom by
R J Acford, Chichester

CONTENTS

FOREWORD

Since its founding in 1860 The Royal Institution of Naval Architects has published many papers on the design and construction of warships of most types and sizes, from early steam-and-sail ironclads to nuclear-powered, missile-armed submarines. Hitherto this source of contemporary thought, experiment, experience, data and discussion, written and debated by those who were responsible for or engaged in the design and construction of the ships and vessels, has been available only to members of the Institution and to those who purchased the various volumes of the Institution's *Transactions* in which the papers were published.

With ever increasing interest in the history of the development of the warship, The Royal Institution of Naval Architects has arranged with Conway Maritime Press Ltd for selected papers to be published, grouped in period and types of ship. This first volume of the series entitled *British Warship Design in World War II* contains papers on several types of ships and craft designed and built during the period 1939-1945 and presents the views of those concerned with their conception, construction and use, affording a unique insight into the problems facing their designers and builders and the success or otherwise of their operation. Interest in these papers has been sustained since their original publication just after the war and copies of the originals have long been exhausted.

It is therefore with particular pleasure that as President of The Royal Institution of Naval Architects I introduce this volume on *British Warship Design in World War II* to a wider public and hope it will be followed by others on warship design from several countries, selected from the Institution's archives.

> Admiral Sir Anthony Griffin
> President

PUBLISHER'S NOTE

The papers reprinted in this volume were originally published in the 1947 quarterly *Transactions* of the Institution (from 1960 the Royal Institution) of Naval Architects. The selected papers are complete, and include the extremely valuable discussions which followed each paper, as well as all the original photographs, line drawings and plans. The only substantial alteration has been to change the position of some of the illustrations and to reduce the size of certain plans to fit more neatly into the page format. Naturally, this volume has been given a new sequence of page numbers.

The Royal Institution of Naval Architects points out that it is not responsible for statements made or opinions expressed by individual authors or speakers.

Ships of the Invasion Fleet
by R Baker, OBE, RCNC, MINA

Originally published in *Transactions*, Volume 89, Number 1,
January 1947, pages 50-72

SHIPS OF THE INVASION FLEET

By R. BAKER, O.B.E., R.C.N.C., Member*

(*Read in Glasgow at the Joint Autumn Meeting of the Institution of Naval Architects and Institution of Engineers and Shipbuilders in Scotland, September 24, 1946, Admiral of the Fleet The Right Hon. Lord Chatfield, G.C.B., O.M., K.C.M.G., C.V.O. (President, I.N.A.) in the Chair.)*

Summary

The paper gives brief particulars of the principal classes of landing ships together with short explanations of the main technical problems occurring in their development. It does not deal with landing craft or barges, except in so far as some of the types described are landing craft carriers. Beside other information the paper includes descriptive photographs and general arrangement drawings. It is mainly a record of what was done in this direction during the war, but mention is made of certain special points which may have a general future interest.

Introduction

Before the war landing ships did not exist; even the names of the types referred to in this paper were unknown. Combined operations had, of course, been considered by the naval staffs before the war began, but the actual developments were on a scale which far transcended anything formerly envisaged, and the main impetus of this development only occurred after the early German successes had made it certain that the western allies would need at some time or other to undertake a major invasion operation on the coast of Europe.

The programme then undertaken to build up the fleet, which was in many ways quite separate and different from ordinary warships, began with the conversion of existing mercantile ships and ended with the design and construction of special types. It began in a small way in this country and ended with the Americans devoting a very large part of their productive resources to it. None of the types developed was perhaps entirely satisfactory as seen in the light of experience, but on the other hand, no type failed and no ship was ever given up by Combined Operations after they had acquired her.

The Japanese in their attacks on China had found it necessary to employ landing craft and landing-craft carriers, but no other navy at that time possessed any ships specially designed for the purpose. The intelligence reports on the Japanese ships occasionally led to suggestions that the British should make similar provision, but the reports were never very concrete and, although some study was given to the problem, nothing resulted except certain plans for the conversion of passenger liners or troopers to assault ships. The conversion then envisaged mainly involved the provision of accommodation for the troops and carrying of suitable assault boats at their davits together with fuel for them; in fact,

no suitable assault boat had been produced when the war broke out. Certain ships had, however, been earmarked as being suitable for conversion to carriers.

The developments described in this paper began in 1940, and from then on the ships used in the Combined Operations naval fleet fell into five main groups.

Group I.—Ships for carrying the infantry with their assaulting craft.

These were originally known as Infantry Assault Ships, later on as Landing Ships Infantry or L.S.I. This group was subsequently sub-divided into:

Landing Ship Infantry, Large	L.S.I.(L)
Landing Ship Infantry, Medium	L.S.I.(M)
Landing Ship Infantry, Small	L.S.I.(S)
Landing Ship Infantry, Hand Hoisting	L.S.I.(H)

Group II.—Ships for carrying the assault craft in bulk, i.e. landing craft carriers.

These were divided into four main types:

Landing Ship Stern Chute	L.S.S.
Landing Ship Gantry	L.S.G.
Landing Ship Dock	L.S.D.
Landing Ship Carrier	L.S.C.

Group III.—Ships primarily intended for the carriage of tanks and motor transport to be landed directly on to the beaches.

This group was by far the most important so far as numbers were concerned, and is divided into three principal types:

Landing Ship Tank, Mark I	L.S.T.(1)
Mark II	L.S.T.(2)
Mark III	L.S.T.(3)

Of these L.S.T.(1) includes two separate classes.

Group IV.—Headquarters ships.

Group V.—Miscellaneous, which included fighter direction tenders, fighter direction ships, repair ships, etc.

The present paper deals only, and very briefly, with Groups I to III. The first ships of each of these groups appeared in the order given above, and although within each group development once begun was continuous

---

* Chief Constructor Naval Construction Department, Admiralty.

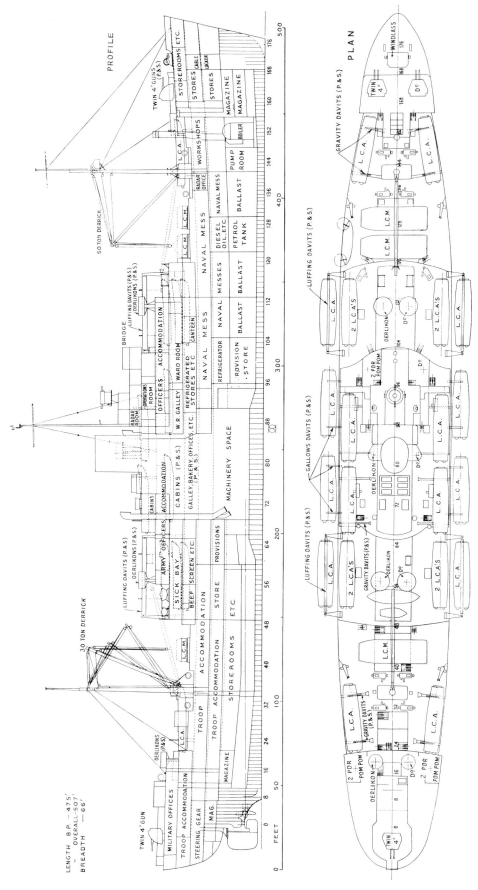

FIG. 1.—"GLEN" CLASS L.S.I.(L.)

throughout the war, the paper deals with them group by group.

Group I.—Types of Landing Ship Infantry or L.S.I.

All of these ships were conversions of available mercantile tonnage, and certain ships had been earmarked for this purpose before the war began, but the landing ship requirement did not arise until the war had been in progress for several months, and in consequence the ships originally earmarked were not available because they had already been put to various other naval uses. The first L.S.I. was asked for in April 1940. The choice was restricted, but the first ships actually fitted were three of the Glen Line, *Glengyle*, *Glenearn*, and *Glenroy*. From the date when these ships were taken over until the end of the war the L.S.I. was continually being improved in detail, but there is no doubt that the Glens, which were large modern ships, were admirably suited for the purpose envisaged.

Prior to this date the three ships had already been taken over by the Admiralty for a special job and a large amount of conversion work had been done on them. This included additional sub-division and the provision of an anti-aircraft armament. The technical problems involved in the actual conversion to L.S.I. were of a straightforward nature, and resolved themselves mainly into the appropriate groupings of the davits and lifting gear, and the arrangement of the troops' accommodation, including washplaces, lavatories, stores, and workshops. The assault craft which they had to carry was the assault landing craft which had been developed towards the end of 1939. This craft subsequently became standard and was known as the L.C.A. Welin-McLachlan davits were fitted to lift these boats which at that time had an all-up weight of about 10 tons; in fact, the boats had been designed to be within this limit so that it might be possible to lift them at the davits of commercial passenger vessels. Provision was also made for motor landing craft, later known as L.C.M., to be carried on as deck cargo and hoisted out by derricks.

The principal original particulars of the class were:—

Length overall	511 ft.
Beam extreme	66 ft. 6 in.
Gross Registered Tonnage ..	9,880
Horse-power	12,000
Type of Machinery	Twin Screw Diesel.

The first of these ships was taken over for her new service in April 1940 and at that time was fitted out to carry:—

Army Personnel	87 officers, 1,000 men
Landing-Craft Crews ..	12 officers, 220 men
Ship's Complement ..	28 officers, 263 men
Gravity Davits	12 sets each capable of lifting 10 tons
Assault Landing Craft (L.C.A.)	12
Mechanized Landing Craft (L.C.M.)	2 Derrick hoisted

In addition the fuel stowage had been increased to about 1,500 tons, giving an endurance of about 15,000 miles at 14 knots.

Fig. 1 is an outline general arrangement of the ships up-to-date at the end of the war.

Fig. 20 is a photograph of *Glenroy*.

Fig. 2 indicates the lay-out of a typical army mess, and

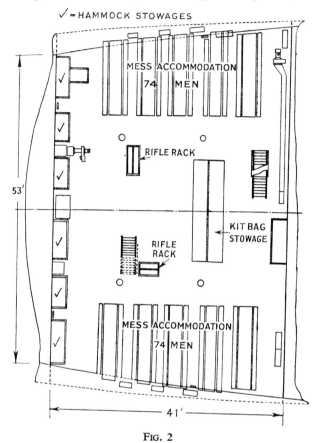

FIG. 2

Fig. 21 a photograph showing details of the type of davit originally provided.

The conversion of the Glens was only a beginning, but the next vessels to be used were of a completely different type. They were the Dutch cross-channel ships which had become available after the invasion of the Low Countries. Two of these ships, *Princess Beatrix* and *Queen Emma*, were fitted out as Landing Ship Infantry Medium, or L.S.I.(M). These ships had been built for operation in sheltered waters only and their carrying capacity was small. The naval requirements represented a very big increase in load and demanded that they should be used all over the world. This made it necessary that steps should be taken to improve their strength and seaworthiness concurrently with the provision of the troop accommodation and the davits.

The ships were practically stripped down and re-built above the upper deck. Additional oil fuel and fresh water tanks were built and petrol for the L.C.A. was carried in special cylindrical tanks with a delivery line to positions near the davits.

Cast-iron fittings in the main services were replaced in

fabricated steel; bulkhead valves were fitted to all main pipes and non-return valves to the ends of suction lines. Geared storm valves were fitted where scuppers, etc., passed through the ship's side.

The watertight doors in the machinery space bulkheads and in the tunnels were removed and the openings blanked off.

The L.C.M. which had been carried on deck and lifted by derricks in the Glens were davit lifted in these two ships. This necessitated the provision of gravity type davits very much stronger than had ever been used before. The advantage of carrying such heavy boats in davits was that they could be launched more quickly and could in fact be used in an assault with the assault boats, but the davit hoisting of the craft did not solve the problem of how they were to be loaded with vehicles, and although the L.C.M. davits were kept in these ships throughout the whole of their service career, such davits did not become standard and other methods, which will be described later, had to be evolved for providing L.C.M. in the assault areas.

Fig. 3 illustrates the general arrangement adopted and Fig. 22 is a photograph of *Princess Beatrix*.

The principal particulars of these ships were:—

Length overall	.. ..	380 ft. (*Princess Beatrix* 380 ft. 9 in.)
Beam	.. ..	47 ft. 2½ in.
Gross Registered Tonnage		4,135
Horse-power	.. ..	13,000
Type of Machinery	..	Twin Screw Diesel
Speed	.. ..	22 knots

The ships were fitted out to carry:—

Army personnel	..	22 officers, 350 men
Landing-Craft Crews	..	5 officers, 55 men
Ship's Complement	..	20 officers, 147 men
Gravity Davits	..	6—10-ton 2—30 ton
L.C.A.	.. ..	6
L.C.M.	.. ..	2 (at davits)

The next step in provision of L.S.I. was the conversion of the Belgian cross-channel ships to L.S.I.(S). These conversions differed only from the L.S.I.(M) in that the ships were smaller still; no provision was made for L.C.M. and eight L.C.A. only were carried in gravity davits.

The structural work involved was not quite so extensive as in the Dutch ships, and consisted of closing up the baggage ports amidships and aft, the fitting of steel weather-tight doors to openings in the super-structure, fitting steel covers to hatches on the weather deck, and blanking off side scuttles in "E" deck. A new small baggage port was provided amidships, port and starboard, and to compensate for the loss of strength doubling plates were fitted to the shell and deck in way of the doors for a length of about 30-feet, and the stringer angles

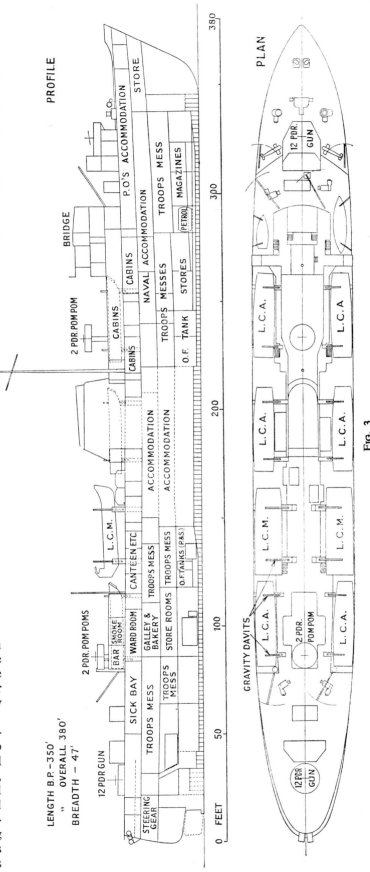

Fig. 3

6

amidships were increased in size. Miscellaneous safety measures were taken as before.

The load draught of the ships after conversion was about two feet greater than when on their original service and care had to be taken that no further nett increase in load took place.

Fig. 4 illustrates the general arrangement of *Prince Baudouin* and Fig. 23 is a photograph of *Princess Astrid*.

The first L.S.I.(H) were also fitted out in 1940. They

was augmented by numbers of passenger and intermediate liners, which were taken up by the Ministry of War Transport as troopers and fitted out temporarily as L.S.I. Such ships wore the red ensign and were dealt with generally by the Director of Sea Transport.

As the war progressed the specifications for the L.S.I. continually increased. These were generally on the lines of trying to carry more troops in each ship and therefore more assault boats in each ship. Further, the L.C.A.

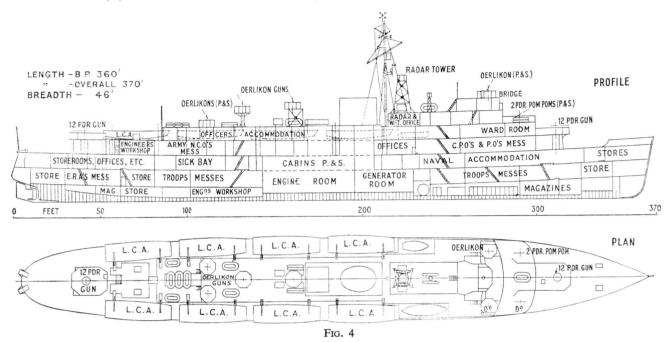

FIG. 4

were conversions of *Royal Scotsman*, *Royal Ulsterman*, and *Ulster Monarch*. The arrangements already existing in these ships made it impracticable to fit gravity davits, so the L.C.A. were carried outboard under spurs. These ships were really improvisations, but they continued in service until the end of the war.

Principal particulars of *Royal Scotsman* and *Royal Ulsterman* were :—

Length overall	340 ft.
Beam	47 ft. 6 in.
Gross Registered Tonnage	3,244
Horse-power	5,200
Type of Machinery ..	Twin-Screw Diesel
Speed	16 knots

They were fitted out to carry :—

Army personnel ..	40–80 officers, 450–750 men
Landing-Craft Crews	14 officers, 68 men
Ship's Complement ..	21 officers, 127 men
L.C.A.	6 officers

Fig. 24 is a photograph of *Ulster Monarch*.

The ships so briefly described formed the basis of all the L.S.I.s used during the war, and the principles developed in them served as a guide in subsequent conversions. When specific operations were being prepared this fleet

itself was much improved as the war went on. The weight of the troops' equipment also increased, so that the original all-up weight of the L.C.A. (10 tons) was at the end of the war almost 14 tons. This involved providing more davits of a heavier pattern, and led to demands that the layout of the davits should be modified so that each set of davits could deal with more than one boat. The gravity davit originally fitted was not advantageous in this respect, as without going to a lot of trouble to fit portable bearers it was impossible for them to do other than lift the boat and stow it. An arrangement, however, was fitted in certain American ships so that each set of davits could deal with 3 boats, one in the davits and two in chocks beneath them. This American davit was similar to the gravity davit but with a cross beam at the head.

Development in this country was on somewhat different lines, but towards the end of the war we were fitting luffing davits of the cross beam type, by using which it was possible to carry one boat slung in the davit outboard and two in cradles one above the other, so that each davit could deal with 3 L.C.A. Fig. 5 indicates the details of this davit as finally fitted in the Glens. The photograph of the *Glenroy* (Fig. 20) was taken at a time after these davits had been installed.

The constant use of comparatively heavy boats under variable weather conditions and during operations led to

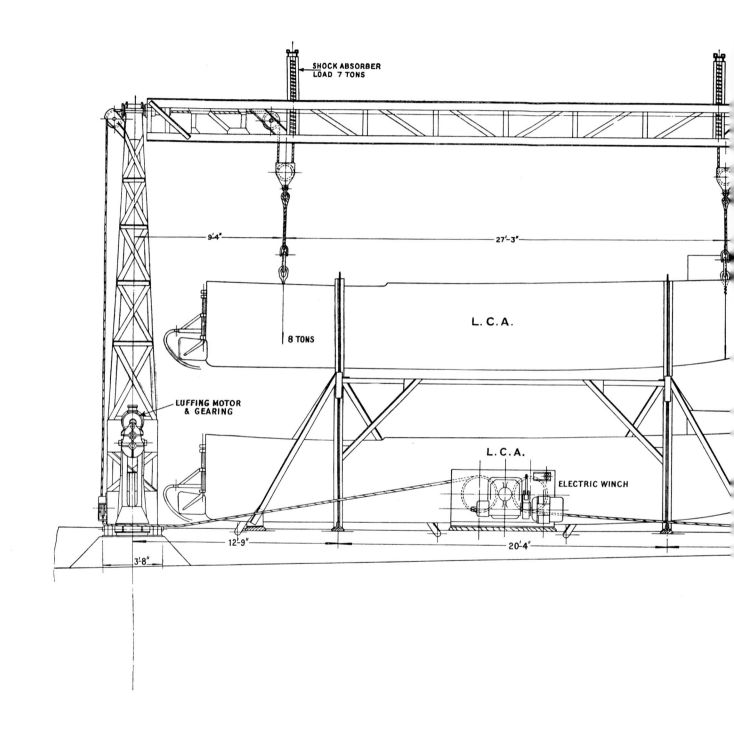

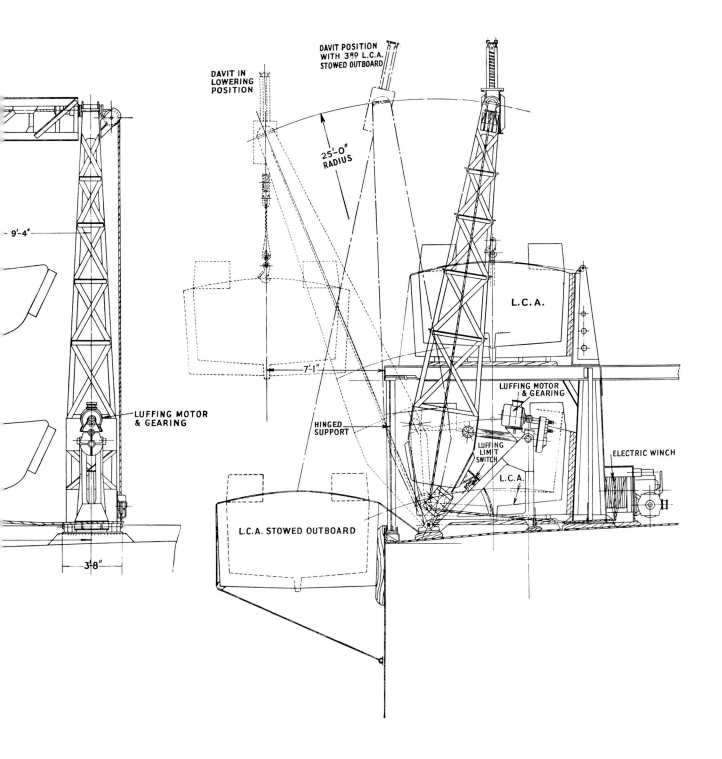

DAVIT IN
LOWERING
POSITION

DAVIT POSITION
WITH 3RD L.C.A.
STOWED OUTBOARD

25'-0"
RADIUS

9'-4"

7'-1"

HINGED
SUPPORT

LUFFING MOTOR
& GEARING

LUFFING MOTOR
& GEARING

LUFFING
LIMIT
SWITCH

L.C.A.

L.C.A.

ELECTRIC WINCH

3'-8"

L.C.A. STOWED OUTBOARD

Fig. 5.

a great deal of study being given to methods of slinging the craft. Davits themselves are well suited for this work when the type of boat is standard, but the American assault boats had slinging positions differently spaced from those in our own boats, which meant that if American boats were used in our ships spreaders were necessary.

selves and the davit hooks were also developed. It was found best to replace chain boat slings by rigid bars. No suitable automatic disengaging gear was produced in spite of prolonged study, but the davits were fitted finally with a specially designed self-locking or moused hook. This hook is illustrated in Fig. 6.

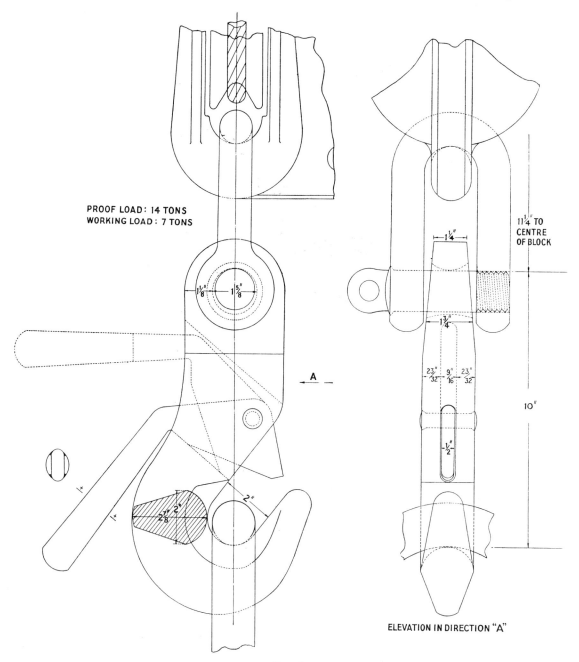

PROOF LOAD: 14 TONS
WORKING LOAD: 7 TONS

ELEVATION IN DIRECTION "A"

Fig. 6

One advantage of the luffing type of davit finally fitted appears to be that with a very small additional complication it would be possible to vary the point of suspension so as to suit any boat that could pass between the legs of the davit.

This question of the method of slinging the boats is not entirely a davit question, but the boats' slings themselves and the davit hooks were also developed.

Before leaving the L.S.I. one outstanding operational difficulty must be referred to. By reason of the nature of the development it was never possible to assemble a homogeneous squadron of L.S.I. A close approach was, however, made to this when in 1943 12 C.I.B. type cargo liners building in America were acquired by the Ministry of War Transport and completed by their builders as red ensign L.S.I. Some of these ships were later on taken over, and after further modification manned by the Royal Navy, and at the end of the war these ships and the Glens represented the last stages in the development of the type.

Group II.—Ships for carrying Assault Craft in bulk

For a comparatively small operation the L.S.I. with its troops, a certain amount of transport, the L.C.A. and the L.C.M. represented a self-contained unit. The troops would be landed in the assault boats, their vehicles and stores by the L.C.M., which would run a ferry service between ship and shore. It is clear that for anything other than a short raid the build-up on shore provided by one or two L.C.M. would be very slow. The realization that this build-up would be too slow created a demand for each L.S.I. to be provided with more L.C.M. than she herself could carry. This problem became more acute in any operation where M.T. ships or freighters were envisaged as taking part with the L.S.I. The problem had been studied before the war by the Japanese, who had produced one or two classes of landing craft transports. In Japanese ships their equivalent of our L.C.M. was carried on the 'tween deck and put into the water by a transporter arrangement working through side ports. This scheme was considered by the Admiralty early in 1940, but little progress was made with it, as it was felt that time would not permit building a special vessel, and we were unable to find a ship suitable for conversion. Other methods had to be adopted; they were:—

(a) *Landing Ship Stern Chute or L.S.S.*—The conception was that landing craft should be carried on deck and launched into the water. The conception was not entirely new, as before the war some thought had been given to the possibility of using whale factory ships for this purpose. Great difficulties were expected with such vessels because of the height of the deck, the steepness of the existing ramps, and the difficulty of altering this slope. However, after the invasion of the Low Countries two L.N.E.R. train ferries were found to be available. They had open decks, moderate freeboard, and when it was found that the propeller shafts were widely spaced it seemed possible that landing craft carried on the deck might be launched into the water through a chute cut in the stern. It was at first proposed that the landing craft should be skidded about the deck and launched over greased ways, but no satisfactory control system for such arrangement could be devised. It was then decided to carry the craft on trolleys running on special rails laid on the deck; the remaining doubt was whether the craft could be satisfactorily launched at sea into a channel as restricted as the one it was possible to provide. This point was checked by full-scale trials carried out by Messrs. Thornycroft in their yard at Woolston. A mock-up of the proposed chute together with its boundary bulkheads was built in the yard and a landing craft successfully hauled up and launched from it.

Once the underlying idea of the conversion had proved practicable the ships were ideally suitable for conversion. When used for the carriage of rolling stock a system of rails and points enabled four rows of trucks to be carried, and it was thought at first that three rows of L.C.M. could have been dealt with in the same way. In the final arrangement, however, points had to be given up because the overhang of the craft fouled the compartments at the ship's side. The craft were therefore stowed in three rows. Launching took place from the middle row only and craft from the side rows were got into the middle by first being hauled forwards to a traversing trolley which moved them from the side to the middle.

The launching was complicated because after each launch it was necessary to recover the trolley which was held by a stop at the bottom of the chute. A very great deal of thought had to be given to the details of the trolleys and of their hauling arrangements, the details of which were worked out by Messrs. Thornycroft, who subsequently undertook the conversion in the docks at Southampton. The ships were in hand during the worst of the bombing there and finally completed early in 1941. Immediately after completion they were put into service ferrying landing craft from port to port, and it was found that although intended for L.C.M. all other types of minor landing craft could be carried satisfactorily. The ships as it turned out, were never used in an assault role. This was largely because of their low endurance and low effective freeboard. When originally built (to Admiralty order) during the 1914–18 war they had boilers fitted for dual firing. During the conversion oil firing gear only was installed, and although the fuel stowage was considerably increased at this time, their endurance on naval service was only 1,350 miles at 11½ knots. Great fears were expressed in connection with their vulnerability to pooping, particularly after the chute had been cut in the stern. The top of the chute was therefore closed by a watertight gate. Experience subsequently showed that this danger was not as great as had been supposed. There is no doubt, however, that had pooping occurred the free surface on the train deck would have entirely destroyed the initial stability and the ships would have been lost by capsizing. In any new train ferries of this type it would be advisable not only to reduce the beam at the waterline, but to make the side structures on the train deck continuous and watertight. Brief particulars of the ships are:—

Length overall	.. ..	363 ft. 6 in.
Beam over fenders	.. ..	61 ft. 5 in.
Gross Registered Tonnage		2,500
Horse-power	.. ..	3,000 I.H.P.
Type of machinery	.. ..	Steam Reciprocating, Twin Screws
Speed	.. ..	11½ knots

The ships were fitted out to carry:—

Army personnel	.. ..	5 officers, 100 men
Landing-Craft Crews	.. ..	5 officers, 70 men
Ship's Complement	.. ..	15 officers, 110 men
L.C.M.	.. ..	13 in number

11

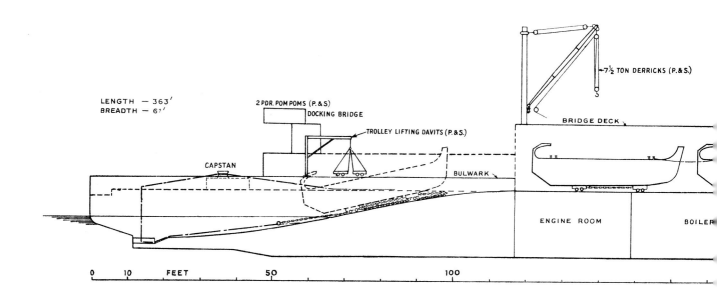

LENGTH — 363'
BREADTH — 6?'

2 PDR. POM POMS (P.& S)
DOCKING BRIDGE

7½ TON DERRICKS (P.& S.)

TROLLEY LIFTING DAVITS (P.& S.)

BRIDGE DECK

CAPSTAN

BULWARK

ENGINE ROOM   BOILER

0   10   FEET   50   100

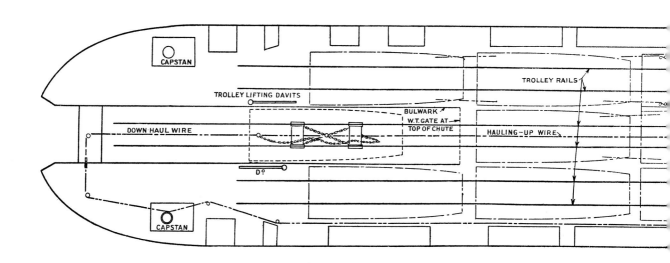

CAPSTAN

TROLLEY LIFTING DAVITS

TROLLEY RAILS

DOWN HAUL WIRE

BULWARK
W.T. GATE AT
TOP OF CHUTE

HAULING-UP WIRE

D?

CAPSTAN

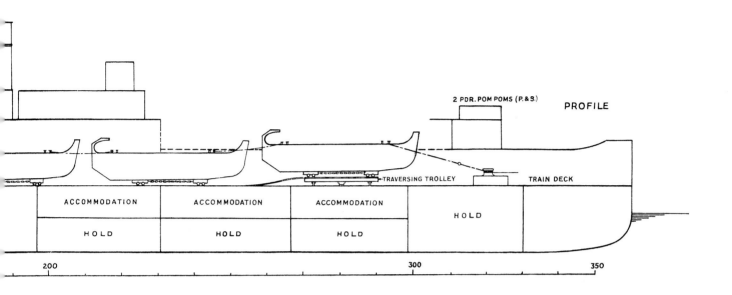

PROFILE

2 PDR. POM POMS (P. & S.)

TRAVERSING TROLLEY

TRAIN DECK

ACCOMMODATION   ACCOMMODATION   ACCOMMODATION   HOLD

HOLD   HOLD   HOLD

200   300   350

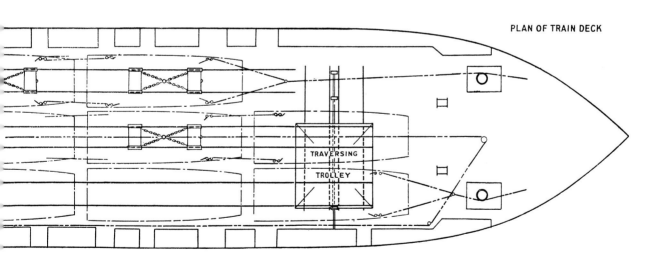

PLAN OF TRAIN DECK

TRAVERSING TROLLEY

Fig. 7

13

It was subsequently found possible to carry 11 L.C.M.(3).

Fig. 25 is a photograph of one of the ships, Fig. 26 a photograph showing an actual launch. Fig. 7 illustrates the general layout of the deck and the hauling, launching and traversing arrangements.

Three years after their conversion, and when the final preparations for invading Europe were being settled, these two ships were further improved by the addition of a locomotive bridge which enabled them to be used for ferrying locomotives and rolling stock as well as landing craft. This modification almost brought them back to their original function. This bridge can be seen in Fig. 25 and is also illustrated by Fig. 8.

(*b*) *Landing Ship Gantry or L.S.G.*—Towards the end of 1940, and before the L.S.S. were complete, plans for combined operations began to be concerned with more distant parts of the world. The problem of carrying small landing craft to distant assault areas became more acute, as experience, even in small-scale raids, confirmed the view that the L.S.I. would never be able to carry sufficient L.C.M. to make it possible for them to operate alone. Large landing-craft carriers were therefore urgently required. Many schemes were considered and finally it was agreed that transport as deck cargo would be essential if any short-term scheme was to be possible. Having obtained a suitable ship and having filled her deck with landing craft two problems remained to be solved, the first was that of lifting the craft over the side, the second that of moving the craft from their stowage positions to the picking up positions. Derricks and cranes were both considered for the first part of the problem, skids, greased ways, trolleys and rollers for the second. Ultimately a new conception was put forward. This was for gantries or transporters which would lift the craft, traverse them outboard and lower them to the water. So far as is known no such scheme had ever been tried at sea before. After it had been agreed to proceed, three tankers then building for the Admiralty were earmarked for the purpose, and gantries suitable for erection on board them were designed and produced by Messrs. Stothert and Pitt of Bath, to outline requirements put forward by the Admiralty.

The craft were stowed on the deck parallel to the middle line. Two gantries were built in each ship, one before the bridge and one abaft. The legs of the gantries were spaced so that the L.C.M. pointing fore and aft could be traversed outboard between them. In order to move the L.C.M. from their stowage positions to the lifting positions under the gantries a system of rollers in inverted channel bars was fitted above the deck of the tanker at a height that did not interfere with the normal working of the cargo arrangements. The craft were stowed in these channels with their bottom rubbers resting on the rollers. They were moved to and fro by means of whips. When under the gantries they were picked up, using a 4-point suspension system. The gantries were arranged so that the outboard ends could

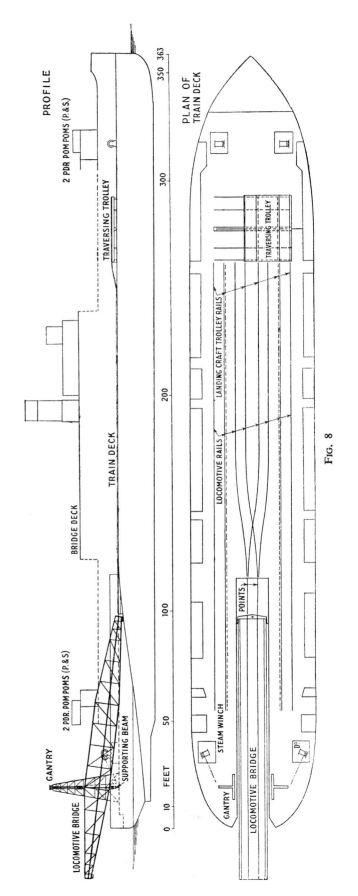

FIG. 8

be folded up practically parallel to the ship's side when the ship was at sea. (See Fig. 28.)

Although the scheme was devised entirely for L.C.M., it was subsequently found effective for the transport of other types of minor landing craft by using temporary collapsible cradles to suit the boats and the rollers. A total of 15 L.C.M. could be carried in 3 rows, 6 forward of the bridge and 9 abaft it. The general scheme worked well and the ships were constantly used for ferrying craft. As originally converted no provision was made for landing-craft crews, but this was added, and later much improved at the expense of oil cargo stowage. Originally it had been believed that the ships could be used for the dual purpose of fleet tankers and landing-craft carriers, but the increasing importance of their combined operations role resulted in them ultimately being used solely as carriers.

Towards the end of the war in the Far East one of the ships was specially fitted as a fresh-water carrier, capacity 3,000 tons.

The interest in these ships lies almost entirely in the gantries or transporters. The reason that these were preferred to cranes or derricks was primarily that the lifting gear in no way restricted the area of deck available for stowage, the lifting arrangement enabled the craft to be placed in the water pointing to the right direction, and hoisting, traversing and lowering were fully under control the whole time. Cranes would have suffered from the disadvantage that it would have been difficult to point the boat and that some stowage would have been lost. Derricks have been used for hoisting boats at sea for many years, but in this particular case they would have caused loss of stowage and it would have been difficult to have controlled derricks sufficiently well to have enabled the discharge of the craft to be performed as an evolution. With the increased mechanization of the Service generally, it is doubtful whether derricks will be as widely used in the future as they have been. For many purposes cranes are much more satisfactory.

Although the gantry ships were not repeated later in the war, they were completely effective. As mentioned above, the boats to be lifted were moved along the deck from forward to aft and the position of the gantries was fixed. It seems possible that a scheme could have been devised under which the gantries themselves could have traversed the deck and picked up the boats from their stowage positions. This was not adopted at the time as it was thought the other method more simple, but it is believed that such a scheme might be developed for future use.

The gantries could lift the craft at 10 ft. per minute traverse them at 90 ft. per minute, and the whole deck could be cleared of craft in about 35 minutes.

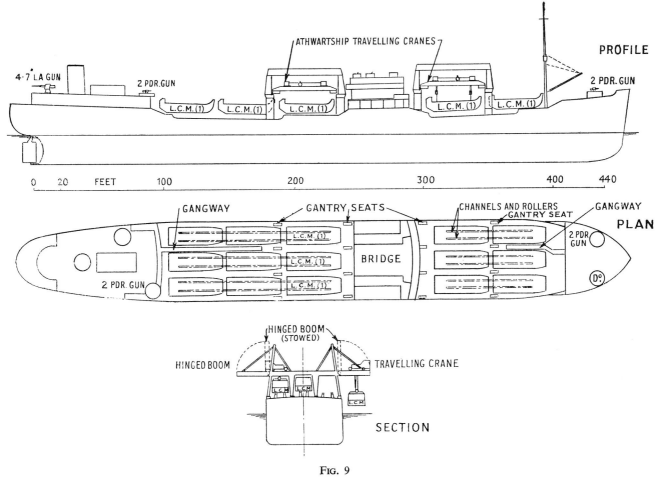

FIG. 9

Brief particulars of the ships are:—

Length overall	..	483 ft. 0 in.
Beam extreme	..	59 ft. 3 in.
Gross Registered Tonnage	..	8,218
Horse-power	..	3,000 I.H.P. (one ship), 3,500 B.H.P. (two ships)
Type of Machinery	..	Steam Triple Exp. (one ship) and Diesel Single Screw (two ships)
Speed	..	12½ and 12 knots

The ships were fitted out to carry:—

15 L.C.M.

Landing-Craft Crews	} ..	16 officers, 250 men
Army Personnel		
Ship's Complement	..	15 officers, 77 men

Fig. 27 is a photograph of one of the ships showing the gantries and craft on board. Fig. 28 shows a L.C.M. suspended from the gantry extension, and Fig. 9 is an outline general arrangement of the gantries and stowages.

(c) *Landing Ship Dock or L.S.D.*—These ships represent the most ambitious attempt at landing craft carriers which we have yet undertaken. The requirement for them dates from September 1941, at a time when tank landing craft had been tried and found satisfactory, but when the idea of tank landing ships had not been fully accepted on account of the difficulty of producing them in large numbers, the belief that they would prove to be extremely vulnerable, and on account of their comparatively greater draught. The object of the L.S.D. was then to have a ship which would be able to carry the largest tank landing craft fully loaded and float them off near the enemy coast so that a raid or assault, using tanks and heavy vehicles, might be possible. Such raids were already possible on enemy coasts near our own bases and the purpose of the L.S.D. was to enable them to be carried out in places far from home. As indicated by the name the ships were in effect large self-propelled ship-shape floating docks. A speed of 15 knots was asked for by the Staff.

The design was prepared in the Admiralty to meet British staff requirements and the ships were then ordered in America under Lend-Lease, the design being further developed by the American Bureau of Ships and subsequently by Messrs. Gibbs and Cox of New York.

Some such scheme for carrying small landing craft had been proposed many years before, but the idea had not been developed. The design, and indeed the operation of floating docks has been largely a specialized business, and when the suggestion was first made in 1941 that a floating dock should be designed as a fully sea-going ship to be operated by ordinary naval personnel, it met with considerable opposition as it was thought that the scheme would be very difficult to develop from a technical point of view, and even if successful technically, the ships would be difficult to handle and prone to accident. The design was, however, completed and the ships were built, and they were used most satisfactorily

both by ourselves and by the Americans. It is evident that the basic principles of the design, which were only arrived at after full consideration of the supposed difficulties, have been proved correct.

One of the first difficulties arose from the fear that the ship might be lost through over flooding. Full investigation, however, showed that this fear was groundless, and the great difficulty was to be able to find means of sinking her to the desired waterline for floating the craft in and out. This arises from the fact that the machinery spaces occupied a large volume under the pontoon deck which could not be flooded, and because the freeboard of the ship when carrying a load was necessarily very much greater than would be required in an ordinary floating dock for harbour use. In the final arrangement steps were taken so that some tanks above the normal flooded waterline could be filled by pumping if necessary.

An interesting stability problem also arose, for the beam of the vessel on the pontoon deck was fixed by the size of the largest craft expected to be embarked and by the width of the dock walls necessary to give stability with the water just over the deck. Had the vessel been built wall sided from this deck downwards, stability in the sea-going condition would have been excessive, and this would have very much increased the difficulty of securing craft after they had been docked down. Great fears were expressed at one time as to the practicability of securing such craft in any case, though in the event this difficulty never really arose. For these reasons the ship was built with a very pronounced flare below the pontoon deck. This flare was also beneficial because it reduced the total volume of water which had to be dealt with every time the dock was used.

One of the requirements laid down in the design stage was that the operation of the dock should be as quick as possible. As finally arranged pumping and flooding were effected through a common main system with branches forward and aft. The total pumping power was 18,400 gallons per minute and the dock could be sunk in 1½ hours or pumped up in 2½ hours. The intakes and exhausts from the machinery spaces were led to positions well above the submerged waterline, and the machinery installation could be run as well with the dock flooded as when the ship was floating normally. If necessary the dock could be operated with way still on the ship.

The actual metacentric heights in the several conditions were:—

Deep sea-going	..	..	..	..	7·7 ft.
Light sea-going	..	..	..	..	8·7 ft.
Worst condition when flooding. (Deck awash)					8·0 ft.

One of the other fears expressed in the early stages was that the water on the pontoon deck would surge to and fro in an absolutely uncontrollable manner if the dock were ever operated in a seaway. To counter this fear the Americans fitted sub-divisional dock gates at about mid-length of the hold. Subsequently, however, these were found to be unnecessary and were removed.

The ships as originally designed were able to carry

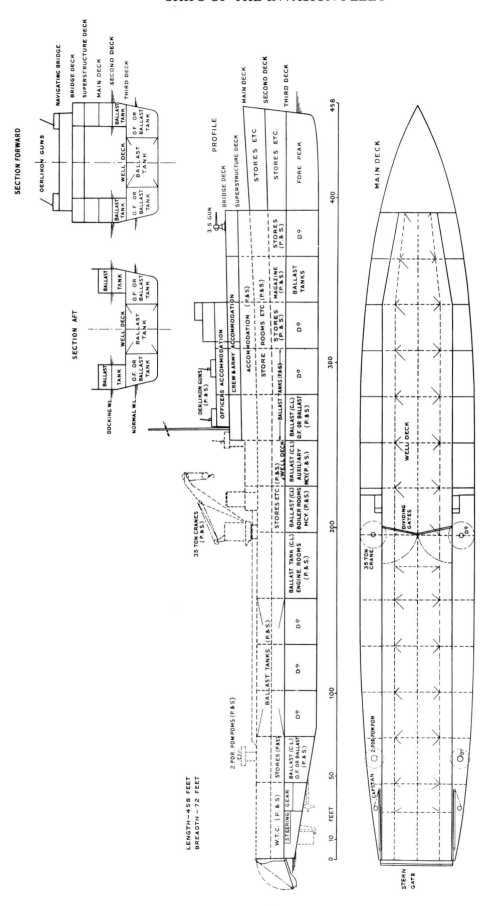

two of the largest tank landing craft then envisaged. When, as the war progressed, the Americans introduced large numbers of amphibious vehicles the ships were found to be ideally suited for their carriage and delivery afloat, and some of the American-operated ships were fitted with portable decks above the pontoon deck so that greater numbers of amphibians could be carried.

In addition to carrying the landing craft, accommodation was provided for the landing-craft crews and army personnel sufficient to man the vehicles embarked in the landing craft. Cranes were fitted on the dock walls so that the ships could be used for carrying motor vehicles dry, dock controls were fitted just as if the ships were nothing but floating docks, and the valves in the flooding system were operated by means of Bowden wire controls which, although giving some trouble through lack of maintenance, were actually most effective.

It transpired that none of the ships was ever used in the assault role for which they were originally intended, because, before they were complete, the principle of the L.S.T. had been accepted by everyone. L.S.D. were, however, invaluable as carriers of minor landing craft, major landing craft and amphibians, and it is thought that this type is not likely to be improved upon in principle for such purposes. Incidentally, of course, the ships could be used as mobile floating docks and repair bases for all types of small craft.

Brief particulars are:—

Length overall	457 ft. 9 in.
Beam	72 ft. 2 in.
Light Displacement	4,270
Horse-power	7,000 S.H.P.
Type of Machinery	Steam turbine, Twin Screw
Speed	16 knots
Maximum Depth of Water over Dock Pontoon	9 ft. 0 in.
Depth of Pontoon deck	20 ft. 0 in.
Freeboard to Pontoon deck	2 ft. 0 in. (18 ft. 0 in. limiting load W.L.)
Dimensions of Pontoon deck	394 ft. 0 in. × 44 ft. 0 in.

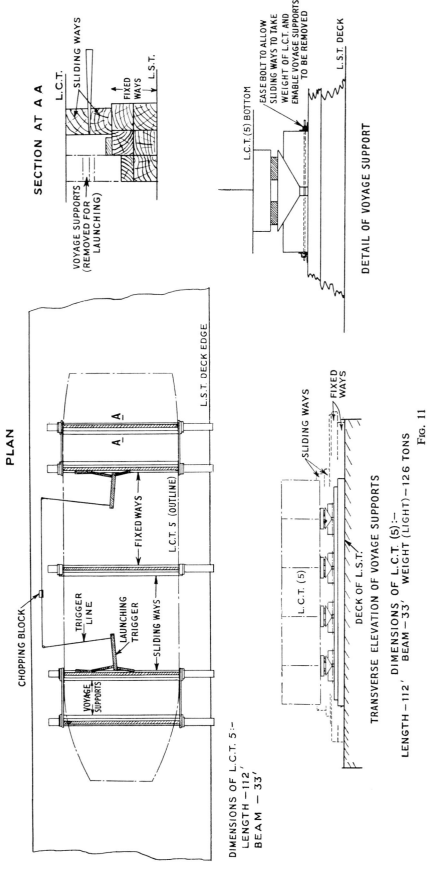

SECTION AT A A

DETAIL OF VOYAGE SUPPORT

PLAN

DIMENSIONS OF L.C.T. 5:—
LENGTH—112'
BEAM—33'

TRANSVERSE ELEVATION OF VOYAGE SUPPORTS

DIMENSIONS OF L.C.T. (5):—
LENGTH—112'   BEAM—33'   WEIGHT (LIGHT)—126 TONS

Fig. 11

The ships were fitted to carry:—

2 L.C.T.(3) or (4) or 3 L.C.T.(5), or 36 L.C.M.

Accommodation was provided on board for the naval and military crews of these craft, viz.:

Army Personnel ..	..	23 officers, 240 men
Landing-Craft Crews	..	36 officers and men
Ship's Complement	..	16 officers, 177 men

Fig. 29 is a photograph of one of the ships, and Fig. 10 an outline general arrangement.

(*d*) *Landing Ship Tank* (*or L.S.T.*) *as Carriers.*—To conclude this section on landing craft carriers mention must be made of two incidental developments.

(*a*) L.S.T. carrying L.C.T., and
(*b*) L.S.T. carrying minor landing craft (L.S.T.C.).

General particulars of the development of L.S.T. will be given in the next section; for the present consideration is only given to this particular function of them.

At the time when L.S.T. were first ordered in America, the British authorities also ordered a large number of 112-ft. L.C.T. The intention was that these craft should be shipped to this country as deck cargo, either in three units in the ordinary merchant ship, each unit requiring a 50-ton crane to lift it, or as a complete craft on the deck of L.S.T., in which case one 150-ton crane would be necessary for disembarkation. One of the requirements, therefore, in the L.S.T. was that she should have a clear deck space suitable for accommodating the craft. Very large numbers of craft were in fact carried in this way, which was, however, of little use if delivery of the craft was required to a port where heavy cranes were not available. It was suggested, therefore, that once the craft had been stowed on the deck it might be delivered by launching it from broadside launching ways. The practicability of this suggestion was thoroughly investigated by means of tank trials which proved it practicable and it was finally adopted with great success. Fig. 11 gives details of the launching ways and stowages provided. To carry out a launch it was necessary to heel the L.S.T. to about 11 deg. by flooding tanks. The launching arrangements were generally similar to those usual in broadside launches, but the ways were greased and grease irons put in when the craft was placed on board. During the passage the craft was carried on wedge-shaped support blocks and at the time of launch she was "set down" on to the launching ways by simply slacking off the bolts in the wedge blocks shown in the plate. The height of drop over the ship's side was about 10 ft. It is thought that this development might be of use in the commercial transport of such craft as dumb barges and river steamers for delivery overseas. Immediately the craft were in the water the engines were started up and they were ready for operation.

Subsequently, a similar scheme was used for the delivery of L.C.T.(5) from this country to the Far East. In this case care had to be taken that the grease did not melt as the temperature rose during the voyage. Tropical tallene was found to be suitable. Fig. 30 is a photograph of a L.C.T.(5) embarked on L.S.T.(2), and Fig. 31 a photograph of the launching ways and voyage supports as installed in L.S.T.(3).

Even at the end of the war there was still a demand for more ships capable of carrying minor landing craft and some of the L.S.T.(3) then completed in this country were specially fitted out for the transport of L.C.M.(7). These craft, which were 58-ft. long and weighed about 28 tons, were stowed transversely on the upper deck of the ships. They were hoisted in by means of a derrick specially fitted and landed on to a trolley or pair of trolleys fitted with hydraulic jacks. The trolleys ran in rails at each side of the deck and were hauled to and fro by means of whips. The stowage was filled from forward, working aft as each craft was jacked down. Fig. 12 shows in outline the arrangement of chocks and trolleys.

Group III.—Ships primarily intended for the Carriage of Tanks and Motor Transport to be landed directly on the beaches.

L.S.T.(1). *Maracaibo Class.*—Now, with the war safely won, it may appear that the L.S.T. is a simple development from the L.C.T., which itself was no great novelty, but conditions in the winter of 1940–41, when the new ships were first developed, should be borne in mind. The first L.C.T. had hardly completed its trials, there was an overall shortage of shipping, and of capacity to build it, and at this time the Prime Minister demanded ships that could land tanks (themselves not yet built) on beaches anywhere in the world. The problem was difficult physically because of the obvious fact that we should have to have an ocean-going ship of limited draught; it was difficult psychologically because it seemed certain that any ship so used would need to be written off after the first assault.

In order to provide something quickly, it was suggested that the Maracaibo oilers would be suitable ships to convert, because of their shallow draught.

Three of them were accordingly taken over and fitted-up to carry 20- to 25-ton tanks and to launch them over the bow. The bow disembarking gear consisted of a very ingenious double ramp arrangement suggested by the D.N.C. Department and developed by Messrs. Clarke Chapman. The tanks were carried abreast the original turret deck of the ships and were enclosed by a new deck and extension of the ship's side. Two of the ships were converted by Messrs. Greenwells of Sunderland and one by Messrs. Vickers Armstrong, Newcastle. The first was completed by the former firm in July 1941, and so far as we know she was the first tank-landing ship in the world.

Apart from the problems of embarking and disembarking the tanks, considerable attention had to be given to the ventilation of the tank deck, particularly when vehicles were warming up, as there was a very high CO concentration in the exhaust gases. In these ships this problem was tackled by fitting exhaust trunks which had

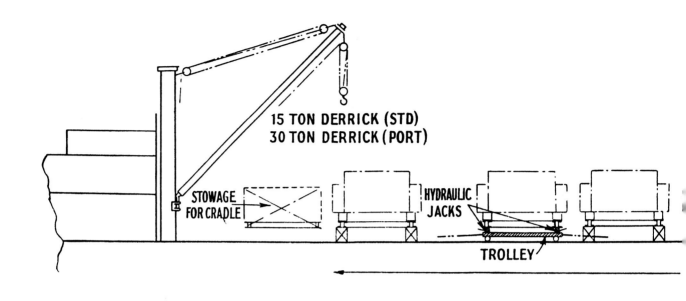

15 TON DERRICK (STD)
30 TON DERRICK (PORT)

STOWAGE FOR CRADLE

HYDRAULIC JACKS

TROLLEY

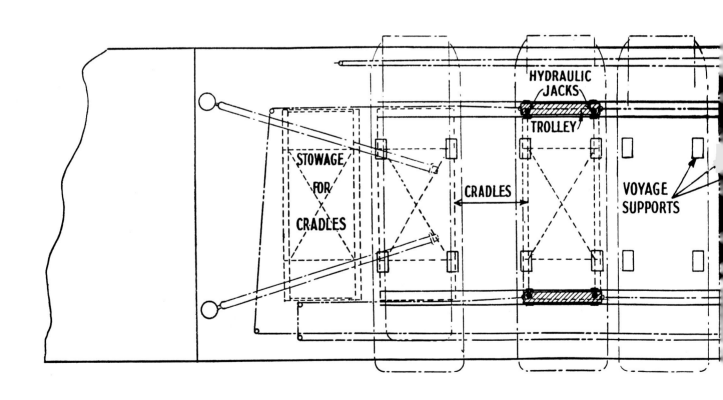

STOWAGE FOR CRADLES

HYDRAULIC JACKS

TROLLEY

CRADLES

VOYAGE SUPPORTS

PROFILE

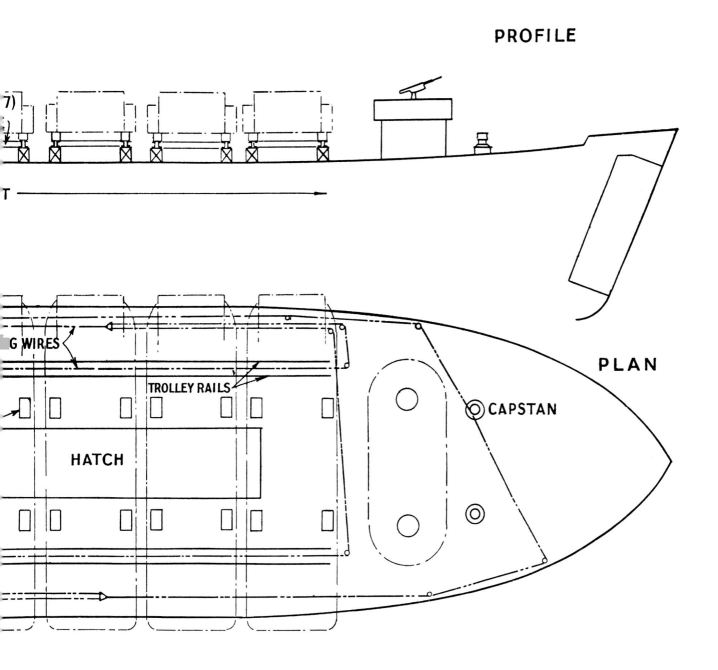

7)

T

G WIRES

TROLLEY RAILS

HATCH

PLAN

CAPSTAN

FIG. 12

flexible asbestos hoods with adaptors at the ends which could be secured to the vehicle exhausts. There were also the questions of securing vehicles when embarked, kedging off the beach, etc., which were worked up from what had been tried in L.C.T.

The principal disadvantages of these ships were their low speed and comparatively great draught. Nevertheless, by using them it was possible to obtain ships which could embark and disembark tanks and other vehicles of all kinds and land them on suitable beaches which had not had any previous preparation. The trials of the Maracaibos proved that large-scale operations over open beaches would be practicable from the seaman's point

They were fitted to carry:—

L.C.M.	.. .. ..	2 in number
Tanks	.. ..	20 25-tonners, later 18 Churchills
or M.T.	.. ..	33 in number
Army Personnel L.-C. Crews	..	12 officers, 195 men
Ship's Complement	..	14 officers, 84 men
Beaching Draughts	..	Forward 4 ft. 2 in. Aft 15 ft. 0 in.

Fig. 32 is a photograph of one of the ships as completed, Fig. 33 a photograph showing tanks embarked, Fig. 13

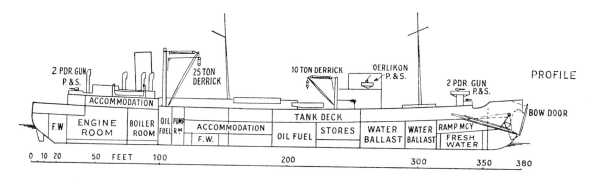

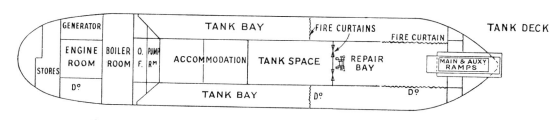

FIG. 13

of view. The trials further proved that such comparatively large ships could be grounded forward and after disembarkation kedge themselves off the beach without outside assistance. The conversions were therefore a most notable step forward in our invasion preparations. Certain problems likely to be met with, however, did not arise in these ships; for example, the question of vulnerability whilst at sea was more or less eliminated by the very close subdivision associated with such ships when on their normal business. The vehicle load was carried on a deck high above the waterline, which involved vehicles ascending and descending long steep gradients whenever the ship was used. These and other features prevented the ships from being regarded as prototypes of future L.S.T.

The principal particulars of the ships were:—

Length overall	.. ..	383 ft. 0 in.
Beam	.. ..	64 ft. 0 in.
Gross Tonnage	.. ..	6,455
Horse-power	.. ..	3,000
Type of Machinery	..	Twin-Screw Reciprocating
Speed	.. ..	10 knots

an outline general arrangement, and Fig. 14 gives some details of the bow disembarkation ramp.

L.S.T.(1). *Boxer Class.*—Concurrently with the conversion of the Maracaibos the design of special ships for landing tanks direct on to beaches was undertaken. The main reason for proceeding with the design before the Maracaibos were tried, i.e. before the principle had been generally accepted, was the feeling that the speed of the Maracaibos would never prove to be great enough. The new ships had a speed of 17 knots. It is significant that when later on a large number of L.S.T. were built the 10-knot speed of the Maracaibos had to be accepted. The design was therefore undertaken without any real back history which could be used for guidance. Many of the requirements were fixed somewhat arbitrarily and, on the whole, the ships were more elaborate than experience afterwards showed to be necessary. Clearly, if a speed of 17 knots was to be achieved the blunt-ended layout of the L.C.T. and of the Maracaibo class would not be good enough, and the requirement for very shallow draught directly conflicted with the speed required. It was arranged in the end that an average slope of beach of one in thirty-five should be assumed, with the draught

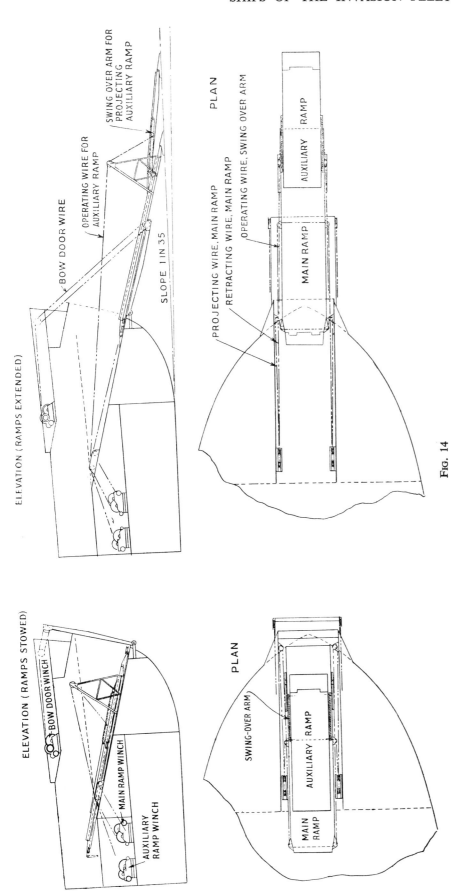

ELEVATION (RAMPS EXTENDED)

BOW DOOR WIRE

OPERATING WIRE FOR AUXILIARY RAMP

SWING OVER ARM FOR PROJECTING AUXILIARY RAMP

SLOPE 1 IN 35

PLAN

PROJECTING WIRE, MAIN RAMP

RETRACTING WIRE, MAIN RAMP

OPERATING WIRE, SWING OVER ARM

AUXILIARY RAMP

MAIN RAMP

ELEVATION (RAMPS STOWED)

BOW DOOR WINCH

MAIN RAMP WINCH

AUXILIARY RAMP WINCH

PLAN

SWING-OVER ARM

AUXILIARY RAMP

MAIN RAMP

FIG. 14

forward not more than 5 ft. 6 in. To enable the vehicles to be put ashore in not more than 2 ft. 6 in. of water it then became necessary to provide a ramp about 100-ft. long.

Considerable thought was given to the problem of where in the ship the main tank load ought to be carried. It was finally agreed that it would be desirable to make the run out as straightforward as possible, that is to say, steep declivities, either up or down, should be avoided. This meant in effect that the tanks should be carried on a deck at or near the water-line. If such a deck had extended the whole length of the ship and the whole beam of the ship, it is clear that the resulting vessel, even if she could have been built strongly enough, would have been extremely vulnerable. The tank deck was therefore subdivided longitudinally and the side compartments were used as machinery spaces and for stores and fuel. This was a development of the system already being used in tank landing craft, and has been adopted in all subsequent L.S.T.

A lift was provided so that the lighter vehicles could also be carried on the upper deck and transferred to the main tank deck for disembarkation. A 40-ton crane was installed so that the ship could, if required, embark or disembark her load of vehicles directly on to a jetty without using the bow ramp.

At the time of the design it was felt that the ships as a whole would prove to be extremely vulnerable, so beside the main bow disembarkation arrangement and the crane, steps were taken so that vehicles could be disembarked into L.C.T. using side ports. The ventilation problem in the enclosed tank space was solved on the same lines as in the Mara-caibos. Fears were constantly expressed that it would never prove practicable to use the ships in the manner intended because such an assault would itself not be possible. Provision was included in the design, therefore, so as to enable the ships to be used as auxiliary tankers or for the carriage of cased aircraft.

At a very early stage it was agreed that three ships should be built by Messrs. Harland and Wolff, Belfast,

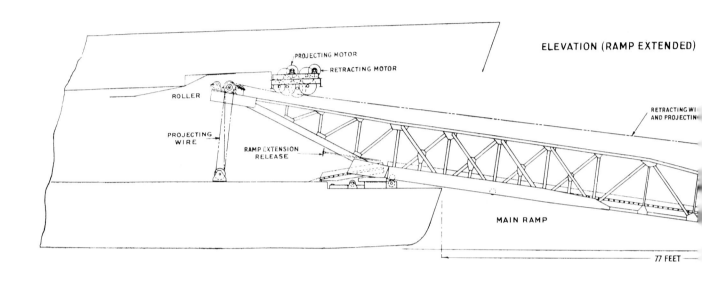

ELEVATION (RAMP EXTENDED)

PROJECTING MOTOR

RETRACTING MOTOR

ROLLER

RETRACTING WI
AND PROJECTIN

PROJECTING
WIRE

RAMP EXTENSION
RELEASE

MAIN RAMP

77 FEET

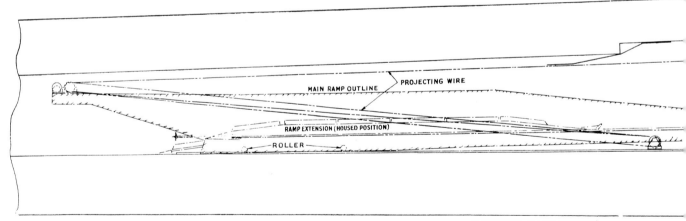

MAIN RAMP OUTLINE

PROJECTING WIRE

RAMP EXTENSION (HOUSED POSITION)

ROLLER

ELEVATION (RAMP STOWED)

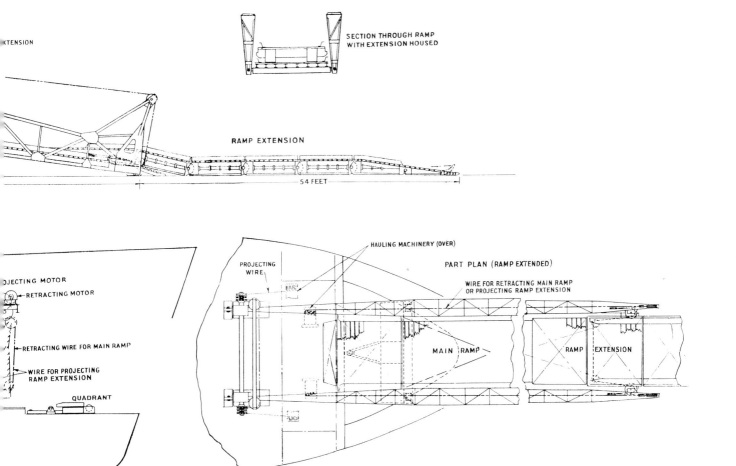

SECTION THROUGH RAMP
WITH EXTENSION HOUSED

XTENSION

RAMP EXTENSION

54 FEET

HAULING MACHINERY (OVER)

PROJECTING
WIRE

PART PLAN (RAMP EXTENDED)

WIRE FOR RETRACTING MAIN RAMP
OR PROJECTING RAMP EXTENSION

OJECTING MOTOR

RETRACTING MOTOR

RETRACTING WIRE FOR MAIN RAMP

WIRE FOR PROJECTING
RAMP EXTENSION

QUADRANT

MAIN RAMP

RAMP EXTENSION

FIG. 15

25

and they were closely associated with the design. It was appreciated that it would be extremely undesirable to try and arrange for a 17-knot ship to be fitted with a square flat end such as had been necessary in the Maracaibos during their conversion, so it was intended to fit a false bow outside the watertight door forming the end of the ship. In the beginning this false bow was to have been hinged horizontally at the upper deck level, but at the firm's suggestion this was discarded in favour of vertically hinged doors meeting on the centre line of the stem. Such doors, although rather a novelty at the time, proved to be entirely satisfactory and became standard in all L.S.T. and also in the larger later types of tank landing craft.

Having decided that the main tank deck was to be at

systems. The device was, however, proved by a full-scale trial carried out at the firm's works.

The ships were ordered in January 1941, but owing partly to the novelty of the various arrangements and the interruptions to the work at Belfast caused by enemy action, the first one did not complete until early in 1943. The class was not repeated because of developments which will be described later, but there is no doubt that the various arrangements made proved to be efficient and satisfactory and the ships, although somewhat elaborate, represented a big stride forward in that it had been possible to compromise on the various conflicting requirements and still produce a workable scheme. These ships were the first tank-landing ships in the world specifically designed for this purpose.

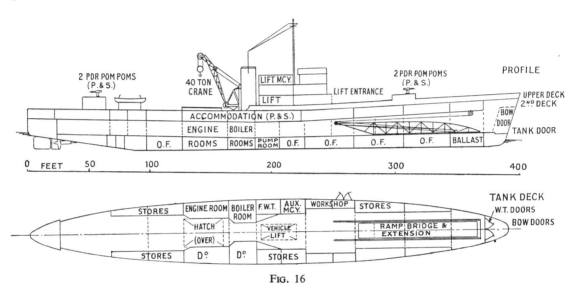

Fig. 16

about the waterline level and that the machinery should be fitted as far as possible in the wing compartments, the problem of the type of machinery became rather acute. The shape of the boiler room as given by the requirement above did, however, suit the shape of Foster-Wheeler boilers, and the ships were propelled by two 3,500 S.H.P. turbine sets and two Foster-Wheeler boilers, one on each side. The uptakes from the boilers ran into a single funnel slightly off the middle line of the ship so as to facilitate the fitting of the crane.

Once the main particulars of the design had been settled the principal outstanding difficulty lay in the design and provision of the bow disembarkation ramp. In the tank landing craft this had taken the form of a single hinged flap. In the Maracaibos it was a slightly more complicated double flap. Neither of these methods would enable a 100-ft. span to be bridged. As a result a cantilever type retractable bridge was suggested and this was subsequently developed by Messrs. Stothert and Pitt, Bath, who included in it an extension causeway making the total length up to about 140 ft. The arrangement was uneconomical in the use of space because of the room it occupied when stowed, and the details of the gear were more elaborate than the details of the other

Principal particulars were:—

Length overall	.. ..	400 ft. 0 in.
Beam	.. ..	49 ft. 0 in.
Light displacement	..	2,840 tons
Horse-power	..	7,000
Type of Machinery	..	Geared Turbines
Speed	.. ..	16¼ (18 knots at beaching draught)

They were fitted to carry:—

Tanks	.. ..	13 Churchills
M.T.	.. ..	27 on Upper Deck
Army Personnel	..	13 officers, 180 men
Ship's Complement	..	26 officers, 143 men
Beaching draughts	..	{ Forward 5 ft. 6 in. { Aft 14 ft. 10 in.

Fig. 34 is a photograph of one of the ships, Fig. 15 gives some details of the bow ramp gear, and Fig. 16 shows a general arrangement of the ships.

L.S.T.(2).—The type of operation envisaged when the L.S.T.(1) were designed was one involving large-scale raids on distant enemy held territory, but during 1941 it became clear that final victory in the war would never be obtained by such means, but would in fact need to be preceded by a large-scale re-invasion of the continent of Europe. The first estimates of the number of tank landing craft which would be required to enable such an invasion to be carried out gave astronomical figures. The figures were so large that even if the whole of the resources of the country had been put to build tank landing craft a very very long time would have passed before our invasion would have been ready. Two possible solutions offered themselves. The first was to build bigger tank landing craft and the second was to get American help under the Lend-Lease Act which had just been passed. These two solutions led to a question being asked, would tank landing craft be able to cross

notable American, contribution to ultimate allied success. The ships far exceeded all expectations in their performance and usefulness. In all over 1,000 were built and they went everywhere and carried everything.

Once again the tanks were carried on a deck near the waterline, but the arrangement of this deck varied somewhat from that fitted either in the L.C.T. or in L.S.T.(1). In these classes the deck was just above the waterline forward, but below the waterline aft, running parallel to the keel line. In the L.S.T.(2) it was arranged parallel to the waterline and just above it throughout the whole of its length. This incidentally enabled a very convenient arrangement to be made in the machinery spaces, locomotive type diesels were fitted in compartments below the main tank deck. The bow ramp arrangement

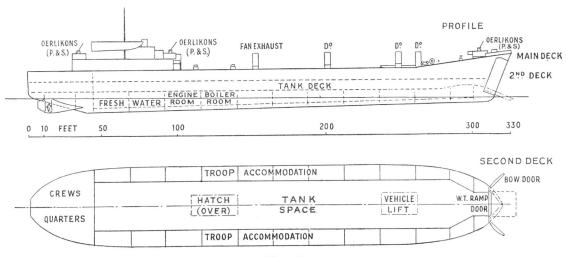

FIG. 17

the Atlantic under their own power? The answer to this question given at the time was, Yes, but only if the craft are made bigger on the lines of the L.S.T.

Resulting from these considerations the Americans were asked to build 7 L.S.T.(1) of the Boxer Class, of which the design was available (these ships were subsequently cancelled and 7 L.S.D. obtained in their place). Next, a small mission was sent to Washington to explain our requirements more carefully to the Americans. The main object of this mission was to invite them to build Atlantic tank landing craft for us, i.e. enlarged tank landing craft as indicated above. The conception of this craft and outline of requirements were provided by the Admiralty. It was for a craft about 300-ft. long, speed 10 knots, and which was simply a compromise between the L.C.T. and L.S.T.(1). It was realized later that it was a misnomer to call a ship 300-ft. long a craft, so the Atlantic T.L.C. was re-christened Landing Ship Tank (2), (L.S.T.(2)). The details of the design of this ship were worked out in Washington in the winter of 1941–42, the British and American authorities collaborating. The first ships were ordered in February, 1942, and were delivered in November, and altogether the conception of these ships must be regarded as a most notable British, and the provision of them a most

consisted of the L.C.T. type but with the additional vertically hinged doors of the L.S.T.(1). The ventilation problem was very thoroughly investigated by the American authorities, and it was found possible to overcome it without the use of special adaptors to the vehicle exhausts or providing powerful supply and exhaust fans to the hangar space. The vessels were all-welded. The kedge anchor layout was similar to that in L.C.T. though the variable speed electric winch provided was very much superior to anything that we had been able to fit in this country. The wing compartments at the sides of the main tank deck were used for the accommodation of army personnel. A very simple type of lift was fitted between the tank deck and the upper deck, which enabled the lighter vehicles to be carried on the upper deck and transferred to the main tank deck for disembarkation as in L.S.T.(1). Gravity davits were fitted suitable for carrying the standard American assault boat, which were used as lifeboats and for general ship services.

The initial programme was a very big one and the requirement was urgent, so that very great pains were taken to ensure that the arrangements were as simple as would be practicable. A cutaway hard chine type of construction was considered, but was dropped as tank tests indicated that it would be from 16–25 per cent more resistful than the ordinary round bilge type, and the diesel engines available had very little margin of power if a speed of 10 knots was to be achieved.

The ships were arranged for a beach slope of one in fifty, with a draught forward of 3 ft., figures which were hardly thought possible when the design was started. Arrangements were made so that they could be ballasted down to deeper draughts for ocean voyages.

Principal particulars were:—

Length overall	.. ..	327 ft. 9 in.
Beam	.. .. ..	50 ft. 1½ in.
Light Displacement	..	1,468 tons
Horse-power	.. ..	1,800
Type of Machinery	..	Twin Screw, Diesel
Speed	.. ..	10 knots

tion was put forward in the autumn of 1943 and it was a requirement that 80 of the ships should be available in the spring of 1945. Under these circumstances it would have been well if we could have literally copied the L.S.T.(2). Two factors, however, prevented us from doing this, one was that the locomotive type diesels for the main propelling machinery were not available, and the other was the comparative lack of welding facilities. Besides this, the Staff were very anxious to have higher speeds if these were at all possible. When the design was investigated it became clear that the only type of machinery which could possibly be available in time was that which had been ordered for the frigate programme, and the only capacity likely to be available for building the ships would be that derived from the same source, so it was that the Board decided to go ahead building landing

PLAN

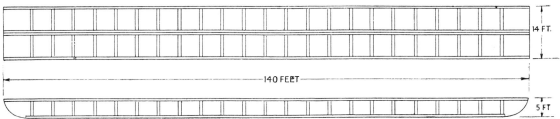

140 FEET

14 FT.

5 FT.

ELEVATION

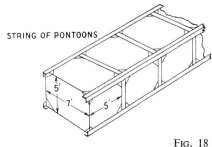

STRING OF PONTOONS

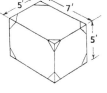

SINGLE PONTOON UNIT

FIG. 18

The ships were fitted to carry:—

Tanks	.. ..	18 Churchills
M.T.	.. ..	27 and 8 jeeps (or one L.C.T.(5))
Army Personnel	..	12 officers, 165 men
Ship's Complement	..	13 officers, 73 men
Beaching Draughts	..	{ Forward 3 ft. 0 in.; Aft 9 ft. 6 in.

Fig. 35 is a photograph of one of the ships and Fig. 17 an outline general arrangement drawing.

L.S.T.(3).—When first we had been successful in getting our allies fully engaged on the programme outlined above it seemed that further development of L.S.T. would not be necessary. This was particularly the case again when the first of the L.S.T.(2) came into service and was so successful. However, toward the end of 1943 there was some difficulty over the allocation of American built ships for purely British operations, and it was decided to undertake a programme of L.S.T.(2) type ships in this country and in Canada. The sugges-

ships with very heavy steam reciprocating engines which handicapped the design considerably.

The design was therefore prepared including this machinery and allowing for mainly riveted work. Meetings were held with the principal British shipbuilders in endeavours to facilitate the work by simplifying the design as far as possible, and as a result of these discussions the ships were actually built with the cutaway hard chine which had been dropped in the American ships. The tank deck, which was arranged above the waterline, was made parallel to the keel, and the upper deck was flat with no round down. It was not possible to get the machinery in beneath the tank deck and the increased weight of the machinery and space required for it resulted in the ships being somewhat larger than L.S.T.(2) for the same load. When the design was commenced it was known that the beaches on which the ships were expected to be used would be very flat. It was not possible to produce a satisfactory vessel with a 3-ft. draught forward and very little keel slope, so the one in fifty slope of keel was maintained and special

28

provision was made to enable the vessels to be able to discharge their cargo when grounded aft. This provision included heavy grounding skegs and means for carrying N.L. pontoon causeways.

These causeways had first been used with the Maracaibos and subsequently with the other marks of L.S.T. because it was found that in general a one in fifty (or a one in thirty-five) keel slope resulted in the ships grounding aft on the majority of beaches and thus discharging the vehicles into comparatively deep water. Various methods have been investigated to overcome this difficulty, but the N.L. pontoon causeways were finally accepted as standard. They were formed of pontoons, each 7 ft. × 5 ft. × 5 ft., made up into strings, and the strings made up again to form rafts. The rafts were secured to the fore end of the ship, the load discharged on to the raft and thence to the shore either direct or by towing the raft.

The combination of the hard chine, full form, and the skegs made the ships very resistful, and although their

ment where possible on those fitted in L.S.T.(2), but the ships suffered from their deeper draught and to a certain extent from the haste in which they had to be built.

The first orders were placed in December 1943, 45 with British builders and 35 with Canadian builders. The first ship, built by Swan Hunter, was delivered in December 1944. During 1944 repeat orders were placed in Canada for a further 36 ships. These programmes were in full swing when the war ended; not all the vessels were complete.

Remarks have already been made on the fittings provided for the carriage of L.C.T. and L.C.M.

These ships will form the backbone of the post-war combined operations fleet and a stepping stone to any future design. There is little doubt, however, that a higher speed and less draught will be called for and from this point of view it is to be hoped that lighter types of machinery will be developed and that British shipyards will be able to undertake all-welded construction.

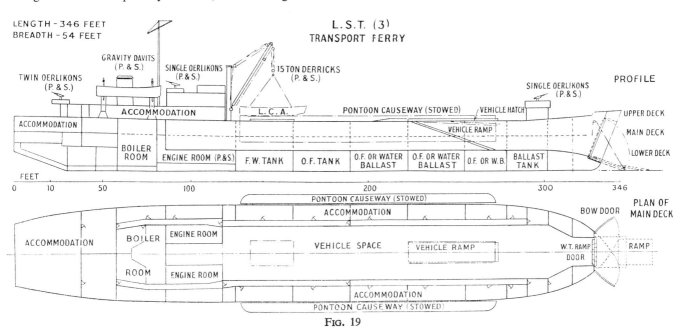

FIG. 19

power was about 2½ times that of the L.S.T.(2), their final speed was very little greater.

The bow door arrangement was similar but the bow ramp was arranged in two parts in an endeavour to increase the number of beaches on which direct discharge would be possible. The machinery for operating the bow doors and ramp was electrical, but otherwise steam auxiliaries were fitted instead of the electrical gear in L.S.T.(2). The general arrangement of the tank deck was similar, but with increased head room, and instead of the lift a ramp was fitted to enable vehicles to be taken from the tank deck to the upper deck and vice-versa (such a ramp had already been fitted in later editions of the L.S.T.(2)). Provision was made for carrying L.C.A. in gravity davits instead of the American assault boats.

Generally speaking the arrangements were an improve-

Brief particulars of L.S.T.(3) are:—

Length overall	..	.. 345 ft. 10 in.
Beam	..	.. 54 ft. 0 in.
Light Displacement	..	2,256 tons
Horse-power	..	.. 5,500
Type of Machinery	..	Twin Screw Steam Reciprocating
Speed	..	.. 13 knots

The ships were fitted to carry:—

Tanks	..	.. {On the general lines of
M.T.	..	.. { L.S.T.(2)
Army Personnel	..	18 officers, 150 men
Ship's Complement	..	14 officers, 90 men
Beaching Draughts	..	{Forward 4 ft. 7 in. {Aft 11 ft. 6 in.

Fig. 18 shows in outline a typical N.L. pontoon cause-way, Fig. 36 is a photograph of L.S.T.(3), and Fig. 19 an outline general arrangement, which also indicates the arrangements for the side carry of the pontoon causeways.

GLOSSARY OF TERMS

1. MINOR LANDING CRAFT.—All types of Combined Operations craft less than 100 feet in length.
2. L.C.A.—Abbreviation for Landing Craft Assault, or Assault Landing Craft, a wood built, 10 knot, 44-ft. boat with steel protection used for landing troops in the assault.
3. L.C.M.—Abbreviation for Landing Craft Mechanised. There were several different models. They were all intended for transport of vehicles, including tanks, between ship and shore. Types referred to in this paper are L.C.M.(1) and (7) British, and L.C.M.(3) American. These are all steel, dimensions vary, with lengths from 47 to 58 feet. Speeds from 7 to 11 knots.
4. L.C.T.—Abbreviation for Landing Craft Tank. There were several different models. They were intended for transport of tanks and other vehicles in direct assaults (or from ship to shore). They were all of steel construction. The first type L.C.T.(1) was 135-ft. B.P., the smallest of subsequent types 112-ft. The largest was developed by U.S.A. to L.S.M. Landing Ship Medium. The L.C.T. formed the basis for all tank and vehicle carrier development.
5. L.S.I.—Landing Ship Infantry, originally known as Infantry Assault Ships. There were several different types. For particulars, see text.
6. L.S.S.—Landing Ship Stern Chute, a ship which can carry Minor Landing Craft on deck and launch them into the water through a chute at the stern. See text.
7. L.S.G.—Landing Ship Gantry, a ship which can carry Minor Landing Craft on deck and hoist them out by means of Gantries. See text.
8. L.S.D.—Landing Ship Dock, a ship in the form of a Floating Dock which can transport Landing Craft and float them out. See text.
9. L.S.T.—Landing Ship Tank, originally called Tank Assault Vessel. Ships for carrying tanks and other vehicles and landing them direct on to the shore over ramps at the bow. See text.

DISCUSSION

Mr. A. C. Hardy, B.Sc. (Member): As one who for over two years of the war worked closely with Mr. Baker, I welcome the opportunity of contributing to the discussion on this paper. It is a fit occasion for a tribute to the splendid work he did in implementing the naval staff's requirements for the construction of one of the most unique fleets the world has ever seen. It was a fleet composed, on the one hand, of a heterogeneous collection of merchant ships and, on the other, of specially built ships for which, in shape, size and function, there exists surely no precedent in the history of naval architecture. The choice of the former, we recall, was not always governed by what was considered strictly desirable for conversion, and sometimes we had to make do with the crumbs from the Ministry of War Transport's table, particularly in the later stages. Some points stand out in the author's paper which seem worthy of emphasis. The first is the value of large and medium cargo liners as a means of carrying upwards of 24 assault craft, a large complement of troops, stores, and even a casualty clearing station with all that that means in generator load. While we may wonder at the reason for initially converting fast special ships like the "Glens" with machinery amidships into fleet oilers, we must agree that their value as L.S.I.(L.) was of paramount importance, though the smaller C.I.(B)s. [ex U.S. Maritime Commission freighters converted in 1943], may have been more handy. We cannot but agree that we were very lucky to obtain those ships which proved in fact most successful. Another point to be emphasised is the value of the cross-channel ships, and particularly of the diesel-driven ones which were converted into landing ships infantry, small medium, and hand hoisting—British, Belgian, and Dutch. Loaded well below the mark and structurally modified, these L.S.I.s were the backbone of any assault force. Their endurance was one of their greatest assets. It is well to remember that they literally went round the world, and that their diesel engines took them there without any trouble at all. The author did not mention the Bel ships, *Empire Charmian* and *Empire Elaine*, which were heavy lift ships with machinery aft converted to carry L.C.M.s. The use of oil tankers also as landing ships gantry for freighting landing craft was an interesting phase in the evolution of the assault fleet. This work was afterwards done by the landing ships dock L.S.D., and continuously round the British coasts by the L.S.S., ex-train ferries. The author rightly stresses the dual international nature of the L.S.T.(2) programme. This is sometimes forgotten, but he is too modest about the part he himself played. In short, the paper is a lesson to the world of the essential ingenuity of British naval architecture, and a tribute to U.S. mass production potentialities. More important still it shows how, what we may term merchant navy power, dovetails with sea power as a whole. It is a lesson too on the need, not only of possessing an adequate merchant navy, but of the necessity for the naval staff to be closely informed about types of merchant ships and their characteristics, and of contemporary developments in design and construction in connection with the ships they may require. There should at all times be the closest relationship between the naval staff and what is going on in merchant shipping in the outside world. I would again like to emphasise how much I enjoyed Mr. Baker's paper, and I sincerely wish to pay a personal tribute to him.

Commander Gordon Norton, R.N.V.R.: The writer claims membership of none of the three professions

Fig. 20.—"Glenroy" (L.S.I.)

Fig. 21.—Welin-McLachlan davits

Fig. 22.—"Princess Beatrix" (L.S.I.(M))

31

named in the Institutions responsible for this discussion, but for the three last years of the war, he was responsible in the Admiralty for co-ordinating the requirements of the naval staff and the implementation of these with the professional and technical authorities.

Landing Ship Infantry. The author refers (p. 7, col. 2) to increased specification entailing carriage of larger number of craft: Fig. 1 shows that eight of the extra craft in the "Glens" had to be carried and secured outboard: these craft are the primary armament of the ships and risk of damage had to be avoided. The net result was that the increase in craft reduced the sea-going capabilities of the ships.

Reference is made (p. 7, col. 1) to a similar restriction in the *Ulster Monarch*, *The Royal Scotsman* and the *Royal Ulsterman*, but the reason here is different. The Dutch and Belgian ships referred to (p. 5, *et seq.*, and Figs. 2 and 4) are promenade deck types, whereas the Harland & Wolff Irishmen are cabin ships, and no ready means could be found of fitting them with gravity davits and inboard secured craft. Nevertheless, though the *Prins Albert* (Fig. 4) type sailed and worked almost to the China Sea, the *Royal Scotsman* rounded the Cape, fought in Madagascar, and for some time sailed and trained in the Bay of Bengal before returning to fight in the Mediterranean.

The behaviour of landing ships as casualties is interesting. At one time or another and in various theatres, the "Glens" were torpedoed, mined, bombed, burnt or stranded; they survived, struggled home and, repaired and refitted, finished the war as staunch as ever. The C.1.B. conversions (p. 10, col. 2) were torpedoed or mined, and sank quietly but firmly, but remained upright.

The two L.S.S. both met trouble, the *Princess Iris*, not loaded, was badly holed and by good seamanship and with all good fortune was beached; the *Daffodil*, with a heavy load of locomotives was mined and seriously damaged; as predicted (p. 11, para. 2) she settled, capsized suddenly and was lost.

Individual ships of the L.S.T.(1) (*Maracaibo*) and L.S.G. were torpedoed and behaved like tankers.

The L.S.T.(2), being so numerous and always poking their noses into trouble, met every kind of accident. Some were lost, but the operational theatres are almost strewn with L.S.T.(2) damaged beyond even wartime economical repair and yet still obstinately afloat. Their greatest danger was fire; think on one hand of the normal Board of Trade fire regulations, and then picture an operationally loaded L.S.T., steaming to an enemy held shore with a cargo partly on deck, but the greater part in one enormous hold—vehicles, mostly jammed so tight that one could squeeze past only with difficulty, petrol tanks full, and loaded with ammunition, explosive charges, canned petrol and much else—and with scores of soldier crews blissfully unaware of fire dangers at sea.

Sprinkler system was of course fitted in the tank hold and fire mains on the upper deck, but nothing could deal with a fire of any size. The U.S. Navy later installed extra drenching and water curtain equipment in their own ships, but we, stretched to the limit with essential repairs, could not face this extra work. It is an important lesson and a great tribute both to the Royal Navy and the Army that intelligent and rigid fire discipline kept fire losses to an insignificant minimum.

Reference has been made to requirements and their implementation, and from a long and varied list two are worthy of reference.

The author refers (p. 14, col. 1, and Fig. 8) to the reconversion of the L.S.S.

The new function was visualized in the War Office, and passed to the Admiralty for agreement. For administrative reasons, the Admiralty added a requirement that the 120 ft. 90-ton locomotive brow should be capable of embarkation and disembarkation from the ship's own resources, but otherwise concurred. Owing to pressure of work at the Admiralty, the scheme was worked out in detail by the railway branch of the Royal Engineers, with the collaboration of the Director of Naval Construction.

The steelwork was prefabricated by a firm that had never set foot in a ship, and was fitted by them with some help from Chatham Dockyard in a six weeks' refit period. With practice, the bridge could be shifted and the ship changed over from locomotive carrying to craft ferrying in less than six hours.

The other case arose from the Royal Air Force who, from the earliest stages of the great Channel operation, wanted facilities for the control of fighter aircraft from the vicinity of the French coast. As originally stated in November 1943, the requirement was for three ships, with working and living accommodation on the simplest scale to accommodate an additional 4 officers and 20 other ranks; they were to have one radar and some R/T and W/T sets. In less than a month, tactical examination showed that two radar sets were needed, many additional lines of communication, full-scale operations rooms, and staff of 18 officers and over a hundred other ranks.

The only possible hulls were L.S.T.(2); there were only three in home waters, and a personal minute from the Prime Minister said that landing ships were only to be used for their designed purpose; and he was in Teheran. The work was placed with Messrs. John Brown & Co., other naval work being cancelled to compensate, and the first of the ships arrived a week before Christmas. At the first meeting, in addition to the firm's representatives and the usual naval authorities, there were nearly twenty other authorities present. The first ship was wanted for training in February.

Masts, generators and two large specially modified radar aerials had to be found and fitted, but, above all, the stability characteristic of the ships had to be altered to give a steady platform for radar operation.

At one time there were seven outside authorities actually at work in each ship. The ships finished on time, and all three played an exceptional part in the re-investment of Europe.

In the combined fleets being assembled for the Japanese war, the tonnage of landing ships, exclusive of landing craft, would have exceeded 5 million tons, and nearly

Fig. 23.—"Princess Astrid" (L.S.I.(S))

Fig. 24.—"Ulster Monarch" (L.S.I.(H))

Fig. 25.—"Daffodil" landing ship, stern chute (L.S.S.)

FIG. 26.—AN ACTUAL LAUNCH FROM A L.S.S.

FIG. 27.—LANDING SHIP, GANTRY (L.S.G.) LOADED

all built after 1941. Great difficulties were met and overcome in the design and building of these ships, but generally it was less a naval problem than one of extra specialized transport. The naval job is to forge a weapon, the transport job to build a tool, and these are basic differences. I very much agree with the author that in any future consideration of these ships, the Royal Navy and the Merchant Navy must seek the way together bearing in mind the problems both of the naval and military staffs.

In my naval duties, I visited almost every shipyard in this country; I always seemed to arrive in the periods of greatest stress, with demands outrageous and insatiable, but everywhere I was met with sympathy and understanding; I shall always think of this industry with the greatest admiration and gratitude.

Professor A. M. Robb, D.Sc. (Member of Council): The author has unwittingly distorted the early history of invasion craft; and the importance of the subject demands that the record be slightly amended. The reference to the "Glen" ships being taken over in April 1940, implies that the invasion of Europe was then under consideration—prior to Dunkirk. In fact the "Glen" ships had been taken over in 1939, for a project which was abandoned after much labour had been expended in elaborate alterations. Early in 1940 the ships were returned to mercantile service in an altered form; and one, at least, had completed a round voyage before they were again taken over. But the taking-over was not for *invasion*. The purpose was ill-defined, but eventually it developed into raiding, a purpose widely different from invasion. The taking over for any purpose might be described as a mere accident, and the ships were not really suitable for conversion to the raiders which at one stage they were supposed to be. Some time after they were taken over a demand was made for the carriage of tank landing craft in addition to the infantry landing craft originally to be carried, and it could be met only by the use of heavy derricks, an arrangement which was far from satisfactory. The first ships which were schemed to suit the purpose of raiding were the Dutch ships *Koningen Emma* and *Prinses Beatrix*. For this purpose— a tip-and-run adventure after a sea voyage—the carriage of the landing craft in safety demanded inboard stowage, and rapid recovery at the end of the raid as well as the inboard stowage led to the adoption of gravity davits for both infantry and tank landing craft; the davits for the heavier craft were the largest that had then been made. The intention was that the tank landing craft should be loaded from a beach at the starting-point and then lifted to the stowage position for the raid; recovery after the raid was to follow the same course. The "Glen" ships and the Dutch ships probably provided valuable experience for the subsequent production of invasion craft. But *invasion* did not come into the picture until some time after these ships had been fitted to carry landing craft.

Major E. F. J. Plowden, R.E. (Associate): Perhaps I might mention a few small points with regard to the L.S.I.s from the experience of the soldier who had to travel in them on business. The soldier in battle order takes up an extraordinary amount of space, and I would put it to Mr. Baker that the minimum width of any companion-way or alleyway should be about 12 feet! It has been found extremely difficult to marshal troops at their action stations as it is nearly always necessary for parties to pass through troop spaces other than their own; so I would suggest that if at all possible each space has an independent means of ingress and egress. This is also very important if a "flap" develops, as it becomes quite impossible to pass troops quickly up to the weather deck in the time that may be available. I had the sorry experience of losing twenty men in this way in 1943.

Steel or brass wearing strips fitted to the edges of companions and ladders can be a grave danger to men wearing steel shod ammunition boots.

More adequate drainage should be provided in troop spaces and latrine accommodation; few people who have not seen them have any idea of the indescribable mess which these places become in rough weather.

In a number of ships the ventilation in the lower troop spaces was grossly inadequate.

Then a most important point is sea kindliness. You will remember that during the first part of the invasion of Sicily a gale sprang up. One of my main worries was not that the gale would interfere with the physical act of landing, but that the troops would be in no condition to work when they got to the beaches on account of sea-sickness. With the greatly increased top hamper on the L.S.I.s it should not be difficult to arrange the small positive GM which is so important in getting an easy motion in a seaway.

Finally, I should like to say how very good the L.S.T.(2) were; the arrangements for accommodation of personnel as well as vehicles were really excellent. We had no difficulty in handling even such cumbrous items as bull-dozers with the arrangements made on these ships, and the author is to be greatly congratulated on their design.

Mr. G. de Rooij (Member): I will not speak about the technical part of the lecture, but I know I am speaking for my friends in the meeting—I am a Dutchman, you know—and I am also speaking for all the naval architects and engineers in Holland in giving expression to our grateful feelings for the part your invasion fleet has taken in the liberation of our small and loved country, and I can tell you that your ships are of much better construction than the invasion ships of the Germans, that never reached your coast.

Mr. H. S. Pengelly R.C.N.C. (Member): This interesting paper by Mr. Baker, who played a sustained and effective part in the development and production of landing ships and craft, is one more example of the tremendous effort required to bring the late war to a successful conclusion, following our early reverses and expulsion from the continent of Europe. I well remember

Fig. 28.—L.S.G. showing L.C.M. suspended from gantry extension.

Fig. 29.—"Highway" (L.S.D.)

Fig. 30.—L.C.T.(5) embarked on L.S.T.(2)

being impressed by a landing ship gantry seen from H.M.S. *Illustrious* in Diego Suarez harbour following the successful Madagascar operations in May, 1942.

My first official contact with combined operations ships and craft was in the autumn of 1944, when it took me a little time to recognize the large number of initials representing the various types and classes in existence and in production. I then found the author to be a fountain of knowledge concerning the capabilities and limitations of this large and growing fleet.

The author states that the arrangements in L.S.T.(2) were kept as simple as possible to facilitate production. The same, of course, applied to L.S.T.(3), although simplicity was not helped by the requirement that the ships were to be capable of world-wide operation, including service in the tropics. It is doubted whether the hard chine, discarded by U.S.A. for L.S.T.(2), greatly facilitated the production of L.S.T.(3); certainly lack of round-down of the upper deck in L.S.T.(3) was false economy and made satisfactory drainage of loose water almost impossible. The author states that the final speed of L.S.T.(3) was little greater than the 10 knots of L.S.T.(2). The 30 per cent increase in speed is not inconsiderable, observing that the light displacement of L.S.T.(3) is some 50 per cent in excess of L.S.T.(2). The photograph, Fig. 36, is of a L.S.T.(C), as shown in outline in Fig. 12.

The paper indicates how early attempts to meet service requirements were by conversions and adaptation of existing ships, never an entirely satisfactory proceeding although the conversions served a useful purpose and provided experience and data for later designs. The final requirements were of such magnitude that it became necessary to produce new designs and to devote a considerable portion of the production capacity of the United States, Great Britain and Canada to building special ships. It is hoped that the experience gained with such ships will not be lost, but rather that while the possible need for combined operations remains, prototype vessels, embodying the lessons of the war, will be designed, produced and tried out in order that bulk production can proceed without delay in emergency.

Mr. L. Woollard, M.A. (Member of Council): The author took a prominent part in the development of many of the landing ships he has described, as well as in that of the landing craft only briefly mentioned in this paper. He has thus a good knowledge of his subject, and I have no criticism to make of his admirable account. I wish, however, to make a few general remarks on the ships in Groups II and III.

All these ships were designed during the war. They were of entirely novel type, and had to be designed very quickly and built very rapidly. There was no time to make improvements, except such alterations as had been found desirable on actual service. This placed a heavy burden on both designers and builders. The latter co-operated with the Admiralty and made it possible to complete a large number of transport ferries, in particular, in a very limited time. I may mention that in all,

including the smaller landing craft which are outside the scope of this paper, the number of different types of vessel designed and built was more than 60.

I omit any mention of Group I—landing ships, infantry —not through any lack of appreciation, but because they are unfamiliar to me, and I hope that some other and better qualified speaker will remark on them.

In Group II the stern chute ships were adaptations of two special ships at the disposal of the Admiralty to enable them to carry and launch the small landing craft designed by Messrs. Thornycroft. This firm also gave us every assistance in working out the detailed arrangements in the ship. An interesting feature was the design of the trolleys carrying the L.C.M. and the method of traversing them and running them down into the water. Their wheels had to be carefully designed and spaced so as to prevent the trolleys running askew and being derailed. These difficulties were surmounted, but the whole arrangement was somewhat of an improvisation to make the best use of the materials in the time available.

The gantry ships were also an early development, in which the installation of gantries enabled tankers to be used also for landing craft long before any such ships designed *ad hoc* could be completed.

The landing ship dock is specially interesting to a floating dock designer. So far as I know the only ship-shape floating dock previously built was a small one, not self propelled, constructed at Sheerness Dockyard about 1920 and used in connection with flying boats. As the author mentions, these vessels succeeded even better than had been anticipated, a matter of some congratulation to him as he spent some time in America co-operating in their detailed design. Though any such design must be uneconomical in so far as the weight of the dock is large in relation to the load carried, they were found useful for a great variety of purposes.

The use of landing ships as carriers is then described. As stated, it was found possible to devise means of launching sideways and dropping overboard fairly heavy landing craft.

Turning now to the more important designs in Group III, the Maracaibo class were forerunners of the landing ships proper, being adapted from the only shallow draught tankers in existence. Their conversion was of great value in enabling the designers to tackle two important problems. The first was the design of the bow doors, which preserved the form of the bow and yet permitted the tanks to be driven away from the ship over a brow. The second was the ventilation of the tank deck, which entailed the dispersal of the fumes given off by a large number of tanks "revving-up" preparatory to departure. We were fortunate in being able to enlist the help of Messrs. Thermotank, who rendered great assistance in devising a scheme of ventilation which was entirely satisfactory.

The first landing ships designed as such were the three of the Boxer class. This design was the most difficult of all due to the conflicting requirements of high speed, shallow draught, and extremely long brow. To the

Fig. 31.—L.S.T.(3) with launching ways on deck

Fig. 32.—Maracaibo oilers (L.S.T.(1))

design of the brow Messrs. Stothert & Pitt gave special attention and produced the ramp about 100 feet long that is described in the paper. Their method of handling the ramp was elaborate and most ingenious and reflected great credit on the firm's designers.

I can only mention the L.S.T.(2), well designed and built in large numbers by our American friends, and very extensively used in the war. I will pass to our own L.S.T.(3), or transport ferries, which represented our final effort in the provision of ships which could carry both tanks and their crews in large numbers. These ships had some interesting features which included the provision of fairly good accommodation suitable for tropical conditions, means for embarking and disembarking rapidly the load of tanks and personnel, and finally provision at the stern for the ship to ground on a hard beach without damage. Fortunately the very long brows in the Boxer class were no longer necessary, this being made possible by the use of the N.L. pontoons described in the paper.

Mr. Baker has given us an interesting and valuable paper, and I wish to thank him for placing on record an account of some of the difficulties and achievements associated with the transport of men and material to a distant and hostile beach.

Mr. R. B. Shepheard, B.Sc. (Member of Council): The author has produced in the space of this paper a most comprehensive record, and with a remarkable economy of words. He has touched on many of the difficulties to be overcome in developing and producing the special craft required, and at the right time. These problems have been amplified during this discussion, which has emphasized the magnitude of the Admiralty's achievement.

The Boxer type was, of course, the first specially designed L.S.T., and as the author has stated, involved consideration of many conflicting and complicated requirements. It was our privilege in Lloyd's Register to be associated to some extent with the design and construction of these and other types of landing ships. There was naturally a good deal of criticism and doubt in some people's minds as to how the "Boxers" would perform, but we have had ample justification from service results of fitness for their intended duties.

In his remarks on the L.S.S., the author comments, "There is no doubt that had pooping occurred the free surface on the train deck would have entirely destroyed the initial stability, and the ships would have been lost by capsizing. In any new train ferries of this type it would be advisable not only to reduce the beam at the water-line but to make side structures on the train deck continuous and watertight." I would like to ask him whether the suggested alterations are proposed to improve the characteristics of the ships as train ferries or as L.S.S.s?

The L.S.D. has an interesting predecessor if only as a conception. In the TRANSACTIONS of the Institution of Naval Architects for 1870, Vice-Admiral Sir Edward Belcher drew attention to the usefulness of a self-pro-

pelled floating dock for Admiralty purposes; his design bears a striking similarity to that of the L.S.D.

I hope that it will be possible to complete the record of these achievements by the presentation to one of our Institutions of a paper dealing with the smaller types of landing craft.

Author's Reply to the Discussion

I do not want to say much. Everybody who has spoken on the paper may be divided into four classes. First of all my associates, and I hope Mr. Shepheard will not mind being included as one of them, as representing those Lloyd's Surveyors who did so much to help us. My associates have all been most kind and I am most grateful to them. Then the soldiers, represented by Major Plowden, who found that the ships were not perfect; of course no one expected them to be, as I mentioned in paragraph 2 of the text. I was, however, very glad to hear what Major Plowden had to say, particularly his kind remarks regarding L.S.T.(2).

Then the Professors. Professor Robb seems to be my only critic, and I am sorry that Mr. Pengelly (who was my Professor at Greenwich) is not here, for I am sure he would agree with me when I say that I never argue with professors under any circumstances!

Lastly, there are the people of Europe, represented by Mr. Roaij, whom I thank for his friendly comment. If we helped in the liberation of his country, that, Sir, is all we were trying to do.

      ·   ·   ·   ·

If I may offer a more extended reply in writing to some of the points raised in the discussion:—

I agree with Mr. Hardy's opening remarks and of the importance to the war effort of the availability of the better type of cargo liners. The Bel ships deserve a mention, but details of them were not given in the paper as their development was not peculiar to invasion operations. I also agree with Mr. Hardy's concluding remarks as to the importance of the naval staff being informed of the capabilities of merchant ship types.

I am grateful to Commander Norton for adding to the value of the paper by giving more details of the service experience of the ship, indicating the extent to which we were able to approach safety under hazardous conditions, and I feel that the Institution as a whole will appreciate his concluding paragraph.

I agree with Professor Robb that in the early days a lot of work was done with the object of providing transport for raiding forces, as distinct from full-scale attempts at invasion. This was rational under the circumstances and I believe the paper describes essentially how the ships developed from small beginnings to a complete Invasion Fleet. Certainly the operational plans affected the ships—but there were far more of such plans and I am grateful to Professor Robb for allowing me to reiterate that many of the ships, at first suggested for specific tasks, easily became "maids of all work"; perhaps the highest tribute that could be paid to them.

Professor Robb's "tank landing craft" should read "mechanised landing craft."

FIG. 33.—MARACAIBO (L.S.T.(1)) TANKS EMBARKED

FIG. 34.—"THRUSTER" (L.S.T.(1)) (SPECIAL ADMIRALTY DESIGN)

FIG. 35.—L.S.T.(2)

FIG. 36.—LANDING SHIP TANK (3) (L.S.T.(3))

Major Plowden's points are all of the most practical value and I think I can promise that they will be borne in mind in the future.

Mr. Pengelly is correct, of course, regarding Fig. 36, and we must all hope that the steps indicated in his last paragraph will be taken so that progress may be maintained.

I am grateful to Mr. Woollard not only for his comments but for his kindness and encouragement throughout the whole of the war-time years.

In view of Mr. Shepheard's remarks it is fortunate that we did not claim originality for the ideas underlying the various types. I have looked up the 1870 TRANSACTIONS and from them it appears that the L.S.D. idea originated in 1823. I do feel, however, that in spite of the similarity between Sir Edward Belcher's proposal and our war-time ships, our ships, when compared with his, do show improvement, as no doubt do our sailors over those of 1870.

My remarks on the train ferries were intended to apply to their commercial use, for however well subdivided such a ship may be below the train deck, and whatever freeboard she may have, if the ship's side plating is carried above the train deck at all, a situation arises in which there are in effect continuous plated bulwarks. When it is realized that any free water on the deck may have an inertia greater than that of the waterplane, the serious possibilities will be appreciated. The inertia of any such water on the deck can readily be materially reduced by making the side houses continuous like floating dock walls, and the advantages of such an arrangement seem to be worth having.

Reducing the beam at the waterline would reduce initial stability and tend to make the ships more comfortable.

The Chairman (Admiral of the Fleet Lord Chatfield): I move the customary vote of thanks to Mr. Baker for his excellent paper. It would have been a great pity if such a well-written and concise record of the most wonderful feat of building these landing craft had not been recorded in the records of the Institution. I think that Mr. Baker's own work in what has been done is recognized by everybody here to have been a very great one, and it has been gratifying to hear several of the speakers pay him the compliments he so thoroughly deserved. I was very much interested in what was said by Mr. Hardy and Commander Norton in regard to the merchant shipbuilding requirements in war, and I have been trying to think what could be done in that respect. The difficulty I see is that these landing craft are really more specialized merchant tonnage than war ships, but there is no doubt that we shall not get landing craft of that type produced in peace time by our shipping companies. If we are going to have any experimental work in developing craft of that nature I am afraid it will have to be done by the State, and if the State has to produce them and pay for them, they will really be a type of warship rather than a type of merchant ship. That only refers of course to the landing craft. I quite agree and fully sympathize with the idea that we want a much closer connection in peace time between the naval staff and the Merchant Navy in working out to what extent our normal carrying facilities in peace can be influenced by the possible requirements of war time. These landing craft were often commanded and manned by soldiers, and where that was not the case they were commanded and manned by that wonderful body which Commander Norton represents here to-day, the R.N.V.R. It all leads to the fact that one has got to get away from the rigid divorce between the Royal Navy and the Merchant Navy. Both services feel they are part of each other and should have their committees and consultations in peace time to work together just as they have had to do, and have done, in war time.

Merchant Aircraft Carrier Ships ('MAC' Ships)

by J Lenaghan, MINA

Originally published in *Transactions*, Volume 89, Number 2, April 1947, pages 96-111

FIG. 1.—*EMPIRE MACCRAE*—GRAIN "MAC" SHIP

MERCHANT AIRCRAFT CARRIER SHIPS ("MAC" SHIPS)

AN INTERESTING PRODUCT URGENTLY INTRODUCED INTO THE WAR-TIME MERCHANT SHIPBUILDING PROGRAMME

By J. Lenaghan, Member*

Synopsis

Merchant ships in war time are assigned many strange tasks, far removed from the functions they were originally designed to carry out in peace time. These new tasks, if they entail substantial structural changes, alter their appearance and seldom permit the ship to combine satisfactorily, to any great degree, the carriage of commercial cargoes in association with their new, or additional, duties.

The war just ended made many heavy calls on all classes of merchant ships, with consequent loss to the total tonnage available for the transport of the nation's normal essential supplies.

This paper describes a war-time production and conversion, unique, and to some extent original, because they successfully combined two functions without detriment to the efficiency of either. It amplifies and records in greater detail the construction of the "Mac" ships referred to in Sir Amos Ayre's paper "Merchant Shipbuilding During the War," read at the Institution of Naval Architects in April 1945.

Introduction

Since the existence of these vessels was publicly revealed for the first time in the spring of 1945, the daily and technical press has circulated widely the story of their development, and in briefly introducing this paper it has been assumed that many members of this Institution are already aware of the function of these ships, and perhaps to a lesser extent of some of the main features in their design.

As their name implies, these vessels are merchant ships so constructed as to enable them to carry aircraft as defensive armament. By the employment of such vessels it became possible when the battle of the Atlantic was at its height to provide air cover over a blind spot in the western ocean, through which convoys had previously sailed without air protection. Unlike the catapult armed merchant ships (C.A.M. ships), which they superseded, the "Mac" ships possessed the advantage of not losing their aircraft after they became airborne. They were produced as an integral part in the expansion of a very heavy programme of additional defensive equipment for merchant ships in the autumn of 1942, and if their appearance (Fig. 1) was severely austere, it was because their equipment concerned *defence* duties rather than *offence*, resulting in a naked tubbiness of aspect as compared with the better proportions of their fighting Royal Navy sisters.

The conversion of merchant ships into aircraft carriers

* Personal Assistant (Technical) to Controller of Merchant Shipbuilding and Repairs.

did not begin with the introduction of the "Mac" ships. The department of Naval Construction Admiralty had already converted a few well-known passenger liners and had acquired and converted, while they were yet on the stocks, a number of vessels of the cargo liner class. One such conversion which largely influenced naval interest in the smaller ship of the tramp class was the conversion of the captured German merchant vessel *Hannover* into an escort carrier, viz., H.M.S. *Audacity*. This vessel had a short but gallant life, and in the series of vessels covered by this paper it is fitting to record that tribute was paid to the part she played in the anti-submarine warfare by naming one of the "Mac" ships after her commander, viz. *Empire MacKendrick*.

Conversions carried out under the auspices of the Naval Construction department went to sea as fighting ships under the white ensign, but the "Mac" ships being dual-purpose ships, combining the carriage of cargo with the flighting of aircraft, retained their identity as merchant ships and continued to fly the red ensign of the merchant navy and to be commanded by merchant navy masters. The retention of this flag was the key and background at the Admiralty for their design and construction within the departments of the Controller of Merchant Shipbuilding and Repairs, and it was the rigid observance of all that this implied, together with a policy of direct personal contacts with all interested departments, rather than by the circulation of the more usual documentary official communications, which eased the burden of additional work in their production, and provided the enthusiasm and interest at both shipyards and repair establishments throughout the full period of the "Mac" contracts.

Policy and Planning

Merchant ship aircraft carriers were first officially considered at the beginning of 1942, but it was not until towards the middle of that year that their immediate need became both apparent and urgent. Once accepted, development of the proposals proceeded very rapidly, and no time was lost in issuing the necessary instructions for the construction of two vessels to be put in hand ready for service in the spring of 1943. It was, however, never intended that their introduction should be more than an interim measure in the anti-submarine campaign. Primarily for defensive and reconnaissance duties with the convoys, they satisfied the requirements of a short-term policy, and filled the gap until naval auxiliary carriers became available, a programme of which was just then begining to take shape in both this country and the United States.

The preliminary naval staff requirements specified that the selected vessels should have a speed of 14–15 knots, and have dimensions capable of providing for a flight deck of not less than 490 ft. length by 62 ft. breadth, and a hangar space for the housing of at least six fighter aircraft. Those vessels, building or in service, which could have satisfied these requirements were already allocated for other equally important duties. Consequently, with the design and production of "Mac" vessels becoming the responsibility of the Admiralty Merchant Shipbuilding Department, capacity for their construction had to be found in yards under that department's control. The majority of these, however, were unfamiliar with naval equipment, and generally physically incapable of producing vessels having dimensions that could meet these specified needs. From a survey of the berth capacity then becoming available, and having regard to the number of vessels required, which had increased from the initial order of two to a total of six within a period of four weeks, and also the dates they were required in service, it was obvious that nothing of larger dimensions than the standard cargo tramp vessel could be produced from the "merchant" shipyards. Modified proposals based on the conversion of the standard tramp were submitted to the naval staff, who not only acknowledged the difficulties placed before them, but, despite a not altogether unanimous reception, boldly agreed to the modifications, and recast their requirements to cover the provision of a flight deck of not less than 390 ft. length by 62 ft. breadth, a hangar

paper is in two parts; Part I describes the grain or cargo ships class and Part II the oil-tanker class.

PART I

GRAIN SHIP MERCHANT AIRCRAFT CARRIERS

General Arrangements

The general layout for the combined functions of these two vessels having no precedent, made it incumbent on the department responsible to see that all fundamentals affecting the design were settled quickly, so that the constructional details could be developed and production of the vessels proceed without delay. From the outline plan supplied to the shipbuilder the usual preliminary general arrangement plan was prepared. This, and its subsequent amendments, were tabled at three conferences held at the Admiralty, on the 7th and 20th May, 1942, and 2nd June, 1942. Points at issue between the departments concerned with the operation of these vessels as aircraft carriers, the production departments, and the shipbuilder of the first vessel, were discussed and settled at these conferences. From the date of the final meeting, the design then basically agreed remained unaltered, apart from details, and generally the same for all six vessels throughout their construction.

A typical layout of the finished arrangements for these vessels is shown in Figs. 2 to 5. Two vessels were ordered from each of three yards; the relative principal particulars for these are tabled below.

TABLE I

Builder	Burntisland Shipbuilding Co., Ltd.	Wm. Denny Bros., Ltd.	Lithgows, Ltd.
Name of Vessel	*Empire MacAlpine* *Empire MacKendrick*	*Empire MacAndrew* *Empire MacDermott*	*Empire MacCrae* *Empire MacCallum*
Length (B.P. on L.W.L.)	412 ft. 6 in.	425 ft. 0 in.	425 ft. 0 in.
Length (overall)	433 ft. 9 in.	445 ft. 8 in.	444 ft. 7 in.
Length of flight deck	413 ft. 9 in.	423 ft. 1 in.	424 ft. 4 in.
Breadth on water-line	56 ft. 8 in.	56 ft. 0 in.	57 ft. 9 in.
Breadth at flight deck	62 ft. 0 in.	62 ft. 0 in.	62 ft. 0 in.
Main draught loaded (service)	24 ft. 6 in.	24 ft. 8 in.	24 ft. 6 in.
Freeboard to flight deck	28 ft. 6 in.	28 ft. 4 in.	30 ft. 1 in.
Total deadweight (tons)	7,930	8,360	7,990

for the accommodation of four "Swordfish" aircraft, and the speed of vessel in service in fair weather to be not less than 11 knots.

The new requirements were intended to cover conversion proposals for both cargo ships and oil tankers, but with the different problems in each type their application followed different courses. For convenience, development of the two types of conversions are described separately, and from this stage onwards the

It having been agreed to accept the hull for the prototype cargo vessel which each of these firms was then building, the development of the design centred on the most satisfactory means of making provision for the following important items:—

(a) Cargo loading and discharging arrangements which would not interfere with, or seriously encroach upon, the aircraft carrier requirements.

MERCHANT AIRCRAFT CARRIER SHIPS ("MAC" SHIPS)

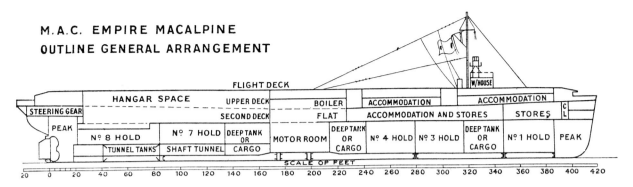

Fig. 2

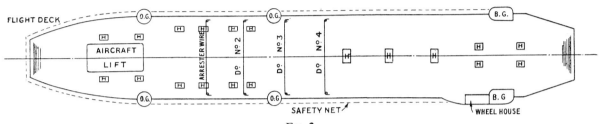

Fig. 3

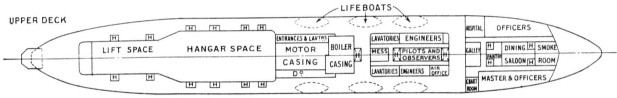

Fig. 4

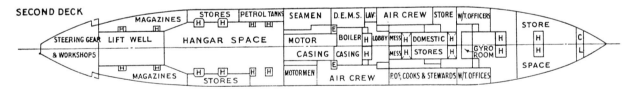

Fig. 5

(b) The siting of the bridge erection without detriment to the navigability of the vessel, and the limitation of the projection outboard (both for this erection and the armament zarebas), beyond the moulded line so that the vessel was not prevented from using commercial quayside berths.

(c) Improved watertight subdivision, and the maintenance of structural strength in way of the sunken hangar space.

(d) The accommodation for two crews, merchant and naval, totalling 107 persons.

(e) Life-saving arrangements to merchant ship standards, including all additional war-time emergency measures.

(f) Mechanical and, wherever practicable, also natural ventilation for crew, cargo and machinery spaces, in addition to the disposal of exhaust gases from main diesel engine and auxiliary boilers.

(g) Space for magazines for safe stowage of bombs, depth charges, ammunition and pyrotechnics, together with sundry small store and locker spaces.

(h) Good steering and manœuvrability qualities for convoy work.

The incorporation of these items would have been comparatively simple and straightforward had there been sufficient time to consider them thoroughly, but with both plans and construction proceeding concurrently, and with dimensions of the ships fixed to that of the selected yards' prototypes, little opportunity was afforded for ideal planning. Floor space for all needs was at a premium and only sufficient to provide satisfactorily for

47

a specification that ensured the efficient working of these vessels' two functions.

Main Propelling Machinery

There were no restrictions laid down as to the type of propelling machinery for these vessels. It was accepted by all from their conception that only diesel machinery could be considered, having regard to the many problems that would arise in getting rid of the boiler smoke, which, because of dimensional limitations in width of flight deck, had to be ejected horizontally from under this deck instead of vertically above the deck, as in the naval aircraft carriers.

The war-time standard diesel tramp had machinery of 2,500 B.H.P., capable of giving a service speed of 11 knots. To have repeated machinery of this power in these ships would have provided no margin of power to enable them quickly to get out of the convoy station for flying patrol duties, nor to overhaul the convoy if, in manœuvring for suitable take-off positions, they had dropped well astern. In the second of the first two vessels allocated for this service the machinery provided in the original merchant ship contract was of 3,300 B.H.P. This additional 800 B.H.P. over the normal standard tramp ship rating was estimated to give an extra 1½ knots to their speed, and to be sufficient to provide the spurt required to satisfy the foregoing two important conditions. All the "Mac" ships of this class had, therefore, the higher-powered machinery installed, the chief particulars of which are indicated below:—

Model Experiments

The hull forms for all six of the selected vessels having been "repeats" of prototype hulls already tank tested, no further experiments in so far as they concerned hull resistance were necessary, nor indeed had changes in form been contemplated would there have been time for such tests. In view, however, of the importance of the above-water structure in aircraft carriers from the airflow point of view, guidance on this matter was sought from the National Physical Laboratory, together with a request that they carry out experiments to observe the behaviour of short ships of this class when moving ahead at 12 knots in rough water.

The Aerodynamics Department of the National Physical Laboratory had ample data, from their previous airflow work, upon which to give guidance on such matters as width and shape of the flight deck terminations. It was important to obtain the maximum length of flat deck for take-off purposes, and with this in view the foregoing department's recommendations in regard to the profile of these endings were readily adopted. Each end of the flight deck was made similar because of the probability that landing over the bows might at some future date be desirable. The width of deck at the ends was determined by the amount of overhang which could be simply supported by the sponson-shaped structure below, between the upper and flight decks.

Solid plating in the sides between the sheerstrake top and underside of flight deck was impracticable. Having regard to the low freeboard of these ships and the

TABLE II

Ships	Empire MacAlpine	Empires—MacAndrew; MacDermott; Macrae; MacCallum; MacKendrick
Propelling machinery—		
Type	Doxford opposed piston four-cylinder	Kincaid-Harland B. & W., six-cylinder single acting
Dimensions	600 × 2,320 mm.	740 × 1,500 mm. Buchi supercharged
Auxiliary boilers	Two	Two
Type	Cylindrical multi-tubular, 12 ft. 0 in. dia. × 11 ft. 6 in. and Composite horizontal, 10 ft. 6 in. dia. × 10 ft. 6 in.	Cylindrical multi-tubular, 10 ft. 9in. dia. × 10 ft. 6 in.
Working pressure	120 lb.	150 lb.
Generators	3 at 65 kW, 220 volt, direct current	2 at 125 kW, 220 volt, direct current

The main engine exhaust and auxiliary boilers smoke outlet were trunked under the flight deck and led from the casings directly overboard, but well abaft of the accommodation spaces. The boiler outlet extended to both sides of the ship with a plate flap fitted within each branch trunk, to permit of the control and diversion of smoke to the lee side in order not to obscure flying operations on the flight deck.

liability of damage to their superstructure, particularly at the fore end, when pitching in heavy seas, openings in the side plating for lifeboats and rafts were limited in size and number, and the areas of solid plating so arranged that the broadside surfaces nearly balanced in a longitudinal direction about the centre of effort. It was anticipated that it might be difficult to control the tendency to cut more and larger openings in this plating as construction proceeded. To offset the unbalancing effect due to this and lessen the angle of helm required to maintain a steady course with a side wind when its direction relative to the ship was nearly broadside, the rudder area was increased 15 per cent over normal requirements, a precaution later confirmed following discussions on this matter with the National Physical Laboratory.

In the initial stages of the development of these vessels it was thought that their short length might cause them to pitch and heave excessively when running at full speed for fairly long periods in the weather conditions normally met with in the north Atlantic convoy routes. The results of the rough-water experiments carried out at the National Physical Laboratory soon settled whatever doubts there were that aircraft on these vessels could be operated only under fair weather conditions. They also showed that at a speed of 12 knots the motion of the ship would not be excessive in wave-lengths of less than 320 ft., but that in regular trains of waves of approximately 400 ft. length synchronism of the natural ship period and period of encounter occurs, and under such conditions both pitch and heave would be objectionable. So also no doubt would be the weather for flying. From the subsequent examination of a number of the service logs for these vessels, and in the absence therein of any reference to an excessive amplitude of stern movement, it must be assumed that nothing exceptional in this respect was experienced. On the other hand, deck landing officers are so expert in the handling of landing aircraft that they can time accurately and take advantage of the phase variation, when for a few pitches the movement of the ship is small and the period long enough to allow an aeroplane to land safely.

On completion of the rough-water experiments, the experimental work was continued with the model run at the ballast draught with varying stern trims, viz. 3 ft., 5 ft. and 7 ft. respectively. The results showed practically no difference in the hull resistance between the 5-ft. and 7-ft. trims, but compared with these the 3-ft. trim showed a 3 per cent improvement. In disposing of the ballast tanks every effort was made to produce this 3-ft. trim for the least favourable ballast condition.

The conversion of cargo ships in war time for purposes other than that for which they were designed very often presents stability problems, and particularly bad in this respect are those which combine large increases to the top weight in association with the carriage of homogeneous cargoes. Aircraft carriers must have ample stability, sufficient to ensure a moderate angle of heel when turning, but not too much to be associated with quick rolling. The optimum safe figure for the metacentric height in these vessels was considered to be about 4 ft.; the actual figures obtained in the ballast and loaded departure conditions of these ships was not less than this.

Aircraft Arrangements

These grain-ship aircraft carriers were the smallest of any aircraft carrier produced before or during the past war, and if to the airborne pilot the flight deck of a fleet carrier appears little larger than a postage stamp, how much more true was that the case in these vessels, and how excellent the pilot's skill in safely landing on this small area, especially with the knowledge that the stops to a plunge overboard were only four arrester wires stretched transversely across the deck at 30-ft. intervals, covering a 90-ft. length of flat deck immediately abaft of amidships, and with no crash or protective barrier fitted at the forward end. From an analysis of a number of deck landings recorded during the working-up trials of these vessels, the landing aircraft mostly appeared to pick up the first arrester wire; failing the first they hooked the second wire, but on no occasion had they to continue on to the third or fourth wire. The take-off trials were equally satisfactory. The average length of run of aircraft, against a wind speed of 25 to 30 knots and with the total inclusive weight of plane approximating $3\frac{1}{2}$ tons, was not in excess of 360 ft. The speed with which aircraft could be flown off and landed on these vessels showed a commendable high standard of efficiency in both the flying and deck personnel, which reached a peak in one of the vessels on which three "Swordfish" aircraft were flown off in sixteen seconds and landed on again in forty-two seconds.

Four "Swordfish" aircraft with folded wings could be comfortably accommodated in the hangar of 142 ft. length by 38 ft. width and 24 ft. height. This was served by a single platform lift, 42 ft. by 20 ft. overall, electrically operated and capable of lifting a fully loaded plane up to 5 tons from hangar floor to flight deck level in fifty seconds. Special ventilation, heating, lighting, and fire appliances, including a sprinkler system, were provided throughout this space.

The combined functions of these vessels presented difficulties in meeting naval practice for the disposition of spaces allotted to magazines, explosive stores and petrol tank compartment, all of which should have been arranged away from the ship's side and below the load water-line. In these ships, however, it was necessary to have such spaces aft, and with space available only at the sides of the hangar between the second and upper deck, there was no alternative but to make the fullest use of this, as indicated on the arrangement plan, Fig. 5.

The special compartment, in which the two pressure-tested aviation fuel tanks were placed, was constructed so that it could be flooded and kept filled with fresh or sea water. The filling, discharging and filtering arrangements, together with all their valves, were led to, and controlled from, a special control room placed under the flight deck and immediately over the tank compartment.

The electrical installations in these vessels, as indicated by the size of the generators in the machinery particulars, was considerably in excess of any war-time tramp ship specification, but was much abbreviated in comparison with the requirements normally insisted upon for the fleet or escort carriers. Flight deck lighting (but excluding the special arrangements for night flying), increased wireless and radar equipments, telephone communication systems and other types of signalling devices were sufficient to ensure that the aircraft could be satisfactorily and safely handled and operated in all reasonable weather conditions. When assessing capacity for the building of these ships, the electrical "contents" for ships of this class were kept prominently in the foreground, and in framing the electrical specification the extent it should cover was determined by the amount that could be installed and completed within the last four months of the constructional period, having full regard for the very limited electrical labour normally employed in the purely merchant shipyard, and the past difficulties in sub-contracting any substantial amount of electrical work to those outside contractors normally associated with merchant ship work.

Production and General

The first programme drawn up to show the probable completion of the vessels indicated deliveries at regular intervals between April and October 1943. That the actual completion dates on the last programme were April 1943 and March 1944 is no reflection on the earlier estimates, but was due to a stretching out of the production period made necessary because of manufacturing difficulties, resulting in a slowing up in the output for certain of the items of special equipment. The first vessel, *Empire MacAlpine*, built by the Burntisland Shipbuilding Co., Ltd., was ordered in June 1942; the keel was laid on August 11th, 1942; the launch took place on December 23rd, 1942, and the completed vessel, after inspection and trials at the shipyard, was handed over to the managers appointed by the Ministry of War Transport on April 21st, 1943. This period of only eight months, covering the worst part of the year, was a very creditable achievement on the part of Burntisland Shipbuilding Co., Ltd., in which both Messrs. Wm. Denny Bros, Ltd., and Lithgows, Ltd., must be associated. All three firms shared in the development and detailed planning of the work, so that the fullest effort could be concentrated on the production of the first vessel, and the problems as they arose solved before the subsequent vessels had advanced too far. The additional total effort entailed in the production of these vessels is perhaps best illustrated by their increased cost as compared with the normal tramp vessel from which they were evolved, and which amounted to approximately 25 per cent. The increased steel-weight content amounted to nearly 20 per cent, while the corresponding reduction in deadweight compared with the basic tramp, after allowance for both the increased lightweight and restricted service draught, was 28 per cent, which in the first vessel represented an actual grain cargo deadweight of 6,450 tons.

A full grain cargo was carried on the maiden homeward passage of the *Empire MacAlpine*; no difficulties were experienced in the berthing of this vessel at either ends of the voyage, and notwithstanding the strangeness of the vessel to the shippers. This cargo was loaded in three days and discharged by suction at a north-west port in twenty-four hours, which included a total of eight hours for stoppages. See Fig. 17.

PART II

OIL-TANKER MERCHANT AIRCRAFT CARRIERS

Proposals for the conversion of tankers into merchant aircraft carriers were under consideration concurrently with the grain ship proposals, but little progress was made in the initial stages because of difficulties in readily procuring the release of suitable modern tankers. Most of such vessels were engaged in the carriage of fuel cargoes of low flash-point, cargoes considered dangerous under normal conditions, but much more so when combined with the operation of aircraft. In the course of the examination of these proposals, a Cabinet decision was issued calling for the fullest possible expansion of the merchant aircraft carrier programme for completion by the winter of 1943. Agreement on all the outstanding technical difficulties quickly followed, and in October 1942 orders were issued for the conversion of nine existing tankers, and for the completion as aircraft carriers of four vessels from the list of tankers in the new construction programme. It was agreed also that the tankers, while in service as merchant aircraft carriers, would carry only heavy-grade oil cargoes having a flash-point of 150° F. and above.

Technical Particulars

Outline proposals for the conversion work on tankers had already been prepared concurrently with the grain ship proposals. These, after approval by the interested departments at the Admiralty, were considerably amplified and taken several stages further by the technical department of the Anglo-Saxon Petroleum Co., Ltd. Full development and final detail plans covering all the nine existing vessels was undertaken by Messrs. Palmers, Hebburn Co., Ltd., in association with Smith's Dock Co., Ltd., North Shields. The plans for the four new vessels were prepared from the Admiralty outline by each individual shipbuilder, viz. Messrs. Harland & Wolff, Ltd. (Govan), Cammell Laird & Co., Ltd., and the two yards of Swan, Hunter & Wigham Richardson, Ltd., Wallsend and Neptune Works.

The principal particulars covering the different tankers are shown in table III.

All the existing tankers had the same dimensions and were of a similar class belonging to the Anglo-Saxon Petroleum Co., Ltd. The selection of so many similar vessels was of great advantage in their planning, and considerably assisted, by the measure of standardization they afforded, the actual conversion work. Outline general arrangement plans, covering both new and existing tankers, are shown in Figs. 6 to 9 and Figs. 10 to 12 respectively, together with their photographs in Figs. 13 and 14. In appearance these vessels appeared

TABLE III

Builder	Existing Vessels	Harland & Wolff (Govan)	Cammell Laird	Swan Hunter (Wallsend)	Swan Hunter (Neptune)
Name of Vessel	*Rapana* Class	*Empire MacKay*	*Empire MacColl*	*Empire MacMahon*	*Empire MacCabe*
Length (B.P. on L.W.L.) ..	460 ft. 0 in.	460 ft. 0 in.	463 ft. 0 in.	460 ft. 0 in.	463 ft. 0 in.
Length (overall)	482 ft. 9 in.	479 ft. 6 in.	481 ft. 7 in.	483 ft. 0 in.	485 ft. 9 in.
Length of flight deck ..	461 ft. 8 in.	460 ft. 0 in.	461 ft. 0 in.	461 ft. 6 in.	461 ft. 0 in.
Breadth on W.L. ..	59 ft. 0 in.	61 ft. 0 in.	61 ft. 9 in.	59 ft. 0 in.	61 ft. 9 in.
Breadth at flight deck ..	62 ft. 0 in.	62 ft. 0 in.	62 ft. 0 in.	62 ft. 0 in.	62 ft. 0 in.
Mean draught loaded ..	27 ft. 6 in.	27 ft. 2¾ in.	27 ft. 7⅞ in.	27 ft. 6 in.	27 ft. 6 in.
Freeboard to flight deck ..	32 ft. 0 in.	31 ft. 6 in.	32 ft. 9 in.	32 ft. 6 in.	32 ft. 6 in.
Deadweight (tons)	11,009	11,246	11,508	11,000	11,450

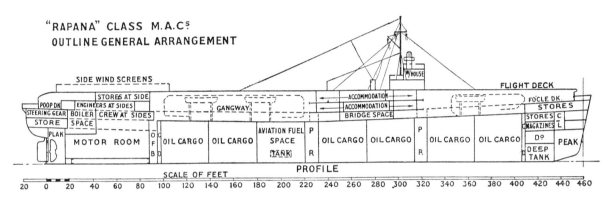

Fig. 6

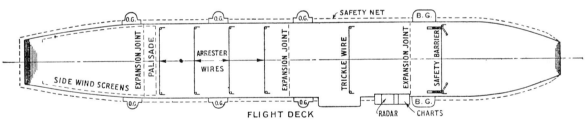

Fig. 7

Dead weight, original vessel .. .. 12,240 tons
Dead weight, converted vessel .. .. 11,010 tons

Dead weight, decrease .. 1,230 tons

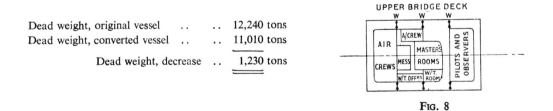

Fig. 8

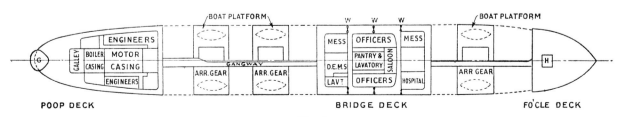

Fig. 9

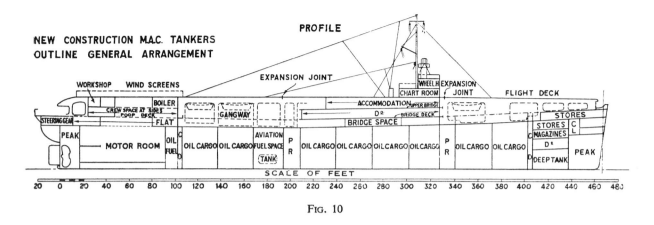

FIG. 10

Flight deck and other arrangements generally similar to existing tankers *Rapana* class

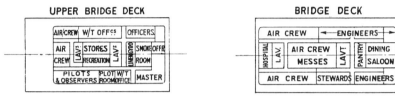

FIG. 11

FIG. 12

to be better balanced than the grain ship, due largely to their longer length, the more open superstructure, and a more elegant two-storied bridge erection.

General Arrangements

The primary difference between the two types of merchant aircraft carriers was the absence of a hangar in the tanker type. To have provided such a space in these vessels would have completely altered the oil cargo piping and associated arrangements, and have extended considerably the period allowed for the conversion work. The increased length of flight deck provided some compensation for the omission of a hangar but introduced other problems. Aircraft continuously parked in the open cannot have the same servicing facilities that are available in a hangar space; only minor adjustments usually are possible, except under the most favourable weather conditions, when certain classes of major repairs might be attempted.

The flight deck was not a strength member; it was arranged in sections with an expansion joint between each, one joint placed immediately forward and aft of the midship erection with, in the case of the existing tankers only, a further joint forward of the poop section. This arrangement enabled the deck, together with all its supports, to be designed for prefabrication, and in the existing tanker conversions, out of a total of 957 tons additional steel, 51 per cent was fabricated by the structural industry and supplied to the ship repairers ready for assembly.

The increased length of these ships called for the addition of two oerlikon guns, making the armament a total of nine guns against seven in the grain ships.

The same considerations in regard to projections beyond the moulded hull did not apply in these vessels, therefore the armament zarebas had no need to encroach on the flight deck and so were extended on sponson supports for their full diameter beyond this deck.

The lifeboats, normally placed aft in tankers, were redisposed in the well spaces, four placed in the after well and two in the forward well just forward of the bridge spaces. Gravity type davits had to be fitted so that the boats could be stowed well inboard and to as high a position to the under side of the flight deck as was practicable (see Fig. 16). The total combined crews numbered 122 men.

The grain ship practice of segregating and allocating blocks of space to the different crews was followed, and the divided accommodation arrangements between bridge and poop space more readily facilitated this in the tankers.

Main Propelling Machinery

The inclusion of a number of existing vessels in this tanker programme precluded any suggestion for increases in the propelling power of the new vessels. All were considered capable of fulfilling the specified 11-knot speed in service and could develop 3,300 B.H.P.

In comparison, the grain ships were better equipped on a power basis, as they had the larger reserve of power above that required for the normal service speed.

The generator capacity in all the existing vessels was increased to cover for the additional electrical load, but apart from this no other major addition was made within the machinery spaces. The main particulars of the machinery installed in the new vessels were as follows (see table IV):—

TABLE IV

Ship	Empire MacCabe	Empire MacColl	Empire MacKay	Empire MacMahon
Propelling machinery Type	Swan-Hunter-Doxford Opposed piston, reversible, two-stroke	← – – Harland-Burmeister & Wain – – → Four-cycle, single-acting		Hawthorn-Werkspoor Single-acting, four-stroke
Dimensions ..	4 cylinders 600 × 2,320 mm. 3,300 B.H.P.	6 cylinders, 740 × 1,500 mm., 3,300 B.H.P.		8 cylinders 650 × 1,400 mm. 3,300 B.H.P.
Auxiliary boilers ..	2	2	2	2
Type	← – – – – – – – – – Single-ended, cylindrical, multi-tubular – – – – – – – – – →			
	12′ 6″ dia. × 11′ 0″ oil-fired	12′ 6″ dia. × 11′ 6″ oil-fired	12′ 6″ dia. × 11′ 0″ oil-fired	13′ 0″ dia. × 12′ 3″ oil-fired
Working pressure ..	150 lb.	150 lb.	150 lb.	180 lb.
Generators	← – – – – – – – 2 at 30 kW and 1 at 35 kW, 110 volt direct current – – – – – – – →			

The auxiliary boiler smoke and main engine exhaust gases were disposed of through discharge trunks carried under the flight deck and extended each side to the after end of this deck. Spark arrester arrangements were provided, and because of the after stowage position for the aircraft, these trunks had to be adequately lagged against the transmission of heat to the deck forming floor of the parking area.

Model Experiments

Apart from the question of combining the carriage of oil cargo with the operating of aircraft, the item most discussed departmentally before work began on these vessels was the hangar problem. The practical difficulties already referred to determined this matter, but in some minds it was felt that exposure of the aircraft to all conditions of weather would result in their damage and immobilize them when most urgently required. The service performances of these vessels showed that there was little justification for this doubt, but that it existed led to a series of model experiments being carried out at the National Physical Laboratory in case this hangar question should arise again at a later date. These experiments were for the purpose of investigating the effect of adding a hangar to tankers already provided with a flight deck, and to ascertain the influence of the hangar on speed, wind resistance and steering, in calm water and in waves. From an analysis made of the several reports on these experiments it was shown that—

(a) The plating-in of the gaps below the flight deck for hangar purposes led not merely to lower wind resistance, but also to greater manœuvrability in high winds.

(b) The presence of a hangar had no appreciable effect on the turning moments.

One of the reports indicated that from a comparison of the values of wind resistance coefficients obtained in these experiments with the results derived from other tests with models of normal type merchant vessels, the values for this deep wall-sided erection on these tankers were remarkably low. There is a corollary here, perhaps not altogether relevant in this paper, which suggests that in the design of superstructure arrangements for all ships in general it might be equally worth while giving some consideration to these as well as to improvement of the under-water hull form.

Aircraft Carrier Arrangements

The stowage or parking area for four "Swordfish" aircraft was arranged at the after end of the flight deck. This space, 100 ft. in length, was closed in by an arrangement of hinged wind screens fitted on each side of the deck, and by a palisade of portable screens placed across the fore end of the space. Eyebolts screwed into flush deck sockets to take the special lashing arrangements were provided within this space as well as in the deck forward of the safety barrier.

The safety net around the outside of the flight deck in the grain ships did not extend forward of the bofors gun positions. In these ships, because of the need for protection around the forward parking space, the net was extended each side to within 12 ft. from the fore end of the deck.

The arrester gear was a repeat of the grain ships, with an additional unit to operate the trickle wire and safety barrier. This barrier was placed across the deck at a distance of about 100 ft. from the fore end. It was supported by substantial side stanchions, raised and lowered hydraulically.

The short hold and 'tween decks forward were the only spaces available for use as magazines and inflammable stores. In the arrangement of these a water-spraying system connected to an independent service pipe line was provided to all the magazine spaces.

With approximately 10 per cent of the deadweight lost as a result of the additional structure, it was possible to use one of the main centre tanks for storage of the aviation fuel tanks. This tank adjoined the main pump room, the entrance house to which was used as the control position for the fuelling system.

The electrical installation, while materially less than in the grain vessels, was nevertheless extensive, and largely influenced the time taken over the conversion of the existing tankers. The main differences in the specifications for the two types of ships were those concerned with the omission of the hangar and its special equipment, and there being no need to provide mechanical ventilation to the cargo spaces.

Production and General

The average time taken for the conversion work on the existing tankers was six months, while the extra time taken to complete the new tankers, as compared with the normal constructional period had they been completed as ordinary tankers, was just under three months.

The names of the tankers withdrawn from the Anglo-Saxon Petroleum Co.'s fleets for this conversion, together with the names of the repair establishments entrusted to do the work were:—

M.V. *Rapana*.	Smith Dock Co., Ltd., North Shields.
M.V. *Amastra*.	Smith Dock Co., Ltd., North Shields.
M.V. *Gadilla*.	Smith Dock Co., Ltd., North Shields.
M.V. *Ancylus*.	Palmers Hebburn Co., Ltd., Hebburn-on-Tyne.
M.V. *Miralda*.	Palmers Hebburn Co., Ltd., Hebburn-on-Tyne.
M.V. *Macoma*.	Palmers Hebburn Co., Ltd., Hebburn-on-Tyne.
M.V. *Acavus*.	Silley, Cox & Co., Ltd., Falmouth.
M.V. *Adula*.	Silley, Cox & Co., Ltd., Falmouth.
M.V. *Alexia*.	T. W. Greenwell & Co., Ltd., Sunderland.

The vessels *Gadilla* and *Macoma*, at the time of their withdrawal, were sailing under the Dutch flag under the management of an associated firm in the Anglo-Saxon Petroleum Co.'s group. These vessels, when converted, continued in Dutch hands, and have the distinction of being the first aircraft carrier vessels to sail under the Dutch flag.

Conclusion

Eleven firms produced these nineteen merchant aircraft carriers within a period of nineteen months. This, if not spectacular, was at least very satisfactory, and could not have been achieved without the goodwill of all the firms concerned, exemplifying to the fullest the results of co-ordinated effort in the production of a "compromise" that successfully fulfilled an emergency need. The battle of the Atlantic was not won by these vessels, but their presence in convoys materially contributed to its success, and this paper would be very incomplete if tribute was not paid to the men who manned them, both naval and merchant, men whose team work and enthusiasm earned for the name of "Mac" ships the high respect of all who sailed in their company.

Written Contributions to the Discussion

Sir Amos Ayre, K.B.E. (Vice-President): It is difficult to say with certainty from whom came the idea of the merchant-aircraft-carrier, but I remember the first suggestion made to me was from Sir Douglas Thomson, Bt., then Parliamentary Private Secretary, Ministry of War Transport, who had been working on the idea with some of his colleagues in the Ministry. It was made at a moment when, at the highest level, the most serious consideration was being given to the question of using certain merchant shipbuilding capacity either for the continuance of the building of merchant ships or for the smaller type of aircraft carrier, for each of which we had the most dire need. The "Mac" ship was a means of meeting both requirements.

The author refers to the retention of the Red Ensign, and I think it can now be said that such was a fundamental condition of our taking on the job at a time when, more than ever, the merchant side had much difficulty in holding on to that part of the industry that had been allocated to it.

There is little doubt these vessels represent the least costly aircraft carriers ever produced, even if they did only accommodate four or five aircraft; this, of course, refers to the total effort in labour, material, and money. But the greatest value in the idea, as it was carried out, was the saving in time required for production. In the latter regard I think the author will agree that but for late deliveries of arrester gear and the elevator, the first vessel would have been ready one or two months earlier than the target date. In other words, a vessel of the type might have been produced in about six months after keel laying. Experience seems to have been that, as a strategic type, it justifies close consideration. We soon had news of the moral effect on those who manned the convoys, and of some wonderful deck-landings, one of them said to have been a record having regard to weather conditions.

If the author has been able to collect the information it would be interesting to add to the present record a note of the speeds which were attainable at the ballast draught, as well as the grain-laden draught which corresponds to the cargo deadweight of 6,450 tons.

Mr. J. L. Adam, C.B.E. (Vice-President): This paper has, of course, the same interest to me as to everyone else interested in the ships built for special purposes during the war.

It has, however, for the technical man interested in ships' structures, a very much greater value. For instance, no one reading this paper can assume that it was a simple matter to add a complete superstructure 15 ft. above the normal strength deck of the hull, although the author has, quite rightly, emphasized the arrangement and operational difficulties rather than the structural problems.

In the grain ships, in which the British Corporation was interested, the flight deck was longitudinally stiffened, and there is no doubt in my mind that with this arrangement, combined with the omission of expansion joints a relatively light deck was able to be fitted, with satisfactory results. It will be seen from the photograph (Fig. 1) and from the remarks in the paper that there could be no continuity in side plating, yet the arrangement had to be such that there was reasonable structural continuity fore and aft and athwartships, between the flight deck and the hull proper. To achieve this, very great care was taken in the arrangement of well-braced fore and aft and transverse girders under the top deck in association with effective webs at the ship's side. This was not altogether easy and it must be remembered also that the flight deck projected some 3 ft. 6 in. each side beyond the upper deck. Longitudinal strength and efficiency must, however, be combined with lateral efficiency if the structure generally is to be satisfactory, and it is only necessary to look at the plan of the upper deck shown in Fig. 4 to realize that here again was no small problem.

It will be seen that, in way of the hangars, the normal girder flange each side is cut down from some 18 ft. of plating each side to 8 ft., and this reduction is not gradual at the fore end. Actually, very great care was taken in designing the structure at the fore end of the hangar space and linking it up with that in way of the motor casing.

As will be gathered from the paper, there were quite a number of other structural problems in the ship, but those I have outlined will show how interesting it was from a hull girder point of view, and I think there is much we might learn from our experience with these ships.

I was prepared to hear of quite a lot of trouble of a minor order in the superstructures, but, in fact, it did not occur.

Sir J. Douglas W. Thomson, Bt.: The first "Mac" ship to go into service was the *Empire Macalpine*, and the management of this vessel was entrusted to my firm—Messrs. William Thomson & Co., Edinburgh. We were not unnaturally anxious that the experiment, which had many obvious difficulties, should be successful, but as it turned out none of the obvious difficulties materialized at all.

For our part we were conscious that the command of the vessel and the operation of the vessel were responsibilities of our merchant navy men who had no knowledge regarding aircraft operation. The crew of the vessel was roughly fifty each merchant navy and fleet air arm, and these were under different codes of discipline and were paid at very considerably different rates. Also the accommodation provided was of the usual type for the two services—the merchant navy men having considerably the better of the bargain. None of these problems provided any real difficulty in practice. We found immediately that the fleet air arm were determined to make the venture a success, and their selection of personnel could not have been more fortunate. In short, both sides of the partnership, both afloat and ashore, were determined that the experiment should work, and accordingly it did work.

The teething troubles were all of a minor character, and the most notable part of the maiden voyage from the Burntisland Yard to the Clyde was the obvious astonishment of various units of the Home Fleet encountered in the Pentland Firth.

The flying trials passed off without any untoward incidents, and the vessel very shortly afterwards sailed on her first Atlantic voyage.

The experiment was, I think, justified by results—the *Empire Macalpine* was able to maintain a satisfactory number of hours of flying reconnaissance in the area in which it was her duty to assist in the protection of her convoy.

As far as cargo was concerned she had consistently good out-turns.

It would have been difficult to find a better example of co-operation and mutual confidence than existed between the two services in the "Mac" ships which we managed, and to all ranks concerned we should all be grateful.

I also feel that the fact that we as managers encountered so few troubles speaks itself for the care taken by the builders and in the design. Readers of Mr. Lenaghan's paper may have the feeling that the conception of the "Macs" was easy and rapid. Most of them, however, will have had experience of trying to get a new idea adopted by several Government departments simultaneously, and will realize that he has glossed over the difficulties encountered and surmounted by the department in which he was working.

Mr. A. L. White, M.B.E.: By reason of my connection with Palmers Hebburn Co., Ltd., I was closely associated with the author in the conversion of the nine Anglo-Saxon tankers to which he refers in Part II of the paper, and I should like to congratulate him on an extremely concise and informative statement. Palmers Hebburn Company, as the paper states, undertook the final development of the basic scheme, and made and issued detailed plans and specifications to all ship repairers concerned with these nine vessels and, whilst the usual minor technical difficulties arose and supply troubles made their presence felt, the programme was carried out with surprising smoothness. In this connection the greatest credit is due to the author and his colleagues of the Admiralty Merchant Shipbuilding and Repair Departments.

These ships were converted to meet an emergency at a time when design was governed to a large extent by the necessity of conserving both labour and materials compatible with producing an adequate unit in the shortest possible time. Had the conversions been done in normal times with a view to long-term service, I think it possible that steps would have been taken to obtain a more efficient grafting of the new structure into the old. The addition of a superstructure equal in weight to approximately 25 per cent of the original lightweight of the vessel was achieved with minimum disturbance to existing structure. The flight deck supports were electrically welded to doubling plates on the weather

Fig. 13.—*EMPIRE MACKAY*—Oil tanker "Mac" ship. New construction tanker

Fig. 14.—Oil tanker "Mac" "Rapana" class

Fig. 15.—M.V. "Rapana" before conversion

decks and the side webs were connected in a similar manner to the deck stringers and sheerstrakes. In no case was the upper deck, or the poop, bridge, or forecastle decks pierced to effect a scarph with the main hull framing. The adoption of this method of connection effected a great saving in time, particularly as it assisted prefabrication and standardization of flight deck structure, but, in my opinion, it seemed inevitable that, even with the judicious introduction of deck expansion joints, the added weight and lack of structural continuity would in service increase stresses in the main hull at certain critical points and under certain conditions of loading.

This opinion is confirmed by my own observation when reconverting two of these ships to normal service conditions. Structure was strained in various places, particularly in the sheerstrake and deck stringers at the bridge front and end, but it can be said that their war service has had little lasting effect and that the initial design decisions, dictated largely by prevailing circumstances, were fully justified.

It is, of course, extremely easy to be wise after the event and it is a practice for which most of us are not entirely blameless. There are no doubt certain aspects of these ships which, in the light of later knowledge, could have been improved, but I fully endorse the author's remarks in regard to the success of this "compromise" and again congratulate him on the very efficient way in which he has presented the facts.

Mr. A. Mitchell, B.Sc., R.C.N.C. (Associate-Member): The extent to which air power over the sea was exercised in the battle of the Atlantic is amply demonstrated by the conversions described in the author's paper.

The ability to operate aircraft from ships is conditioned largely by speed of ship and length of flying-off deck. In the "Mac" ships both these factors approached the minimum simultaneously, and the resultant aircraft carrier was limited to the operation of relatively slow-flying aircraft, of a type which had, however, demonstrated its value for anti-submarine patrols.

These "Mac" ships, sailing regularly with ocean convoys, made such a contribution to the anti-submarine protection that fewer of the fully equipped escort carriers were necessary, and the call on the merchant shipbuilding effort for fast ships was lessened at a critical time.

The experience gained by the Admiralty in the escort carrier conversions was made freely available to the Controller of Merchant Shipbuilding and Repairs, and the special precautions as to stowage and handling of petrol and explosives and fire prevention in the hangars, incorporated in H.M. ships, were applied to the similar problems in the "Mac" ships.

The aircraft lifts fitted in the grain ships and the arresting gear for both grain and tanker types, were fortunately available from the equipment ordered in anticipation of a considerable increase in the escort carrier programme—it is probable that some of the

earlier "Mac" ships escorted across the Atlantic the arresting gear for the later ships of the type.

It is satisfactory to note that the equipment provided was so expeditiously fitted and applied to such extremely good purpose.

Mr. P. Ledgard (Member): This paper gives another record of a project boldly conceived and executed during the late war.

It is gratifying to see that the author has found time to prepare this paper, which I am sure will become a worthy addition to the literature of this Institution.

There are a few notes which I would like to add to the section dealing with the subject of merchant aircraft tankers as a contribution to this paper.

It has been rightly expressed that these vessels were primarily cargo carriers with special equipment installed for purely defensive purposes only. This was, of course, novel for this class of vessel and provided many problems during their construction and conversion. It was only by the keenness and excellent co-operation which existed between the Admiralty Merchant Shipbuilding Department and tanker companies, shipbuilders and ship repairers, that these were solved so readily. Hence the short time taken in getting these vessels into service.

Mention has been made about the stability of the grain carrier "Mac" ships as having an optimum safe metacentric height of about 4 ft. The figure for the loaded conditions of the conversion "Mac" tankers was about 2 ft. and ·3 ft. for the new construction tankers of 61 ft. beam.

I understand that these vessels proved to be comfortable in service and steady under flying operations.

Care, however, had to be exercised during loading or ballasting the conversion "Macs", as it would have been possible under orthodox procedures of filling cargo tanks to produce a condition approaching negative stability.

To overcome this, instructions were given to fill not less than four tanks to about half their depth at the beginning of loading, after which the remaining tanks could be safely filled, completing the tanks mentioned last.

The reverse order had to be carried out during unloading.

The increased G M in the new construction tankers of 61 ft. beam made it possible to load and ballast in the usual way.

All these tankers were of the three tank abreast type, having two longitudinal bulkheads. The question therefore of safety, with wing tanks bilged due to possible damage by enemy action, became more pronounced.

Provision against any tendency to capsize was made by either having all wing tanks loaded to a height, in relation to the water-line, which would balance entry of sea water and loss of oil cargo, or alternate wing tanks full and empty alternately, producing the same balance with two wing tanks open to the sea. This assumed a length of damage greater than one tank length equal to 31 ft. Such practice was, incidentally, the usual one for tankers in general and no mishap due to bilging of wing tanks has been brought to my notice.

A figure of 10 per cent is given for reduction in dead-weight carrying capacity after the addition of defensive equipment. When one considers the value of these vessels under war service as completed, a reduction of this order can indeed be considered worth while. The new construction "Mac" tankers were nearer to 7 and 8 per cent.

Regarding the streamline effect of the flight deck structure, it was observed during the various trials that the course-keeping properties of these tankers had been improved by the addition of this deck. In one particular instance the wind speed over the flight deck was more than required by the officers for aircraft take-off. The ship's speed was therefore reduced to about 6 to 8 knots, or as low as the diesel propelling machinery revolutions would permit. There was not the slightest difficulty in keeping this vessel into the wind at such a speed.

It is understood that the flight deck kept remarkably dry in rough seas. On the other hand, where the sides were plated for a short distance between the forecastle and flight decks, the safety net structure was damaged in certain vessels of the converted "Mac" tankers. The reason for the dryness of the flight deck can be attributed to the waves being free to pass over the tank decks, because the maximum open space was provided below the flight deck in order to free any gas vapour arising from the cargo. In fact, it was one of the primary factors in the design of this class of "Mac" ship to keep the tank deck clear of any enclosing structure. No damage occurred to the safety nets of the new construction "Mac" tankers, because the platforms for these nets were stopped clear of side plating and wire net protection inserted. Any seas sweeping up the sides were, therefore, impeded as little as possible.

While on the subject of flight decks, I would suggest that a perspective sketch of their structure, giving the scantlings, would be of value to the Institution, because there were practically no data to be obtained on this subject during the development of the structural arrangements. Theoretical considerations were insufficient for ready assessment of scantlings and the vast experience of Lloyd's Register was brought to bear on the problem.

The resulting structure proved adequate in service and gave no trouble of any kind, even when certain vessels were diverted on special occasions for carrying aircraft as freight across the Atlantic.

The new construction tankers had the least scantlings, because it was not necessary to mass-produce the steel-work, as was the case of the tankers withdrawn from their normal service.

It should be noted that the framing of the flight decks was disposed in a longitudinal direction; besides being useful for fabricating purposes the effect was to give an exceptionally fair deck for the aircraft to run along.

All the additional deckhouses amidships, although extended over the oil compartments, were arranged in such a manner as to allow all the tank hatches to be in the open. This entailed special consideration to breakwater arrangements for the supporting structure forward and prevention of locked seas on deck.

It will be noted that the petrol tanks are situated in one of the centre cargo compartments, about amidships. There were a number of advantages for this position, such as its proximity to the cargo pump room for placing petrol pumps for servicing aircraft, flooding valves for quickly surrounding the petrol tanks in case of emergency, and good leads to atmosphere for the cargo tank and petrol tanks' independent gas vapour lines.

Also, an empty tank amidships, when carrying heavy oil cargoes, gives good distribution for reducing stress on the hull, due to longitudinal bending moments. Incidentally, the observed movements at the expansion joints appeared to have been about $\frac{5}{8}$ in. to $\frac{3}{4}$ in. at sea.

The waste gas discharges from the main diesel engines and auxiliary boilers brought their own problems for these vessels, with propelling machinery aft. They were, however, surmounted, as well as the safety measures necessary for fuelling aircraft and servicing generally in this region.

One of the agreeable surprises in these vessels was the way in which the naval staffs and merchant navy personnel merged together in successfully operating the units of this new and untried fleet. It was certainly a pleasure to work with them during the various sea trials and observe the resource and skill in which they carried out their duties.

I understand that these tankers have now been converted back with little difficulty to ordinary tankers again. This possibility of reconversion was borne in mind during the design stage of the defensive equipment. It is, therefore, pleasing to know that the shipowners have now been able to augment their tanker fleets again with these fine ships without undue delay.

Mr. J. F. C. Conn, D.Sc. (Member of Council): The author has given an excellent paper on the "Mac" ships, which were few in number but important in their effect. During trials Swordfish aircraft took off from and alighted upon their decks with surprising facility. The success of the "Mac" ships was due perhaps to:—

(a) The courage and resource of the Fleet Air Arm pilots.

(b) the Swordfish aircraft performance; and

(c) The efficient arrangements made for the operation of these ships as aircraft carriers.

The technical peculiarities of the vessels are interesting. To build such extensive superstructures successfully was no mean feat. Only the "Mac" tankers are shown in the diagrams as having expansion joints, since the flight deck on these ships was not the strength deck. Can the author give any results of service experience with these ships which would shed light on the merits and demerits of expansion joints?

It is unfortunate that no midship section drawings are reproduced in the paper. The value of the latter would be enhanced if these were added. Does the author agree

FIG. 16.—LIFEBOAT STOWAGE IN TANKER "MACS"

FIG. 17.—DISCHARGING GRAIN FROM A "MAC" SHIP AT A NORTH-WEST PORT

that, if circumstances had permitted, a longitudinal system of framing would have been desirable?

In those sections of the paper dealing with model experiments the author has shown the practical advantages of such tests. The highly significant results given on page 104 are worthy of notice. These should be carefully studied by those designers who seek to obtain the optimum above-water form of hull.

Captain R. C. Bayne, R.N.: Arising out of this excellent and lucid paper, a few remarks on some of the problems which faced the Admiralty in connection with the staff requirements for these ships may be of interest.

In the earlier part of this paper, under "Policy and Planning," reference is made to the modified proposals, based on the conversion of the ordinary standard tramp, which were submitted, and to the reception they received. It was at this stage that difficulties in planning began and some tricky decisions had to be made. Later, when the Tanker "Mac" ships were considered, other problems arose.

Innumerable meetings were held in the Admiralty at which all interested parties were represented, and where opinion seemed to be nearly always equally divided between those who believed in the "Mac" ship and those who did not, or between those who wanted to fit them like men-of-war with every conceivable device, or those who appreciated that simplicity was essential if something was to be produced quickly. To illustrate some of the problems:—

Speed of 11 knots.—The Air Staff, in general, were horrified at the idea of such a speed, pointing out that no carrier had yet been produced with a designed speed of less than 19 knots and that 14–15 knots originally agreed was a minimum. The other side replied that 15-knot ships were not available and were all wanted for bringing food into the country, and that if the lower speed was not acceptable the scheme might have to be dropped. This also was not acceptable, and so, after much wrangling, the Air Staff finally said if there was no other way they would accept the 11-knot vessel with certain provisos, but pointed out that they had doubts whether the resultant ship would be very much use as a carrier. Undoubtedly a bold step but one that was fully justified in the light of events.

Asdics.—Should the ships be fitted with asdics? In conformity with normal naval practice at the time, asdics were strongly advocated by some, it being pointed out that they might make all the difference between a ship evading a U-boat or being torpedoed; and that these were valuable ships whose loss could be ill afforded. Against this it was stressed that asdics meant added complications in building or conversion, would probably delay completion to an undesirable extent, and that the time factor was all important. After lengthy argument it was finally decided not to fit asdics and to accept the risks. (No ship was in fact torpedoed. H.M.S. *Audacity* was not a true "Mac" ship, as she flew the white ensign and was termed an escort carrier.)

Radar.—This went through much the same vicissitudes

as asdics. Though its fitting would cause added complications, particularly to the bridge structure, etc., and an increase in complement (for men to man the set) it would not delay completion, and so a decision to fit radar was taken. There is little doubt that this was a wise one.

Night Flying Equipment.—As night attacks by U-boats were frequently carried out on convoys, night flying equipment was considered very desirable. Such equipment fitted to meet normal naval standards, however, entailed complicated arrangements of deck lighting and wiring, etc., and owing to a shortage of electricians in the shipyards it appeared that the fitting of it might delay the ships. In this case a compromise was reached and emergency deck lighting of a very simple nature was finally fitted. Subsequent operations showed that this decision greatly increased the usefulness of these ships.

The above are only a few brief examples of what nearly every feature and item of naval equipment fitted in these ships went through. "Mac" ships turned out to be very austere, not only because of their functions, but also because of limited resources and the importance of speed in their production. Though no one will deny the praise due to those who designed, built and manned these ships, some credit should, it is felt, also be given to those who decided the policy and planned them, and who had to make so many difficult decisions "in the dark."

Commander Lord Gifford, R.N.: It gives me great pleasure to make some written comments on the excellent paper which Mr. J. Lenaghan has written on the subject of merchant aircraft carriers, because of the very happy association which was formed, on account of these ships, between the Department of Merchant Shipbuilding and Repairs and the Air Department in the Admiralty. This association developed into a very personal one between the author and myself, assisted by a very small and select little group. The two of us were left to get on with the job, and I think we did so with the minimum of red tape.

We also made good friends with a number of shipbuilding and ship repairing firms, many of whom had never, in their wildest dreams, thought that they would be called upon to build an aircraft carrier. The ship owners too entered into the spirit of this revolutionary experiment with zest and enthusiasm.

This spirit was equally noticeable among the crews of the ships, both Royal Navy and Merchant Navy, and I would venture to say that the "Mac" ships did more to cement good relations and understanding between these two services than any other single undertaking throughout the war.

The moral effect on the convoys was excellent, and I was told that on one occasion, when a convoy conference was being held in America, the Naval Control Service Officer, having issued his instructions, inquired if any master wished to ask a question. A master rose and asked if there was going to be a "Mac" ship in the convoy. When he was given an answer in the affirmative, some 50 masters, who were present, leaped to their feet and applauded. I think this is very remarkable, as the merchant navy is not, normally, very demonstrative.

It is true that the hardest part of the Battle of the Atlantic was over by the time that most of these ships came into service, but aircraft from them made a number of submarine attacks, and it is almost certain that there was one victim. How many attacks were prevented by the almost continuous escort which the "Swordfish" were able to provide, no one can tell, but it must have been a considerable number.

One cannot pay too high a tribute to the air crews who operated from these ships in the Atlantic. On many occasions they brought their aircraft back safely, in conditions of wind and sea which previously had been thought quite impossible. The "String Bag," as the "Swordfish" was rudely called, certainly added a feather to the cap of Fairey Aviation, Ltd. for their performance in the "Macs". No other aircraft could have landed in such conditions. Their slow landing speed and robust construction enabled them to come down safely with the ship pitching or with the minimum of wind speed over the deck. This tribute must include the deck landing control officers, who skilfully chose the moment when the deck was level to bring the aircraft down safely.

At one time it was considered that the air officers should have a separate mess. I was always against this, and it was eventually arranged that the merchant navy and fleet air arm officers should all mess together. This had excellent results, and many ships' officers took their turn in the air as unofficial observers.

One enthusiastic 2nd officer proudly appeared on the bridge, as his ship steamed up the Clyde, with a "Swordfish" aircraft embroidered in yellow silk on his tie.

The Royal Netherlands Navy played their part in the scheme, as has been stated by the author. The enthusiasm shown and the experience gained in the *Gadilla* and *Macoma* has had a sequel in the taking over by the Dutch of a light fleet carrier. During the trials of the *Gadilla*, H.R.H. Prince Bernhard, of the Netherlands, inspected the vessel, and insisted on landing on the deck himself.

Many naval officers were sceptical as to whether the merchant navy master could successfully operate an aircraft carrier, but their fears were quite unfounded. The masters of both the grain ships and the tankers played their parts well. Each of them was given a course at the Western Approaches Technical School and in a white ensign carrier.

My last view of one of the "Mac" ships was in the Red Sea in the summer of 1946, when returning from the Pacific in H.M.S. *Victorious*. The latter was carrying 600 Australian brides of naval officers and ratings instead of aircraft, and we passed the *Macoma*, reconverted to her normal vocation. I made a signal "what have you done with your flat top?" to which the Dutch master replied "It iss better without the flat top!"

Author's Reply

Sir Amos Ayre refers to the late delivery of arrester and elevator gear and the effect on delivery of the first vessel. The subsequent vessels suffered more from these delays than the *Empire MacAlpine*. In the latter vessel these equipments were actually completed after the vessel had left the builder's hands, but I doubt if their programmed dates had been adhered to, and, having regard to the newness of the type of vessel to the builders, if construction from keel to completion could have been carried out under seven months. The grain "Mac" in ballast draught had no difficulty in maintaining a speed of 13 knots, and their grain-laden draught, corresponding to a cargo deadweight of 6,450 tons, was 24 ft. 6 in.

Mr. J. L. Adam naturally draws attention to the structural arrangements in these vessels. The flight decks in all but two of the vessels were longitudinally framed, and I agree this was the most satisfactory and lighter arrangement. The constructional arrangement in way of the hangar space in the grain vessels provided many problems; adequate compensation was made for the large cut this space made in the upper deck plating, transverse strength was maintained by side webs and deep overhead beams across the hangar space, and all side and longitudinal girders were carefully scarphed into the structure, particularly at the fore end, in way of the casings.

Sir J. Douglas W. Thomson, as stated by Sir Amos Ayre, was one of the initial sponsors of the "Mac" ship. His personal interest continued until the need for these ships had passed, which, together with the enthusiasm of the staff officers and crews of his firm, Wm. Thomson & Company, Edinburgh, contributed largely to their success.

Mr. A. L. White's remarks refer to the nine existing tankers withdrawn from service for conversion. It was always my impression that the flight deck supporting structure on these vessels was too rigid and heavy and I have no doubt, with these vessels rolling in a seaway, considerable stresses were imposed on the deck connections at the foot of each side web. Practical difficulties prevented many of the webs being positioned over the main hull side transverses and bulkheads, and the absence of this continuity between the added and existing structure could account for the evidence of straining in the stringer and sheerstrake, observed by Mr. White in the reconversion of these vessels back to normal tankers.

Mr. A. Mitchell, of the Naval Construction Department, advised the Merchant Shipbuilding and Repairs Department on the special equipment required for these vessels. My only comment on his remarks is to express thanks for his help so generously given throughout the construction of these vessels.

Mr. P. Ledgard adds greatly to the value of this paper by his remarks on the "Mac" tankers. As he states, the supports for the flight deck in the new construction tankers were not only considerably lighter in weight than those added to the existing tankers, but they were merged in with the main hull structure and formed a very compact and balanced superstructure. No evidence of straining, as reported in Mr. White's remarks, was observed in the reconversion of the four new tankers named in Table III.

Dr. J. F. C. Conn: No special observations were made on the behaviour of the expansion joints on the tankers but I have no doubt, having regard to the open type structural arrangements of the flight deck supports and the need to restrict the depth of the longitudinal side girders under this deck, that expansion joints were necessary. Mr. Ledgard gives figures noted at the joints in the new tankers; similar figures were also reported for the converted tankers. The main framing was transverse, in accordance with present tanker practice, with longitudinal frames on bottom shell, upper deck and flight deck. I do not think there would have been any particular advantage in departing from this.

Captain R. C. Bayne's contribution provides a side-light to the arguments which went on behind the scenes in the development of these ships. Departmental differences were many, but in the end all co-operated to the fullest to make the completed vessels a success, and none more so than that section of Trade Division Admiralty for which Captain Bayne was responsible.

Commander Lord Gifford was in close touch with these vessels throughout their active service as "Mac" ships, and I am grateful for his remarks on their performance. The wisdom of associating large numbers of naval and merchant personnel in ships of this class was doubted by many; that the experiment was successful is amply confirmed by Lord Gifford's remarks.

I am sorry I cannot include the further sketches requested by Mr. Ledgard and Dr. Conn. The structure on each type was varied in detail, and if I were to include the structural details of any one type it would be necessary, if justice is to be done to this aspect of the problem, to cover the structural arrangements in each class—grain ships, new tankers and converted existing tankers.

In conclusion, I wish to express my thanks to the contributors, all of whom were directly associated with the planning and development of these vessels.

British Submarine Design during the War (1939-45)
by A J Sims, OBE, RCNC, MINA

Originally published in *Transactions*, Volume 89, Number 3, July 1947, pages 149-164

BRITISH SUBMARINE DESIGN DURING THE WAR (1939–45)

By A. J. SIMS, O.B.E., R.C.N.C., Member*

(Read at the Spring Meeting of the Eighty-eighth Session of the Institution of Naval Architects, March 26, 1947, Admiral of the Fleet The Right Hon. Lord Chatfield, G.C.B., O.M., K.C.M.G., C.V.O., President, in the Chair.)

1. General

In his paper "The Royal Navy at the Outbreak of War,"† Sir Stanley V. Goodall, K.C.B., O.B.E., has given some details of the two latest types of submarines—the "U" and "T" classes—in service at the outbreak of the recent war. An examination of the tables provided with that paper will show that three of each of these types were completed at that time.

There were also twelve "S" class submarines, six minelayer submarines of the *Porpoise* class, and three fleet submarines of the *River* class. The remainder of the submarine fleet comprised the "O," "P" and "R" classes—programmed in the later 1920's—and a number of "H" and "L" classes completed or laid down during the 1914–18 war.

* Chief Constructor, Naval Construction Department, Admiralty.
† I.N.A. Spring Meetings, 1946.

The pre-war designs of "S," "U" and "T" classes formed the basis of all submarines which completed during the war in time to take part in operations. Many changes in the features of these submarines were, however, required as the war progressed, and this resulted in the designs being completely reviewed on several occasions. The advances of offensive and defensive qualities brought about by war experience were embodied as quickly as design considerations and the limited available building capacity permitted.

Several new designs were produced for special purposes, but during the first half of the war the decision was always that their advantages were not sufficient to counterbalance the disturbance of the building programme. Towards the end of 1941, however, it was decided to proceed with the design of the "A" class with a view to its insertion in the building programme at a

TYPICAL PARTICULARS OF WAR-TIME SUBMARINES

	"S" Class	"T" Class	"U" Class	"A" Class	"XE" Class
Length overall	217 ft. 0 in.	273 ft. 5 in.	196 ft. 10 in.	281 ft. 8½ in.	53 ft. 1½ in.
Beam extreme	23 ft. 9 in.	26 ft. 7 in.	16 ft. 1 in.	22 ft. 3 in.	5 ft. 9½ in.
Standard displacement (tons) ..	715	1,090	545	1,120	—
Surface displacement (tons)	814	1,321	658	1,385	30·3
Submerged displacement (tons) ..	990	1,571	740	1,620	33·6
Oil fuel carried (tons) (normal stowage)	44	132	55 (c)	159	—
Surface S.H.P.	1,900	2,500	615 (a)	4,300	42
Maximum surface speed (knots) ..	14¾	15¼	11¼	19	6½
Submerged S.H.P.	1,300	1,450	825	1,250	30
Maximum submerged speed (knots)..	9	9	9	8	6
Torpedo tubes	6 bow 1 external (b)	6 bow 5 external (b)	4 bow (b)	6 internal 4 external	—
Torpedoes carried (total)	13	17	8	20	—
Guns	1 3-in. 1 Oerlikon (b) 3 Vickers GO	1 4-in. 1 Oerlikon (b) 3 Vickers GO	1 3-in. 3 Vickers GO (b)	1 4-in. 1 Oerlikon 3 Vickers GO	—
Crew	48	61	33	61	4

Notes.

(a) "U" class had diesel-electric drive—the remainder direct drive.

(b) Slight variation in torpedo and gunnery armament occurred between vessels in each class.

(c) Maximum fuel stowage (including use of No. 5 Main Tank).

time when the builders could take it in their stride. These submarines were about to be delivered at frequent intervals when the war ended.

Reference must also be made to the "Midget" submarine designs of the "X" and "XE" types, and with this should be associated the design of "Chariots"—the name given to the British type of "human torpedo." These vessels required a diversion of design effort disproportionately greater than their size, but naval history now testifies that this was worth while.

2. "S," "U" and "T" Classes

The principal particulars concerning these classes are given in the accompanying table. There are several minor differences between vessels of any one class.

The "S" class submarine (see Fig. 1) was designed for offensive patrols in confined waters. The small pre-war building programmes between 1929 and 1935 had afforded the opportunity of successfully eliminating minor troubles with this class and of bringing the design continually up to date. Operational experience during the opening months of the war showed that these submarines were very suitable for North Sea work, and they were economical as far as production was concerned.

The design was, therefore, further reviewed early in 1940 in order to incorporate such war experience as had been obtained, and the decision given that submarines of this class were to be inserted in the building programme.

"S" class submarines were built in fairly large numbers up to the end of the war, the last vessel being delivered just after the conclusion of hostilities.

The last vessel, however, was greatly different in detail from the first. The hull construction showed a complete transformation from riveting to welding, with consequential improvement in the robustness of the hull against counter-attack, and an increase in the diving depth. The submarines built at the beginning of the war had welded frames and riveted pressure hull seams and butts, as experiments had shown some doubt as to the wisdom of welding pressure hull plating at that time. With the advance of welding technique as the war progressed the complete adoption of this process became possible.

A stern-firing external torpedo tube was added to the submarines built in the early part of the war, but this was later precluded by the decision to substitute a 4-in. gun for the 3-in. gun in certain vessels.

With the movement of the war to the Far East, the endurance was appreciably increased by converting certain of the main (ballast) tanks to oil-fuel tanks. Experience prior to the war had shown the difficulty in carrying oil fuel in riveted external tanks, since "working" of the structure—aggravated by bumping when alongside—had given rise to leakage through the rivets. The possibility of tell-tale tracks being left in war had made it necessary to stow all the oil fuel inside the pressure hull. With the adoption of welded external tanks, however, the difficulties with the riveted structure almost entirely disappeared, and it was again possible to carry oil fuel outboard.

Further alterations made in this class are discussed under Section 4.

The original "U" class submarines were intended primarily to replace, for both pro-submarine and anti-submarine training purposes, the historic "H" class which had given such outstanding service during and since the 1914–18 war. At the same time they were designed for short-distance war-time patrols.

The first three vessels, *Undine*, *Unity* and *Ursula*, were completed in August, October and December 1938, respectively, and were the only ones available at the outbreak of war.

During the war the design (see Fig. 2) was progressively kept up to date, and submarines of this class were built in fairly large numbers. From the table it will be seen that they had diesel-electric drive, and the simplicity of the machinery arrangements greatly facilitated rapid production. These submarines—of limited operational qualities—were destined to prove very suitable for work in the Mediterranean, especially during those periods when it was possible to operate from Malta.

In the pre-war submarines of the class the external torpedo tubes had caused the superstructure forward to be of a rather bluff shape, and this involved some disadvantages in periscope depth-keeping (aggravated by the comparatively short periscopes with which this class had to be equipped), in the visibility of the rather prominent bow wave, and in the loss of speed in a seaway. Later vessels had the bow fined, the length being slightly increased as a result. The fitting of other operational equipment made it necessary to forgo these tubes in later submarines of this type.

The already good diving qualities of the "U" class were improved by the addition of a quick-diving tank, which also assisted in giving better control during torpedo firing. This tank enables the submarine to be made deliberately heavy, and has been a feature of British submarines for some time.

The construction of this class was interrupted before they were adapted for complete construction by welding. The partial measure of welding the pressure hull frames and butts of plating was adopted in later war-time construction "U" class, but the pressure hull plating seams were riveted throughout.

The "T" class submarines (see Fig. 3) are of the patrol type and were designed to replace the "O," "P" and "R" classes. The first vessel—*Triton*—appeared in the 1935 building programme. Further vessels of the class were included in subsequent pre-war and war-time building programmes, and it was only when the preparations for building the "A" class were well advanced that it was decided not to order further vessels of the "T" class.

At the commencement of the war only three vessels of the class had been completed—*Triton*, *Triumph* and *Thistle*—although several others were in various stages of construction. Every effort was made during the war to obtain larger numbers of this very successful and very useful type of submarine, but the need for numbers made it necessary to curtail the programme to some extent in favour of the more easily built "U" and "S" classes.

As in the "S" class, it was possible to change over to complete welding in the "T" class with the resulting improvement in hull strength. The endurance was also increased for work in the Far East by converting certain main tanks to carry oil fuel.

The "T" class have, generally, two external torpedo tubes forward, and the effect which these had on the bow casing in the earliest vessels of the class was similar to that in "U" class. Later vessels were fined at this position, the lip ends of the tubes projecting to some extent through the casing and suitable fairing being provided. Two external tubes were also provided amidships—pointed forwards in earlier vessels but aft in later vessels in order to provide a stern firing salvo. This salvo was augmented in later vessels by the provision of an additional tube at the after end of the casing.

3. "A" Class

As already mentioned, it was not until the end of 1941 that certain considerations caused the construction of a new type of submarine to be approved. War-time pressure had enabled major strides to be made in welding technique, and this offered the prospect of improved hull strength. The adaptation of existing hull designs to the complete use of welding produced a much improved answer, but not the best which was possible. Moreover, the development of a new design in association with the use of welding enabled the construction of the hulls to be appreciably speeded up.

There were further arguments in favour of a new type of submarine. The war in the Far East made it desirable to produce a submarine of a higher surface speed and endurance. Again special attention had to be given to habitability, as the environmental conditions likely to be encountered would be much more severe than in home waters or even the Mediterranean. Many improvements had taken place in the scientific apparatus for offensive and defensive purposes, and every effort had been made to keep the old designs up to date. The congestion was, however, becoming acute, and it was clear that a new design would enable equipment to be disposed to better advantage.

These were some of the factors which led to the "A" class. The design was developed with all possible speed, but the vessels were not inserted in the new construction programmes until the builders were able to accept them with the minimum disturbance to their output of submarines.

It is of interest to note that the introduction of means whereby the diesels could be run with the submarine submerged at periscope depth (the equivalent of the German "Schnorkel") was given serious consideration at the inception of the design; indeed a system on this principle was considered for British submarines during the inter-war period. Evidence had become available on the performance of this gear in the Dutch submarines which came to this country in the early period of the war. The review of the problem showed that there was no technical difficulty in meeting the requirement with sacrifices in certain directions, but that while it was comparatively safe to re-charge the batteries with the submarine on the surface, the fitting of the gear was not justified. It should be emphasized that the Germans fitted "Schnorkel" when the strength of our antisubmarine attack made the presence of their submarines on the surface too unhealthy to be accepted.

Some latitude had to be shown in the procedure adopted to fabricate the hulls in order to suit the individual capabilities of the building yards. In the most advanced technique, the pressure hull portion of the submarine was divided into a number of sections—each of cylindrical or conical shape. Each section had its plates running fore and aft and was assembled in such a way as to give downhand welding throughout. Automatic welding was employed as far as possible. The circumferential joints had to be manually welded at a later stage on the slip after the sections had been fitted out as far as was practicable. These joints had to be welded in situ and consequently provided the most difficult welding in the ship. Accurate preparation beforehand, therefore, was given special attention so as to obtain the greatest guarantee of good-quality work.

At the slipway the sections were transported into position by travelling gantries and arrangements were made to facilitate downhand welding of the internal structure such as bulkheads, floors, flats, engine and motor seats, etc. This work was carried out on the upper part of the slipway, after which the sections were moved down the slip to their final position before they were joined together.

Sections of the external tanks and superstructure were also prefabricated in order to save time at the slip.

Reference has already been made to the high standard of habitability required in this design. The success obtained in the air-conditioning of the existing types of submarines was carried a stage further in that a special air-conditioning compartment was introduced. Here the air was drawn from the main body of the submarine, reduced in temperature and humidity and—if necessary—adjusted in carbon dioxide and oxygen content, and then re-circulated to the submarine again. The opportunity was taken to give careful consideration to the details of this system, and many trials beforehand were carried out to ensure that the optimum distribution of air to the various compartments, and efficiency of the system as a whole under the cramped conditions obtaining in submarine design, were produced. The arrangement of accommodation also represented a step forward from previous practice. All of the accommodation was placed in the forward half of the submarine except for a small number of bunks aft. All noisy machines were kept away from the mess spaces, and every member of the crew was provided with a bunk.

The provision of good fresh-water storage, electric distillers, cold cupboards and domestic automatic refrigerators were other contributions to habitability in the tropics.

The sudden ending of the war prevented operational experience with this class from being obtained, the first submarine being completed just before the end of the war.

4. War-time Improvements

Reference has already been made to some of the improvements introduced in our submarines as the war proceeded, and the following supplementary notes may be of interest:—

(a) Welding

The decision to change over from riveting to welding was made after a very careful review of the performance of welding under the peculiar conditions associated with the submarine's functions and of the ability of the shipbuilders to accept this change. There were many anxious moments in the period immediately following the decision. The enthusiasm which has, however, been shown by the builders, together with the searching information provided by radiographic examination, have given confidence in the results obtained. The welded hulls have shown their ability to withstand punishment, and improvements in diving depth have also been obtained. It needs to be stated firmly that there is every reason to believe that the strength of the "A" class hull is at least equivalent to, if not better than, the strength of any submarine produced by our enemies.

Some of the diving depths quoted for German submarines are the result of their preferring, by diving deeper, to accept an extremely low factor of safety technically, in order to obtain such safety as they could from our devastating anti-submarine measures.

(b) Improved Radar and Radio Equipment

Keeping pace with the important developments in these fields taxed the resources of designer, production expert, builder and refitting yard alike. It was essential that the submarine service should have the best equipment available at the earliest possible moment. Those who have seen a submarine's control room will realize some of the difficulties in incorporating new equipment. Our building and refitting authorities were particularly patient under the several demands made upon them, and our submarines were kept up to date with marked success.

(c) Silencing of Auxiliary Machinery

The need for the highest degree of silencing of those items of auxiliary machinery which may have to be operated in the presence of enemy forces was emphasized in the early stages of the war, and much effort was devoted to achieving this. The first method of attacking the problem was to reduce the noise made in the machines themselves or to choose alternative equipment which was inherently more silent in operation. The second approach was to mount the equipment on special flexible mountings which would greatly reduce the noise transmitted through the hull of the submarine to the sea.

(d) Shock Mounting of Equipment

With the greater accuracy and intensity of the enemy's anti-submarine measures, it was increasingly necessary to ensure that equipment was comparable in robustness to the pressure hull itself. Much experience in this connection had been obtained by pre-war tests against submarine targets. Moreover, the measures adopted for reducing sound emission were also helpful in increasing resistance to shock of the auxiliaries concerned, despite the fact that optimum sound isolation and shock mounting techniques are rarely compatible.

When possible, submarines which had been heavily attacked were examined on their return to determine what lessons could be learned from the defects sustained, and many improvements were introduced as a result.

(e) Torpedo Equipment

The measure of flexibility in torpedo-tube armament which the external tube affords was exploited to vary the arrangement of this armament to some extent as operational requirements demanded. Our pre-war completed submarines had no stern salvo. The "T" class, however, had the rather remarkable bow salvo of ten torpedoes. By the addition of an external torpedo tube aft and the turning around of the two midship bow firing external tubes, a stern salvo of three torpedoes was provided in many of these vessels. A stern firing tube was also added to many of the "S" class until this had to be forgone in the face of other requirements.

(f) Diving Times

Close attention was given to the factors determining the diving times for the various designs. The rate of flooding the main tanks, the flooding and venting of the superstructure casing, and the speed of angling the vessel as she submerges, are all important factors. There are many other details which require to be borne in mind. In British submarines, diving times are taken to the depth at which the tops of the raised periscopes are just above water, and this is a greater depth than is usually allowed for in recording the times of diving for submarines of other navies.

(g) Guns

The opportunity provided in the war for the use of the gun was surprisingly frequent, and this caused much consideration to be devoted to this subject. In "A" and "T" classes the efficiency of the 4-in. gun was improved; in "S" class the 3-in. gun was replaced by a 4-in. gun where possible; in "U" class the 12-pounder gun was replaced by a 3-in. gun.

Our submarines were provided before the war with two portable Lewis guns erected when required in sockets on the bridge. Tests having shown that with regular maintenance the Oerlikon could be kept efficient if permanently sited outside the ship, the after end of the bridge of most of the existing operational submarines was modified to take it. In addition, improved portable guns were provided for use from the bridge itself.

(h) Accommodation

The conventional layout of accommodation in submarines prior to the outbreak of war was to place the

Fig.—1. "S" Class Submarine.

Fig.—2. "U" Class Submarine.

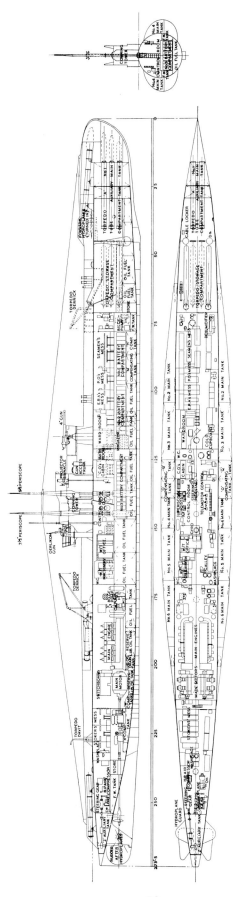

Fig.—3. "T" Class Submarine.

officers' accommodation in the foremost mess where traffic through the submarine was least. War experience showed that it was more important that this should be near the bridge, and the alteration was made in later vessels.

The principle was carried still further in the "A" class, where the commanding officer has been provided with a cabin in a pressure-tight compartment within the bridge structure.

Reference has already been made to the improvements in the accommodation of the crew.

(i) Freon Air-conditioning Units

"S," "T" and "A" classes were each provided with two in number 55,000 B.T.U./hr. Freon air-conditioning units—one forward and one aft. The "U" class were provided with one such unit.

The size was standardized in the interests of mass production—there being as a result a slight inconsistency in the aggregate air-conditioning capacity provided in the various classes.

These plants have been a great success—principally as regards the reduction in humidity obtained. The greatest testimony to this is that the crews of submarines in the Far East have often preferred to sleep in their congested but air-conditioned vessels rather than in the roomier but ordinarily ventilated depot ships.

(j) Air Purification

The problem of restricting the carbon dioxide build-up and the oxygen decline in the closed-down submarine increased in importance. It came particularly to the forefront during the Norwegian campaign, when our submarines had to operate under conditions of almost continuous daylight, and charging of the batteries became difficult. Occasions arose when it was not practicable to charge on a given night, and the submarine's air had to last the crew for periods up to 40 hours.

Space required to carry means of carbon dioxide absorbent and oxygen replenishment is considerable, but has been accepted.

5. "X" Craft

The design, production and achievements of these craft have now found a special place in the history of submarine warfare. The "Midget" submarine has always attracted the ingenuity of the inventor. Its construction, however, is surrounded by special problems which increase rapidly in severity as the size of the vessel is reduced. The normal submarine requires careful attention to detail in order that all available space may be used in the most economical manner; most items of equipment have to be specially designed to eliminate every unnecessary demand on space, even if some accessibility for ready maintenance has to be sacrificed thereby. Such considerations become more acute in the "Midget" submarine. Safety margins are necessarily reduced, accessibility is restricted, accommodation is more cramped, limited maintenance is possible, and drastic pruning of the equipment provided in the bigger

submarine becomes essential. Yet there is a definite limit to the extent to which these reductions can be made —a limit which is often put too low by those inexperienced in submarine design.

The magnitude of the achievement in producing the "Midget" submarine is shown by the fact that at the outbreak of the recent war there was no design of such a craft available for the British Navy. Yet "X" craft carried out the memorable attack on *Tirpitz* in 1943— this despite the stress of design work in other directions, the congested building programme, and the far-reaching requirements which these craft entailed.

The development of the vessels was inspired by Admiral Sir Max Horton, K.C.B., D.S.O., who became head of the submarine service early in 1940, and who had long believed in the capabilities of this type of craft. A small submarine for river use was under development at the beginning of the war for Army requirements, the design having been undertaken by Commander C. H. Varley, D.S.O., R.N. The trend of the war caused this requirement to lapse, and the project was taken over by the Admiralty for certain naval objectives. Several alterations were made, the design being overhauled by Commander Varley with the immediate assistance of specialists from Messrs. Vickers-Armstrongs, Ltd., Barrow-in-Furness, and with advice from the technical departments of the Admiralty. The production of two prototypes, X3 and X4, was undertaken by Commander Varley with Admiralty assistance and with the help of Portsmouth dockyard.

Enough experience had been obtained by early 1942 to embark on the design and production of operational craft. The new design was produced by Messrs. Vickers-Armstrongs, Ltd., Barrow-in-Furness, in which experience up to date was fully incorporated as far as was possible. The design was checked by the Admiralty technical departments, and twelve submarines of this type were eventually built.

The operational craft were 51 ft. 4 in. long, 5 ft. 9½ in. beam, 27 tons surface displacement and just under 30 tons submerged displacement. They were built in three sections in order to assist construction and ease the considerable problem of accessibility for fitting-out. The sections were subsequently bolted together, the intention being to leave as little work as possible to be completed after this had been done.

A 42 horse-power Gardner engine gave the craft a speed of just over 6 knots on the surface. A 30 horse-power main motor gave a submerged speed of just below 6 knots.

After hydroplanes only were provided. Hydroplanes and steering gear were both hand-operated.

The success of the operation against *Tirpitz* caused the suitability of the design for operation in the Far East to be considered. As a result, a slightly modified design was produced, and the resulting vessels were known as "XE" craft. They were slightly increased in size in order to accommodate Freon air-conditioning plant, increased fresh water, additional air purification equipment and certain other features.

This re-design was undertaken by the Director of Naval Construction, and the outline particulars of the resulting craft are given in the table.

Twelve vessels of this type were built or being built by the end of the war, and experience in the Far East showed the design compared favourably with its predecessor.

6. "Chariots"

The "Chariot" is essentially a specially designed torpedo-shaped craft in which the crew in special self-contained diving dresses ride astride its top. The craft is capable of being brought to a low buoyancy condition in which the heads of the operators are just above water, and the crew can then remove their face-pieces in order to have freedom of observation and normal breathing. The craft can also be operated to the depths which such a diving dress allows.

Craft of this type were used by the Italians soon after their entry into the war, and captured portions enabled their capabilities to be assessed.

The "Chariot" was provided with a large detachable head containing the explosive. This could be secured to the ship being attacked, and the vessel could then retire, control not being seriously affected by the removal of the head. The overall length of the craft was 22 ft. 3 in. and maximum breadth 2 ft. 4½ in.; its total weight including the head was 3,500 lb. Propulsion was by a 2 B.H.P. main motor giving a speed of 2¾ to 3 knots, and sufficient battery was carried to give an endurance of 5 to 6 hours at full speed.

Special care was taken to provide the crew of two with such body supports as would enable them to operate the craft with as little discomfort as possible.

7. Conclusion

The foregoing gives an indication of some of the submarine items dealt with during the war. It is, perhaps, unnecessary to state that they are but a part of the whole story. For example, considerable effort was expended in dealing with *ad hoc* problems involved in equipping submarines for special operations, improving design details as war experience was gained, exploring designs for special objectives, and so on. The liaison between the submarine officer and the designer was very close at all stages of the war, and the efforts of the latter received their greatest impetus from the outstanding work which the submarine officers and crews were able to accomplish.

DISCUSSION

Sir Stanley V. Goodall, K.C.B., O.B.E. (Vice-President): As Mr. Sims has said this paper only gives a part of the story of British submarine design during the war. Taking this as a cue I will endeavour to walk delicately.

In the design part of the paper more could be said regarding the complete adoption of welding. In submarines complete welding offers more advantages from the military standpoint than in any other form of warship. But the hazards of submarine service, even in peace-time, make it imperative that such a big change in practice should only be adopted after very full consideration of all that is involved. In the first place, we had to find a more weldable steel than that used for riveted pressure hulls. A good deal of preliminary work was necessary; for example a team of radiographers had to be formed; under Dr. W. R. Harper this team proved of great value. The importance of accurate circularity had to be appreciated. Close investigation into design details in way of openings and discontinuities, etc., was very necessary because local weakness in the case of a welded submarine may prejudice the whole scheme, and lead to disaster. We know now that weaknesses of that nature did occur in some of the German designs.

We heard a great deal about German designs until a U-boat was captured almost intact in 1941. After that, uninformed talk about the superiority of German submarines died away. Immediately this U-boat was available I gave instructions that samples of steel from the pressure hull were to be taken, tested and analysed. Shortly afterwards I received a request from our new Honorary Member (Mr. Churchill) for an explanation as to why the hulls of German submarines were built of steel which was so much better than ours. I was able to reply at once that the statement which had worried him was quite untrue. There was nothing out of the ordinary about the steel of this German submarine; it was, in fact, rather dirty.

With regard to production, I would like to call attention to the fact that the construction of submarines, their machinery, and their equipment is essentially a matter for specialists. The loss of H.M.S. *Thetis* just before the outbreak of war had a serious effect on wartime production. Two most valuable members of my staff went down with the ship and Messrs. Cammell Laird's submarine team was very sadly depleted.

We had at one time during the war to consider the possibility of increasing the number of firms on submarine production, but taking into account all our other commitments the only possible extensions were at Walker where Messrs. Vickers-Armstrong built submarines as well as at Barrow and at the Royal Dockyards Devonport and Portsmouth.

When the war started it was intended to settle down to a steady programme of "Ts" and "Us," but the reintroduction of the "S" class spoiled this plan. The author gives the impression that "S" class submarines were re-introduced for production reasons, but actually they were built because they were a type more suitable for work in the North Sea. So far as production was concerned, their reintroduction interfered with the steady output of the "T" and "U" classes. To illustrate what could be done, however, it may be stated that at one time Messrs. Vickers-Armstrong, from their two yards, were delivering U-class submarines at the rate of one every two or three weeks.

Reference is made in the paper to alterations made during construction and the patience exercised by the firms in submitting to the various new requirements. That is a very sore point with shipbuilders because not only is work stopped or completed work undone, but the effect on the men is bad psychologically. If nearly finished work is scrapped, and the men see a ship they were pressed to complete delayed, they get disheartened, and it is more difficult to urge them to finish another job they are told is badly needed.

The Midget class is extremely interesting: Those not intimately acquainted with submarine designs are apt to forget the extent to which submarine principles can be shed in designing and building small submarines. For that reason, I think some errors were made and some effort was wasted at the outset of the programme.

We did intend to make a great effort at mass production of the "A" class, and the firms concerned entered into the matter most enthusiastically. At Chatham and at Barrow the system of submarine construction was drastically changed with this object in view. But submarines never had the highest priority except for one short period when the "A" class was under construction. Unlike Germany—where the major effort was submarine construction—in this country there was a big merchant shipping programme and a vast programme of repairs, both of warships and merchant ships, in addition to a multiplicity of new warships of all types. Therefore, submarines generally had a poor place in the priority list, but the "A" class were shown to be successful both in design and production methods, and if the war had gone on they would have done very good work in the Far East.

In conclusion, I should like to refer to a statement which the author makes in the very last sentence of the paper concerning liaison between submarine officers and designers. This was close at all stages of the war, as the author says, and I can speak for the Corps in general when I say that the favourites amongst those they serve are the "submariners." They know that these men in peace and war entrust their lives to the designers and that submarine officers with their intimate and varied experience can give them invaluable help in making the designs successful. This remark applies particularly to Mr. L. C. Williamson, who was my Assistant Director in charge of submarines during the war. The submarine section of the Royal Navy owes him a very great debt, and so do I.

Sir Charles S. Lillicrap, K.C.B., M.B.E. (Vice-President): I propose to make a few general remarks only. During the war security considerations naturally prevented the publication of details of our naval shipbuilding, but in the Admiralty we have always appreciated the desirability of releasing information as soon as possible. So since the war, first Sir Stanley Goodall, and later on, various members of my staff have read, or will read, papers giving what information we can about our war-time programmes.

Mr. Sims's paper comes into this category; it will be followed to-morrow by several others so that you may feel by the end of these meetings some of the symptoms

of indigestion. Do not let that disturb you for it will be a very long time before you get such a meal again.

Whether we like it or not the words submarine and German will always be associated together, because in two world wars the circumstances of Germany have favoured the exploitation of the submarine arm. The submarine has been accorded an eminence in German fleets that it could not have in ours, and it would not be surprising if German designs were to be thought superior to ours, not so much in points of detail but in broad conception. Further, it would not be surprising if German submarine tactics were found different from our own, because of their greater opportunities. Valuable and welcome as the author's paper is, therefore, I feel very strongly that it would be improved considerably if he could be persuaded to add comparable figures and particulars of contemporary German submarines; or perhaps write for us, for comparison, a similar paper on them.

Putting this question on one side, I believe that our submarines throughout the war enjoyed the confidence of the "submariners," and no doubt this was largely due to the close liaison between the submarine officer and the designer, a liaison which we sometimes find it hard to maintain for surface ships, and which will, I fear, be even harder to maintain in the future as ships get more and more complicated. Mr. Sims's drawings can clearly be recognized as submarines. Could anyone recognize modern destroyers as counterparts of their sisters of the 1914–18 war?

As pointed out by the author, shortage of suitable building capacity meant that for a large part of the war, design and methods of construction were frozen, so that it was not until near the end of the period that we were able to follow the Germans and Americans and produce all-welded types.

A great deal of publicity has been given to the failure of all-welded surface ships—too much cannot be given to the other side of the picture. Welding in our submarines was introduced gradually and with adequate care in the design and inspections. So far as the Germans were concerned this was their major war effort. There were no failures. We cannot go back; future ships and submarines which are not practically all-welded will carry too heavy a load to compete with more modern structures.

Engineer Rear-Admiral S. O. Frew, C.B.: There are two points I should like to deal with. First of all, the question of improved habitability conditions, particularly in those submarines that existed before the war. In the early days of the war there was no air conditioning, and under tropical conditions the crew were stripped of all clothing except for a loin cloth—which was invariably used for mopping their brows! As a result, we had skin troubles, heat exhaustion, etc., and at the end of a patrol the personnel were in rather a shaky condition. Consequently, spare crews were of great importance, and we had to have two or three spare crews available for operations. But the introduction of air conditioning vastly improved the humidity and lowered the temperature slightly. The operational conditions generally were very much improved. With patrols in the Pacific, extending as they did up to 50 days, and where the temperatures were high, it was imperative that air conditioning should be introduced. The result was that when crews returned from a patrol they were fresh and ready to go out again, and the reserve personnel was halved. That was of vital importance, and although the author has only dealt slightly with that aspect it is one I should like to emphasize.

My other point is about machinery noises. I think that perhaps our biggest headache was associated with the singing propeller, particularly under submerged conditions. I do not know whether the author has anything in mind whereby the disadvantages from which we suffered during the war in this respect can be reduced or overcome by an improved design of submarine propeller.

Captain Lord Ashbourne, D.S.O., R.N.: I want to refer to some of the criticisms of submarine design that we have heard both during and since the war. Compared with German and American submarines, ours were criticized as having an inferior speed on the surface and as having a less maximum diving depth. There is, of course, substantial foundation for this criticism, but I think we want to be very clear and understand that the Germans and Americans did not get their extra speed or diving depth for nothing. The Germans had to give up battery capacity and the Americans had to go to what we regard as large submarines. We, on our side, were unwilling to accept either of these limitations.

The German submarine was designed primarily to operate in the broad spaces of the Atlantic and therefore had to have high surface speed in order to intercept our convoys. Again, the German submarine had to have great diving depth in order to increase its chances of escape from our very effective anti-submarine forces.

The American submarines were designed primarily for the Pacific where size was not a matter of great importance. Indeed, as far as habitability is concerned, it was an advantage, quite apart from the tactical advantage of high surface speed. American submarines had enormous distances to cover from their base to their patrol areas which medium size submarines would have taken a disproportionate time to carry out. Our submarines, on the other hand, were designed for world-wide operations and they did, in fact, operate from the arctic to the equator. Their principal duty was offensive patrol, and for that purpose they had to operate for weeks and months on end completely unsupported and frequently, if not usually, close to the enemy's coast. For that purpose, large battery power and long diving time were absolutely essential; I do not believe that anybody ever heard of any of our submarine commanders complain that they had too much battery power. Of course, we "submariners" always want great battery capacity and we would like to go much faster on the surface; we always want more torpedo tubes and more guns and, of course, we are not prepared for a moment to go to a

large submarine. Designers, however, very rightly point out to us that we cannot have it both ways.

There are two other minor points I might mention, in comparing our submarines with those of other countries. Firstly, there is the position of the captain of the submarine during an attack. In our case we have always had the captain in the control room, and in the very closest contact with the first lieutenant and the men under him who are responsible for diving the submarine. On the other hand, most foreign countries prefer to have the captain in the conning tower. For this purpose the conning tower is enlarged so that it will accommodate the captain and his attack team and the various control instruments. This has the advantage of segregating the attack team and the captain from the remainder of the boat, and they are unhindered by the other activities that go on inside the submarine. Further, this arrangement gives an increased periscope depth. Which is right and which is wrong it is not possible to say, but I am quite sure that our arrangement suits our temperament better and I doubt if we shall change it.

The second point is the position of the gun. Foreign countries usually have it on the casing whereas we prefer, when considerations of top weight permit, to put it well above the level of the casing, and in some cases even up to the level of the bridge. This has the great advantage of allowing the gun to be manned very much sooner after surfacing than would otherwise be the case. Another advantage is that we can fight the gun in very much rougher weather, and I am sure that we have the better arrangement here.

Broadly speaking, I consider our submarine design has proved robust and dependable and, in every way, equal to the functions it was required to perform.

Before sitting down, I should like to pay a tribute to Mr. Sims, whose skill, energy, and enthusiasm has been so largely responsible for these very excellent results.

Commander P. J. Cowell, D.S.C., R.N.: The Flag Officer, Submarines, who has read this paper, would have liked to have been present this morning, but was unfortunately unable to attend.

I should like to add a note, from the operational viewpoint, on the designs described in the paper. There is no need to add to the numerous reports already given on the successes achieved by "S," "T," "U" and midget class submarines, but it would be fair to pay particular tribute to the "U" class submarines which, as already stated, started life as training submarines. These vessels were extensively operated in the Mediterranean with an effect fully appreciated by the enemy in Italy and North Africa.

Perhaps not so well appreciated is the severe punishment to which some of our submarines were subjected.

Spearfish was subjected to a very heavy depth charge attack, some of the charges exploding practically in contact with the hull.

Triumph was mined on the surface, the fore-end was completely blown off and the torpedo tube compartment flooded.

Tally Ho had all her main tanks on one side of the ship ripped open by a Japanese destroyer.

Terrapin was depth charged to such an extent that the ship's side was forced in until it came up against the torpedo tubes.

Stubborn and *Ultimatum* were both heavily depth charged and forced to twice their designed depth.

All these ships returned safely to harbour and were capable of being refitted—a tribute to both the design and the shipbuilder.

It is noted that the list of war-time improvements is an impressive one, and that the building and refitting authorities were particularly patient in incorporating the necessary modifications. It may be truly said that quite a number of items could be added to the list and that the operational authorities were and always will be particularly impatient. It is in war that we learn lessons fast, sometimes too fast, and only the close liaison between the user and designer which exists in the submarine world can keep the unforeseen snags to a minimum.

Nevertheless additional requirements will arise in time of war and their need for speedy installation in the submarines then existing cannot be over emphasized.

The paper does not include numbers of submarines, omitted presumably for obvious reasons. From the submarine officer's standpoint we shall never have enough submarines and, owing to production difficulties and the changing theatres of war, those which can be produced may not be of the most suitable type.

It may be that for the future we shall have to change our concept of the "all-purpose" submarine, but any design must take into full consideration the need to step up production in war time.

Even with the advent of the atomic age, when much is heard of the argument that a Navy is no longer of use, I am fully confident that the submarine has a great future and that we are a long way from finality in its design, but even after listening to the discussions on Mr. Church's paper,* just read, I do not think we shall have single cabins for all!

Mr. F. O. John (Member of Council): I have listened to Mr. Sims's paper with the greatest interest and am reminded of the very strenuous days we had in Cammell Laird's works trying to build submarines in the minimum time. I think we had considerable success, in spite of the many alterations that came along as the result of wartime experience. We built many "T" class, a great many "S" class and a few "A" class, and they all gave a good account of themselves. We completed one "S" class about every six weeks for several years. About half of them had riveted hulls, but the remainder had the seams and butts welded. This was something of an innovation, and the work had to be done with extreme care and in correct sequence. The actual welding was done under special supervision. We had one charge-hand supervising the work of about 10 welders, and he

* "Improved Crew Accommodation for Ocean-going Cargo Vessels."

had to see that each run was de-slagged and carefully inspected before proceeding with the next. The time and date of each inspection was carefully recorded in a diary. We tested several of the hulls to an internal air pressure of about 150 lb. This in itself was something of an innovation but we had no trouble and everything went very well. The Admiralty, as you know from the paper, adopted X-ray examination very extensively and, as a result, our methods and our welding improved. The men were given the opportunity of seeing the X-ray photographs and quickly realized that only the very best welding would be accepted.

As regards the "A" class, we did not follow the methods stated in the paper. We fabricated large portions in the shop, and transferred them to the slip and welded the parts together in place. We made light steel portable covers which were lifted by crane over those portions being welded, so that work could be carried on under conditions approximating to those in the shop.

Much could be said about the methods we adopted but a discussion of that now would be out of place. There is little of a controversial nature in the paper but there is a great deal which shows the brilliance of our Admiralty naval architects, and the members of the R.C.N.C. are to be congratulated on the splendid success which our submarines achieved during the war.

I will conclude by thanking the author very much for his excellent paper and the Director of Naval Construction for allowing so much valuable information to be included in our TRANSACTIONS.

Mr. G. de Rooij (Member): Before asking the author a few questions may I, in my position of Director of Naval Construction of the Royal Netherlands Navy, thank you for the great assistance the Dutch fleet and also our submarines have had from the British Admiralty, not only from naval officers but also from the Director of Naval Construction and his staff.

On page 67 the author says that "automatic welding was employed as far as possible." May I ask which parts of the hull were automatically welded and which system of automatic welding was used?

Perhaps the author knows that our submarines, built after 1935, were constructed from high tensile steel, electrically welded for the greater part. Some portions of the pressure hull were of armoured steel, also electrically welded. I should like to know whether high tensile or armoured steel was used for British submarines, and whether these parts of the structure were also electrically welded. Also, could the author tell me which kind of welding joints were used for the butts and seams—overlapped joints or V-joints? And were the latter with or without an underlaid strip? Again, were the roots of the V-joints chipped out and welded again?

On our submarines we have used with great success the hydraulic movement of rudders, periscopes, anchors, and oerlikons. Have you also experience of this system?

During the war, our Navy took over one "S" class boat and one "T" class boat from your Navy, and we have had very good results with them. I am pleased to have this opportunity of thanking the British Admiralty for all the help and assistance they have given us in this respect.

The President: We have had a very interesting paper and have also been fortunate in hearing some of the skilled users of submarines—the naval officers—who have given us their views. Of all the dangerous operations carried out by the Navy during the war against new weapons, there was nothing to compare with the tasks which devolved on the submarine officers and their men, and it is very pleasant to hear this morning the tributes paid by naval architects to the users of submarines; and by the users to the work of the naval architects. I should like also to thank our friend, Mr. Rooij, of the Netherlands Navy, for his kind appreciation of the help the Royal Netherlands Navy received from the British Navy during the war.

I should now like to propose a hearty vote of thanks to Mr. Sims.

Written Contributions to the Discussion

Vice-Admiral C. B. Barry, C.B.: I would like to say how extremely sorry I am not being able to be present in person to make my remarks on the paper which is being read by my old friend, Mr. A. J. Sims, who has now been dealing with submarine matters for a number of years and has the confidence of the officers of the submarine branch to a quite particular degree. I can think of no one better qualified to read this paper than he.

I want to pay a tribute to the long and most outstanding work in designing submarines that has been carried out by the late Deputy Director of Naval Construction, Mr. L. C. Williamson. I have known Williamson well ever since he first took on designing submarines—I think about 1930—and the longer I knew him the more did my affection for him grow, also my admiration of his great qualities as an imaginative, sound, and never-to-be-defeated designer. His whole heart was in the job and his success was conspicuous. Everyone in submarines will miss him greatly and I wish him all happiness in his retirement.

I would also like to mention G. W. Pamplin, who was the author's predecessor. He was in charge of the submarine section from well before the war until 1944 and the work he did was indeed most successful. As one of the war-time Flag Officer Submarines I would like to express my appreciation of his work.

A matter that I would like to stress is the very satisfactory way in which our submarine designs, produced before the war or early in the war, continued to give satisfactory service throughout the full strain and stress of that period, and to record that it was only necessary to review these designs at intervals to effect detailed improvements and to make modifications for introducing the latest aids to attacking, and to incorporate the newest radar and asdic. This is indeed satisfactory when you think of the tremendous punishment which these submarines had to stand up to during the late conflict when,

although as is inevitable, a number were sunk, a very large number emerged from the most terrific attacks battered but intact.

A tribute must also be paid to the Royal Corps for the way in which they invariably responded to requirements called for by the varying conditions of the war, however difficult those might be. I think particularly of such things as air conditioning all our submarines going to the East, which proved so singularly successful, and adding the necessary extra fuel which so greatly improved endurance all round.

One of the most remarkable successes in the submarine branch was the introduction of the X craft or Midget submarines. These remarkable little craft were, I think, unique in that they achieved success on every single operation on which they were employed. It is not generally known that the same X craft—I think it was X24—twice penetrated the forty odd mile long fjord, right into the middle of the town of Bergen, where it arrived on both occasions in broad daylight and manœuvred amongst a mass of merchant ships, tugs, motor boats, and so on. On the first occasion it blew up a large merchant ship alongside a coal jetty and put the coal jetty out of action as well as the ship, and on the second occasion it destroyed the cruiser floating dock. These two remarkable exploits were never published for the very good reason that, so far as we could make out, the Germans had no notion that a Midget submarine had caused these two explosions which were believed by them to have been both due to sabotage, and so there was no need to disillusion them.

Another thing about the X craft was their quite remarkable manœuvrability in spite of not having any fore hydroplanes. They could be twisted and turned about, put ahead and astern at any depth desired, keeping all the time level and at the same depth. As can be imagined this was of extreme value to them when groping about under the bottoms of the ships they were attacking. Altogether the production of these craft was a most outstanding success.

Finally, as a submarine officer of very long standing, I would like to say how excellent has been the co-operation, understanding, friendship, and will-to-succeed that has always existed between those in the submarine branch of the Royal Navy, and the designers, building and refitting authorities; I am sure it is as good to-day. With this happy state of affairs existing things are bound, generally, to go right. With regard to myself, I have had the privilege of knowing well many members of the Royal Corps and working in the closest conjunction with them, and I would like to take this opportunity to say how happy and in every way delightful have been these pleasant associations.

Mr. C. W. Moss (Member): The author is to be congratulated on producing a paper which gives an overall survey of war-time activities on submarine design, a subject which unfortunately is too infrequently dealt with.

It is gratifying to know that the pre-war designed "S," "U" and "T" class—the latter two classes can be considered immediately pre-war—formed a nucleus for war-time submarine development. This argues much for the versatility of design which permits adjustments to be readily made to meet the many phases of submarine warfare, without a major alteration to the fundamental design.

The advent of Italy into the war, the capitulation of France, and the entry of Japan into the war, must have embarrassed to no small extent the requirements of the submarine service.

Events proved conclusively that the three immediate post-war designs were readily adaptable to the change in circumstances.

The "U" class, primarily built for pro-submarine and anti-submarine training, proved their worth as offensive units of the Mediterranean and off the Scandinavian coast, and the sterling deeds performed by some of the earlier craft when the dice was heavily loaded against us, have heaped laurels on the prestige of the submarine service.

The "S" and "T" class also proved to be craft of sound design and readily adaptable to changing circumstances without a major interference with production, and when the history of the submarine service during the last war is made available, I have no doubt we will find that whether in the Mediterranean, the Atlantic, or in the Far East, they proved their worth despite anti-submarine ingenuity.

Welding research on submarine construction having duly removed the prejudice from the minds of the authorities, permitted the development of the "A" class submarine which incorporated from the operative angle the results of war-time experience, higher surface speed and endurance, and increased diving depth. The design of this class revolutionized submarine construction and presented the opportunity of extending mechanical welding to a degree impossible in the previous classes.

Conservatism in development has never paid a dividend, and I think it is true to say conservatism in welding lost a lot of ground in submarine war-time production, since the fundamentals covered in the design of the "S," "U" and "T" class could have been incorporated without loss of efficiency, if the same principles of pressure hull form and fairings embodied in the "A" class had been adopted.

The major advantages can be summarized as follows:

(a) Adaptability for massed production with consequent saving in building time.
(b) Economy in man power.
(c) Elimination of many skilled operations on hull construction, with the result that in time of emergency the personnel required to accelerate production could be readily trained from the unskilled classes, including women. The design permitting sectional pre-fabrication with simplicity of unit production operations, which allowed whole sections to be built in any structural engineering establishment having the required crane capacity.

The principle of sectional pre-fabrication was envisaged before we had knowledge of German methods of submarine production. Examination of the reports which have been made by various shipbuilders and technicians as to the methods adopted by the Germans, leave me convinced beyond doubt that the "A" class design enabled this country to produce submarine hulls of a higher standard than the German counterpart by the development of a more advanced building technique.

The author's remark regarding the ability of the shipbuilders to accept the change from riveting to welding is inconsistent with fact. There has always been enthusiasm by the shipbuilders associated with submarine construction for the adoption of welding on account of the advantages offered in this highly specialized branch of the shipbuilding industry.

The results obtained on the introduction of the "A" class and the wide field available for the exploitation of ingenuity, with the impetus given as the result of the wealth of research covering radar, radio equipment, torpedo control, and other features of ingenuity, in which some of us associated with the building of submarines are permitted to show interest, bids fair for the future of submarine design in the capable hands of The Royal Corps of Naval Constructors.

The author's reference to "X" craft and "Chariots" is interesting and the former, from my personal knowledge, indicate that the close liaison which exists between the Admiralty and private industry on design and production, pays a dividend.

Mr. H. J. Tabb, R.C.N.C. (Member): Towards the end of 1943 I was appointed Principal (Ship) Overseer at Messrs. Cammell Laird and Co. Ltd., Birkenhead. The vessels then under construction including several aircraft carriers, destroyers and "S" class submarines. By that time the construction of submarines was nearing its peak, and vessels were being completed at intervals of about five weeks—in fact during December 1943, two submarines and one destroyer were handed over to the Admiralty. The author has mentioned the many changes made necessary by the progress of the war, and I think it is true to say that no two vessels were identical. In spite of these constant, if necessary, irritations to the shipbuilder, the average fitting-out time after launching was eleven to twelve weeks. The measure of these achievements is increased when we remember that, by the unfortunate sinking of H.M.S. *Thetis* in 1939, a great proportion of Messrs. Cammell Laird's submarine experts was lost, so that the submarine organization had virtually to be built up afresh on the outbreak of war.

The author has referred to the change over from riveting to welding. This was undoubtedly a great step forward, and materially assisted production by facilitating pre-fabrication of such items as bulkheads, flats, engine bearers, etc., also complete bow and stern sections within the limits of the capacity of the shipyard cranes. Platers' work was also reduced. In riveted submarines it is essential that all pressure hull butts and seams should make edge to edge contact to a high degree of accuracy.

so that the rivets are not unduly stressed when the vessel is submerged to maximum-depth. This feature was obviously against speedy construction, but was completely eliminated by welded butts and laps. The introduction of welding also resulted in the saving of time for testing—a matter of relatively greater importance in a submarine than in a surface vessel. The carriage of external oil fuel has been mentioned by the author, and in riveted ships it was essential that the external tanks should be endurance tested with diesel oil for forty-eight hours to prove their tightness. This laborious test, involving the handling of many tons of diesel oil when the ship was in dry dock, was dispensed with after experience with welded ships showed it to be quite unnecessary.

It was important, of course, that the standard of welding should be the highest possible. The pressure hull of a submarine must always remain its last line of defence, and the incorporation of the most advanced offensive weapons and scientific equipment is of no avail if the vessel has little resistance to attack. Generally it was found that no more than about 10% of the shipyard welders were of the required efficiency. The standard attained, however, was raised considerably by the rigid application of inspection methods, including X-ray examination. During a period of about 1½ years, the average number of defects (cracks, porosity, undercutting, slag inclusions, etc.) found by X-rays was reduced by 75% and many of the more severe defects were completely eliminated.

Trials of new submarines were generally reduced to the minimum, so that the vessels were passed into service with the least loss of time. This involved a passage from the Mersey to the Clyde followed by full power and diving trials. A trim dive was also carried out in Liverpool Bay so that the vessel was ready to dive immediately on passage if the presence of hostile (or sometimes friendly) aircraft made this advisable. The almost entire absence of any major troubles during these trials, and the subsequent good service of the vessels in all parts of the world, is a tribute both to the excellence of the design and the good work of the shipbuilder.

The first "A" class submarine was laid down sufficiently early so that it could be progressed concurrently with the later "S" class vessels. This was desirable as the prototype was bound to involve many problems which could not be solved in the drawing office or even by the excellent full scale mock-ups. The method of hull construction was generally similar to the "S" class, with prefabrication of units to the maximum extent permissible by crane capacities, but it was notable for the considerable increase of Unionmelt welding, on the pressure hull and elsewhere, wherever this process could be safely accomplished in the welding shop. As in the "S" class the welding was at all stages closely supervised by the shipbuilders and by the Admiralty overseers, and an even greater degree of X-ray examination was possible. One problem was the maintenance of strength during launching, when a considerable area of pressure hull plating was left loose for shipping main engines and motors.

This was overcome by the provision of a temporary plate made watertight by a rubber joint, secured by hook bolts and provided with heavy longitudinal girders firmly welded to pads on the pressure hull at the forward and after ends of the loose work. These girders were afterwards cut away without damaging the pressure hull. No undue breakage was observed, but after shipping machinery a further problem was presented in the welding of the closing plate. This was the most difficult welding operation encountered, since ultimately the joint was tied in all directions. A technique was carefully worked out however and strictly followed, and X-ray examination showed the final welds to be clean and free from cracks. A certain amount of breakage was caused by this welding operation, however, and it was not possible finally to chock the main engines until the welding was complete.

Mr. W. R. G. Whiting, M.B.E., M.A. (Member of Council): As a matter of historical interest it may be pointed out that external torpedo tubes were installed in the "W" class in 1914. This was a feature of the Schneider-Laubeuf prototype, but at that period British experience with torpedoes carried externally was not altogether satisfactory and this easy method of increasing offensive power was not pursued until after the first world war.

It appears from the paper that the basic hull designs of that war, viz. "L" and "H" types, have persisted without fundamental change up to the present day. That hull design reached comparative finality at so early a date is a great tribute to the original designers and to the consistency of Admiralty policy.

The submerged speeds quoted in the table of particulars appear somewhat high in comparison with those understood to have been reached by earlier submarines of similar underwater power. If correct is this to be attributed to form or to reduction of appendage resistance?

Mr. W. Hamilton Martin (Member): It is interesting to realize from the paper how refrigeration has even found its application in H.M. submarines for cold cupboards and domestic automatic refrigeration, and for air-conditioning of living spaces, reducing temperatures and humidity when required.

What has been achieved so far is indeed noteworthy. A great deal more remains to be done in this field.

In such craft floorspace is always at a premium, while silence of operation is an absolute essential.

Minimum attention, upkeep and overhaul is desirable and, if possible, no mechanically driven parts should go to make up such refrigerating or air-conditioning units.

Air-cooling only should be used; water-cooling, apart from its added complication, being altogether too inefficient when in semi-tropical or tropical zones.

The entire refrigerating cycle should preferably be a closed one so that no leakage of refrigerant is possible.

It would appear that a system of continuous absorption refrigeration would offer a sufficiently sound basis from which to evolve satisfactory means for preservation of food and drinks, for freshwater-cooling—and also air-conditioning, units of which could be built to fit into panels between frames against the vessel's shell, thereby materially reducing the floor space normally required by such refrigeration and air-conditioning plant.

The inherent silent vibration-free automatic operation, without any moving part or need of water-cooling, and demanding little or no attention, upkeep or overhaul, would seem to recommend this system especially to the submarine service. Its weight would also be relatively low. The practical limits of such a system deserve closer investigation as to its possible adoption in this field. If successful, it would no doubt find its way likewise into the future large airliners.

One can foresee for such units many applications in warm climates in other than shipboard use, especially if they can be operated by a heat source such as oil, electricity, gas, steam, exhaust gases, etc., and work as an independent unit.

Mr. D. W. Avey, R.C.N.C. (Associate-Member): This subject is deserving of a full discussion in view of its complexity, and the many widely differing branches of engineering involved. Submarine work requires particularly close co-operation between the designers and the builders, and this need increases with the continual improvements and additions to the operational equipment so that the available space is used to the best advantage.

The all-welded pressure hull is a noteworthy achievement, the standard of welding required for submarines being exceptionally high. Among the problems of submarine pressure hull construction in this connection are:—

(i) The exceptional undesirability of irregularities, cracks, slag inclusions and porosity in the welding, because of the pressures sustained at deep depths and the shock stresses which may be experienced.

(ii) The large plating thicknesses involve large contractions and high cooling rates.

In addition to radiographic inspection several submarines in the earlier days of all-welded hulls were tested by internal air pressure at 150 lb/in². H.M.S. *Turpin* at Chatham Dockyard was an example and several methods for the build-up of pressure were considered.

The method adopted was to use the dockyard air service to its limit and then boost the pressure with special air compressors. The volume to be pressured was of the order of 40,000 cubic feet and so the test was a considerable undertaking. Moreover, it had to be carried out when the submarine was well advanced in the fitting-out stage, and special precautions had therefore to be taken with equipment which was not designed to withstand pressures of this order. Certain hull valves had to be gagged, as the pressure was applied in the reverse direction to that for which they had been designed.

Many revolutionary changes were made in the constructional procedure, the submarine form being particularly adaptable for sectional building. At Chatham the pressure hull was built in sections varying between 10 and 28 ft. in length, this limitation being governed by the capacities of the slip lifting appliances. This procedure allowed of better access and working conditions, and the longitudinal growth of the ship forward and aft from amidships enabled fitting out—especially in the control room—to be unimpeded by progress on the hull work.

The internal portions of the longitudinal seam welds in each section were hand-welded, and the external portions machine-welded using the hand-welding as the backing. This meant that general economy and time saving were greater for the longer sections of the ship. Temporary extension plates fitted to the seam ends enabled the starting and stopping positions of the machine-made runs to be kept clear of the section.

For the cylindrical circular sections, excepting those containing main transverse bulkheads, the fillet welds of the frames to the hull plating were also made by a welding machine, the machine being fixed whilst the section revolved. The section was supported by two pairs of rollers, one pair forming the drive and being actuated by an electro-hydraulic variable speed gear. A structure rigged through the section, and independent of it, supported the welding machine which was repositioned for each frame fillet weld. The machine was adjusted for voltage and rate of electrode feed, whilst the peripheral speed of the section was the equivalent of the rate of electrode travel. The operation was therefore analogous to a lathe action, being made possible by the accuracy with which the sections were constructed.

This practice could not be applied to those sections at the ends of the submarine where the form changed. In the majority of these cases each section was up-ended, which allowed the simultaneous welding of several frame-to-plating fillets in downhand positions.

Main bulkheads were moulded, welded and built into the sections as complete units. Other parts of the structure sectionally fabricated before shipment included the ballast keel, minor bulkheads, flats, the engine and main motor seats, bow and stern structures, the bridge and superstructure, and portions of the external tanks.

Author's Reply to the Discussion

I should like to thank the many speakers who have taken part in the discussion—speakers who are representative of designers, users, and builders. As a result, much information has been added to the account which I have given of our submarine design activities during the recent war. It is unnecessary for me to comment further on many of the points made.

Sir Stanley Goodall has referred to the new steel produced when it was decided completely to weld our submarine pressure hulls. It had been the practice to specify the steel used for this work by its physical properties only, leaving the chemical composition to be decided within limits by the steel makers. Welding, however, made it inevitable that some control should be imposed on chemical analysis. In particular, the carbon content of the steel had to be limited to 0·21 per cent.

The assistance given by radiography in obtaining a high standard of welding in this important application cannot be over-emphasized. Early radiographic examination caused some anxiety regarding the standard of work being produced. All concerned, however, were very quick to co-operate to effect the necessary improvement. The builders themselves showed keenness to obtain good radiographic results, and the welding staffs were encouraged to examine the prints obtained from samples of their work. The improvement achieved in a relatively short time was very great. It is a subject, however, in which we cannot afford to relax in any degree whatsoever, and the utmost vigilance is required to maintain our present standard, or better still, to improve it.

Sir Charles Lillicrap, Director of Naval Construction, has referred to German designs. I rather hesitate to include a table giving a comparison between British and German submarines of the 1939–45 war. Such a table might be misleading without full explanation and it would not be easy to condense all the essential data into this form. It is suggested that the Institution might like to include a paper on the subject of German submarines of the recent war in a future series of meetings.

Sir Charles has further emphasized that we cannot go back from the decision to weld our submarines. A riveted submarine would now seem almost prehistoric in comparison with a welded vessel. Some of the advantages of welding as applied to submarine construction are obvious—others are not quite so apparent. We have, of course, increased the thickness of our pressure hulls, and experience has shown that apart from this factor welding has increased the robustness of the structure to withstand the very rigorous conditions of a submarine's wartime service. Even if the pressure hull thickness had not been increased, there would be great advantages in the symmetry of joints and sections which welding allows, and also in the elimination of the caulked riveted joints. With the adoption of welding, testing of the rather complicated tank structure of a submarine's hull has been greatly eased, and the variation of pressure on the structure as the vessel dives deep has had no effect on tightness of joints.

Engineer Rear Admiral Frew has referred to the improved habitability of our submarines. We had a form of air conditioning in our vessels at the outbreak of the war, but our early experience with it in the Far East showed that it had certain disadvantages, and it soon became apparent that we should have to take advantage of the superior performance of Freon refrigerating plant. As Admiral Frew has said, this decision enabled the reserve crews in the Far East to be halved—in itself an important factor at a time when submarine personnel were not plentiful. Subsequent experience showed that as a result our crews preferred to sleep in their submarines rather than in the more spacious—but non-air conditioned —depot ships.

Admiral Frew has also referred to the singing propeller. We had a great deal of trouble with this in the "U" Class. Although it was known that the conditions under which the propeller had to work were such as to create the possibility of singing, experience before the war had given no hint that we were likely to have any trouble in this respect. Early in 1940, however, reports were received of singing from certain propellers, the phenomenon being cured in many cases by replacing the propellers by spares. It was clear, however, from the number of reports received that general action was necessary to put the propellers beyond the possibility of the phenomenon occurring. Such action had to be taken very quickly in view of the rapidity with which the "U" class were being delivered at the time.

The Superintendent, Admiralty Experiment Works, Haslar, carried out extensive investigations in many directions. There were the hydro-dynamic characteristics of the propellers themselves; the hysteresis qualities of the material; the effect of shape of stern on uniformity of flow to the propellers; the influence of free flooding holes and minor appendages in way of the propellers; and the possibility of avoiding resonance from the structure by extra local stiffening. The investigations included theoretical work, model experiments, and ship trials. In addition hysteresis tests on specimen materials were carried out by the Professor of Applied Mechanics at the R.N. College, Greenwich.

As a result the disability was overcome by (a) the adoption of fine edges to the propeller blades, and (b) by more exact machining of the blades. In later vessels of the "U" Class, the stern was lengthened to give an easier angle of approach of the water to the propellers. As regards (a), the edges were reduced in thickness from $\frac{1}{8}$ in. to, at first, $\frac{1}{16}$ in., and afterwards to $\frac{3}{32}$ in. (b) ensured uniform characteristics from all three blades. These measures completely eliminated the singing tendency, but research into the problem still proceeds, since the remedies have the disadvantage that the edges are more readily damaged by waterlogged wood, etc., and singing then reappears—generally with greater violence.

The subject is too extensive to be dealt with at any greater length as a reply to the discussion. It is hoped that a paper describing the investigations will be prepared by the Admiralty Experiment Works in due course, giving complete details of this nuisance, its cause, and its cure.

Captain Lord Ashbourne has referred to some of the features which we have to consider in our submarine design and which need to be remembered when comparing our submarines with those of other Powers. If our submarines could be bigger, we should have greater scope for higher surface speeds and rather greater diving depths. The American submarines in the recent war were larger than ours and the Americans were clearly right in pursuing that policy. I do not think, however, that the American submarines would have been suitable for much of the work which our vessels had to do. The American submarines were built primarily for service in the Pacific where they achieved outstanding success. Our submarines had to be smaller for the more confined waters in which they were largely employed.

The discussion of the relative merits of the conning tower control position and the control room position is one which has gone on for many years. The policy in some navies has been for the commanding officer to carry out the attack from the conning tower and to leave the control of the vessel to the first lieutenant in the control room below. We have always put the attacking position in the control room where the commanding officer with his greater experience is immediately to hand in case of emergency. We feel this is the better answer.

Reference has been made by Commander Cowell to the damage sustained by some of our submarines. We have a great admiration for the crews who brought them home. Every effort was made to use each such occasion to introduce improvements whereby a similar incident would have less severe consequences next time.

The introduction of war-time improvements in submarines—as indeed in all ships—is a difficult subject. It is one in which the greatest consideration has to be shown by all interested parties. The tempo of war in itself brings great improvements. Moreover, it is experience in the early phases of a war which shows what modifications are required best to combat enemy measures. Alterations and additions to our submarines are, therefore, inevitable, and we must be prepared for some of these if those who fight our ships are to be given the best possible material. On the other hand, we must not ask the builders to incorporate any unnecessary requirement if we are to avoid having the bad psychological effect on workmen referred to by Sir Stanley Goodall. Each improvement needs to be very carefully examined to ensure that it really is worth while before its incorporation is approved—or even advocated.

Commander Cowell has further mentioned the fact that in future we may have to change our concept of the all-purpose submarine. There is little doubt that if we could multiply the types we could make each more powerful for its specific task. It is always a problem to decide exactly how far to go in this direction. The difficulty—as in other types of warships—is that if a given submarine is too specialized in its application, it is likely to be an embarrassment to the administrative authority when a vessel of a different type is required for current operations in the area. However, the designer always hopes that greater specialization in performance will be accepted in order that he may make the best of his opportunities.

I need add little to Mr. John's remarks except to refer once again to the fine output of submarines from Messrs. Cammell Laird & Co., Ltd., despite the setback they received as a result of the *Thetis* disaster.

Mr. Rooij's remarks concerning the relations between the Dutch designers and the Naval Construction Department are much appreciated. The Dutch submarines and their crews who fought with us during the war were much admired by our submarine service and we were glad to give such assistance as was within our power.

The Unionmelt method of automatic welding was employed in our pressure hull construction and was used mainly for the welding of the seams.

It has not been our practice to introduce high tensile or armoured steel in pressure hull construction. We have used what is virtually a superior grade of mild steel in order to obtain good welding qualities and robustness against shock.

We employed the butt joint throughout in pressure hull construction—the single V in the case of seams which were automatically welded and the double V in the case of circumferential butts which were manually welded. Lapped joints were never used in pressure hull work. Normally our practice was not to fit straps to the welded joints, but there were a few of the earliest of our welded submarines in which we considered it desirable to introduce narrow straps to the pressure hull welds. This practice has long been given up.

As regards the hydraulic movement of rudders, periscopes, etc., our practice for a number of years has been to make the greatest use of this method of operation. Our centralized telemotor system operates the hydroplane gears, the main vents, the torpedo tube front doors, the auxiliary tank kingstons, the periscope hoisting gear, the steering gear (secondary operation), certain hull valves, etc. The system has been brought to a high state of reliability and gave satisfactory performance under the arduous conditions of the war.

Vice-Admiral Barry has made kind reference to the work of the Royal Corps in the submarine field. Good liaison with ships' officers is relatively easy to achieve in the submarine service and we know that only by taking full advantage of this can the best results be obtained.

Mr. Moss has referred to the delay in making the decision completely to weld our submarine hulls. I can sympathise with him in the impatience he felt in this connection, and it is correct that Messrs. Vickers-Armstrongs, Ltd. put forward a scheme on these lines early in the war. To appreciate the difficulties attending a decision on this subject, however, it is necessary to recapture some of the atmosphere of the 1940–42 period. Our submarines were being called upon to perform tasks involving great hazards. The Norwegian campaign, for example, required them in many cases to operate close inshore under conditions of almost continuous daylight when it was very difficult to re-charge batteries. Our losses were fairly heavy and it was an uphill struggle to keep the production of new submarines abreast of such losses. In addition, we had many testimonies to the strength of our riveted hulls against the severe treatment to which they were subjected. Although we had the possibility of changing over to welding very much in mind at the time, it would undoubtedly have temporarily upset production at a very critical period. I think the decisions made were correct, especially as some of our submarine builders preferred to retain riveting at that time.

Both Mr. Tabb and Mr. Avey have added to the value of my paper by including some account of their experiences with submarine construction at Messrs. Cammell Laird & Co., Ltd., and H.M. Dockyard, Chatham, and I do not think that I need to add any remarks on their contributions.

With reference to Mr. W. R. G. Whiting's remarks,

the speeds I have quoted for our war-time submarines have been obtained on trials. I would hesitate to ascribe this to reduction of form resistance or of appendage resistance since this latter has had of necessity to be high to meet indispensable staff requirements.

Mr. Hamilton Martin has made some interesting remarks on refrigeration. The absorption refrigeration system has been given close study but it is doubtful whether its advantages are sufficient to justify its application in submarines. One value of the Freon refrigeration system is that if the charge of refrigerant leaks into the submarine due to depth charge attack or other cause, the cares of the ship's officers are not increased as a result. This is unlikely to apply with the absorption system.

Corvettes and Frigates
by A W Watson, MBE, RCNC, MINA

Originally published in *Transactions*, Volume 89, Number 3, July 1947, pages 165-185

CORVETTES AND FRIGATES

By A. W. Watson, M.B.E., R.C.N.C., Member*

(Read at the Spring Meeting of the Eighty-eighth Session of the Institution of Naval Architects, March 27, 1947, Admiral of the Fleet the Right Hon. Lord Chatfield, G.C.B., O.M., K.C.M.G., C.V.O., President, in the Chair.)

§ 1

This paper describes the development of the designs and of the construction of British corvettes and frigates built for the 1939–1945 war. As the war progressed, vessels of these types were needed in increasing numbers for patrol and escort duties, capable of meeting attacks from submarines and aircraft. Two corvette and two frigate designs were built, namely:—

>Flower class corvettes.
>Castle class corvettes.
>River class frigates.
>Loch class frigates.

A total of about 700 vessels was ordered—mostly from shipbuilders not usually engaged in warship construction. First-class mercantile practice, complying with the requirements of Lloyd's Register and of the British Corporation, was adopted as a basis for the construction. It was never practicable to utilize the shipbuilding capacity normally engaged in warship construction.

§ 2

The above total gives an indication of the extent of the shipbuilding war effort required for these four classes, quickly showed the imperative need for adding to and improving the fighting equipment, and for increasing complements. Developments in tactics involved the provision of new weapons and devices, and the result was that the resources required for the manufacture of equipment and the time and resources required for "fitting-out" vessels after launch increased considerably, and became much greater than would be needed for merchant vessels of comparable size. The details of the equipment had to be kept constantly under review, to reconcile the conflicting requirements of operational authorities on the one hand for changes improving fighting and sea-going efficiency, and of shipbuilders on the other hand contending for the limitation of changes in the interests of rapid production.

§ 3

The leading particulars of the designs are given in the following table and the general arrangements are shown in Figs. 1, 2, 3, 4 and 5.

§ 4

Consideration was given in 1939 to alternative designs of vessels intended for coastal patrol, to have speed and seaworthiness superior to that of large trawlers. Among

TABLE I

Item	Corvettes		Frigates	
	Flower Class	Castle Class	River Class	Loch Class
Length, B.P.	190 ft.	225 ft.	283 ft.	286 ft.
Beam, moulded	33 ft.	36 ft. 6 in.	36 ft. 6 in.	38 ft. 6 in.
Depth moulded to upper deck	17 ft. 6 in.	17 ft. 6 in.	17 ft. 6 in.	17 ft. 9 in.
Load displacement, tons	1,170	1,580	1,865	2,260
Oil fuel stowage, tons	200	480	440	724
Propelling machinery, I.H.P.	2,750	2,750	5,500	5,500
Speed, knots	16	$16\frac{1}{2}$	$20\frac{1}{2}$	$19\frac{1}{2}$

and of the importance of selecting designs capable of achieving maximum performance and suitable for rapid production from the resources available.

To assist in reducing the time for building and the personnel required for manning, simplicity and a small complement were requirements at the outset. These soon became unattainable targets. War experience

the alternatives reviewed was a sketch design proposed by Smiths Dock Co., Ltd., South Bank, Middlesbrough, based on the whale-catcher *Southern Pride* designed and built by the firm. This sketch design was adopted as the basis for the Flower class, and the detailed design was worked out by the firm, in co-operation with Admiralty Design Departments, the British Corporation, and Lloyd's Register. The hull dimensions and layout

* Assistant Director of Naval Construction, Admiralty.

differed considerably from those of the parent whale-catcher, an increase in length of 30 ft. giving better proportions for speed, more space and better watertight subdivision. The four-cylinder triple-expansion engine of *Southern Pride* was adopted, patterns for this engine being available. To obtain an increase in the power of *Southern Pride*, the engine speed was increased to 185 R.P.M., estimated to raise the output of the engine to 2,750 I.H.P. Steam was supplied by two cylindrical oil-fired boilers in separate watertight compartments.

§ 5

Reports of behaviour at sea of the first corvettes showed the performance to be generally satisfactory, but the need for employment on ocean patrol instead of on coastal patrol made it essential to provide for a substantial increase in complement, as well as to incorporate improvements in fighting equipment. The chief alterations authorized were:—

Forecastle extended.
Bridges modified to improve asdic control.
Depth charge armament increased.
Protection for personnel against machine-gun fire and bomb splinters.
Deepened bilge keels.
Increased electrical power.
Steam heating and artificial ventilation in living spaces.

The alterations were incorporated in vessels under construction where this could be done with a minimum disturbance to delivery. In vessels on order, and not too far advanced in the preliminary stages of construction, opportunity was taken to alter the hull sections forward above the load water-line to give them increased sheer and flare and so further improve the seaworthiness.

§ 6

These alterations to the Flower class were made without modifying the principal dimensions or under-water form. The increased dimensions adopted for the Castle class design, as proposed by Mr. William Reed of Smiths Dock Co., Ltd., made it possible to provide vessels of more suitable size for ocean service. It was also possible to remedy the congestion of living spaces in the Flower class, to carry more oil fuel, and to modernize the armament and A/S equipment.

§ 7

The first frigate designs were considered towards the end of 1940, when a review was made of the prospects of building vessels more suitable for service in the Atlantic than the 16-knot Flower class corvettes and with higher speed. Higher speed was always a target, but designs providing for this had geared turbines and water-tube boilers, which had to be rejected in 1939 in favour of the Flower class. The naval staff set a speed target of 22 knots, and a number of alternatives for convoy escorts approximating to this speed were examined. It was recognised that 22 knots could only be obtained with designs having lengths beyond the capacity of the corvette building berths, and with turbine machinery. The acceptance of a compromise design with two sets of corvette machinery estimated to achieve 20 knots was therefore best suited to production by the corvette group of shipbuilders and machinery contractors, and vessels built to this design became the River class frigates. The design was worked out in detail at the Admiralty, and although simplicity and merchant ship practice were retained as far as possible, provision had to be made for fitting out the frigates more closely to warship practice. The speed requirement of 20 knots made economy of weight of even greater importance than in the corvettes, and the principal hull scantlings specified were accordingly based on those of lightly built warship designs that had already been found satisfactory.

§ 8

Although the first River class had a large endurance, the expectation of German submarine attacks on trade being extended to world-wide limits, requiring convoy escorts to cover the greatest possible distances, called for still more endurance. It was found possible to provide this by a re-allocation of suitable compartments combined with the omission of the mine-sweeping equipment, and all River class ordered after the first twenty-four had their fuel stowage increased to 650 tons.

§ 9

The Loch class were substantially reproductions of the River class with considerable changes in the construction of the hull, designed to favour the maximum and most expeditious production. The intensification of German submarine attacks in 1942 made it necessary to accelerate and increase the escort vessel building programme to provide additional protection to vital ocean communications. A target of 200 vessels for completion by the end of 1944 was set for accomplishment by the group of shipbuilders engaged in building corvettes and frigates. It was realized that this programme was beyond the capacity normally available in the shipyards, and special arrangements were made to utilize the capacity of structural engineering firms for the supply of prefabricated parts of the hull structure on a large scale, and for provision of a greatly extended range of fittings and equipment by the Admiralty. The Admiralty also undertook to create new "fitting-out" establishments for completing vessels afloat.

§ 10

Before describing the new system of construction of the Loch class hulls, particulars of the system adopted for the corvettes and River class frigates may be noted. These are shown in Figs. 6 and 7. The connections are mostly riveted, but liberty was given to shipbuilders with welding resources to substitute welded construction for decks, bulkheads, engine seatings, etc. A comparison

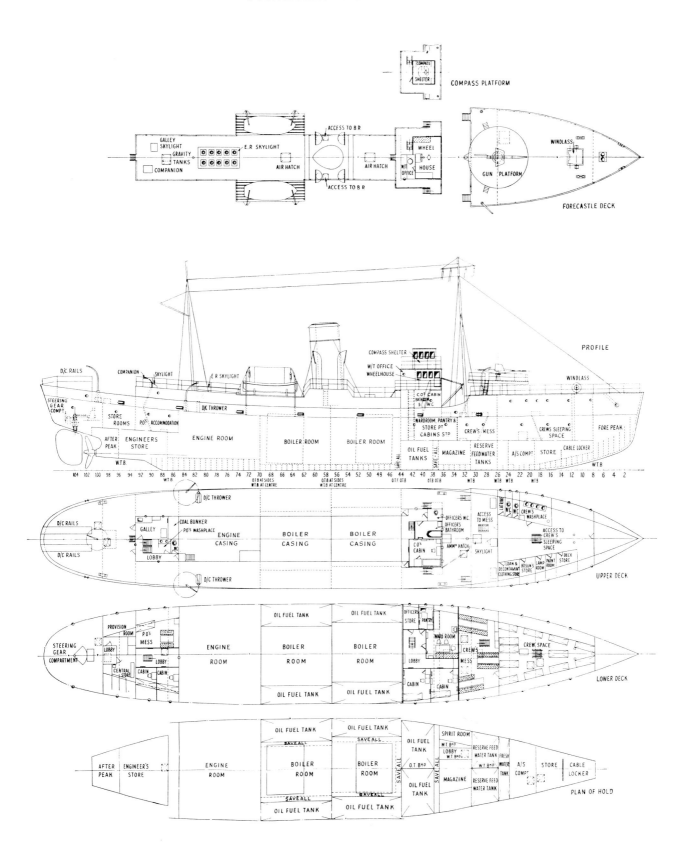

FIG. 1.—"FLOWER" CLASS CORVETTE DESIGN. GENERAL ARRANGEMENT

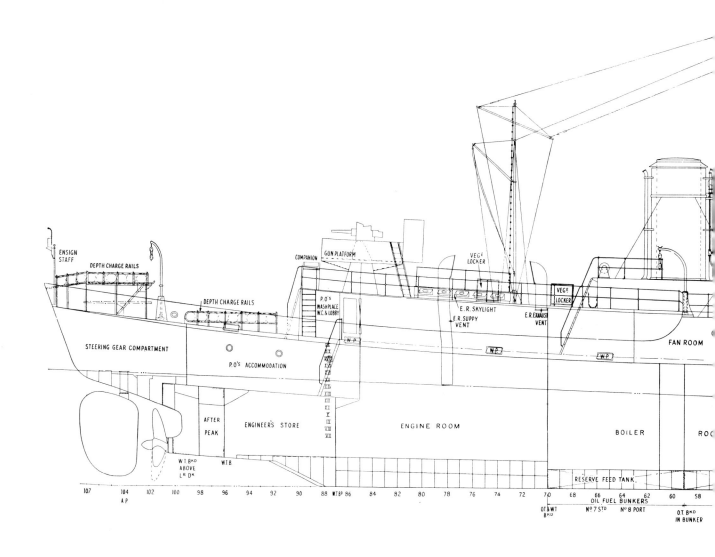

ENSIGN
STAFF

DEPTH CHARGE RAILS

DEPTH CHARGE RAILS

COMPANION

GUN PLATFORM

VEG^E
LOCKER

VEG^E
LOCKER

E.R. SKYLIGHT

E.R. SUPPY
VENT

E.R. EXHAUST
VENT

FAN ROOM

STEERING GEAR COMPARTMENT

P.O'S
WASHPLACE
W.C. & LOBBY

W.P.

W.P.

W.P.

P.O'S ACCOMMODATION

AFTER
PEAK

ENGINEER'S STORE

ENGINE ROOM

BOILER

ROO

W.T. B^KD
ABOVE
L^R D^K

W.T.B.

RESERVE FEED TANK

107   104   102   100   98   96   94   92   90   88 WT8^D 86   84   82   80   78   76   74   72   70   68   66   64   62   60   58
         A.P.

OT.&WT
B^KD

N^O 7 STD

N^O 8 PORT

OIL FUEL BUNKERS

O.T. B^KD
IN BUNKER

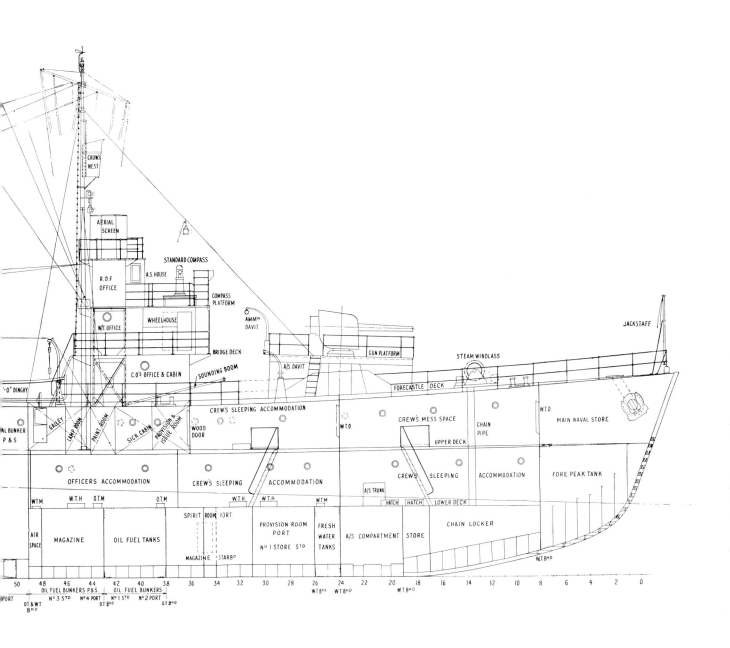

CROW'S NEST

AERIAL SCREEN

STANDARD COMPASS

R.D.F. OFFICE

A.S. HOUSE

COMPASS PLATFORM

W/T. OFFICE

WHEELHOUSE

AMMᴺ DAVIT

BRIDGE DECK

GUN PLATFORM

STEAM WINDLASS

JACKSTAFF

C.O'ˢ OFFICE & CABIN

SOUNDING BOOM

A/S DAVIT

FORECASTLE DECK

-'-0" DINGHY

CREW'S SLEEPING ACCOMMODATION

CREW'S MESS SPACE

CHAIN PIPE

W.T.D.

MAIN NAVAL STORE

GALLEY

LAMP ROOM

PAINT ROOM

SICK CABIN

PROVISION & ISSUE ROOM

WOOD DOOR

W.T.D.

UPPER DECK

NL BUNKER P & S

OFFICERS ACCOMMODATION

CREW'S SLEEPING ACCOMMODATION

CREW'S SLEEPING ACCOMMODATION

FORE PEAK TANK

A/S TRUNK

W.T.M.

W.T.H.

O.T.M

O.T.M

W.T.H.

W.T.H.

W.T.M

HATCH

HATCH

LOWER DECK

AIR SPACE

MAGAZINE

OIL FUEL TANKS

SPIRIT ROOM PORT

PROVISION ROOM PORT

Nᵒ 1 STORE Sᵀᴰ

FRESH WATER TANKS

A/S COMPARTMENT

STORE

CHAIN LOCKER

MAGAZINE STARBᴰ

W.T. Bᴷᴰ

50   48   46   44   42   40   38   36   34   32   30   28   26   24   22   20   18   16   14   12   10   8   6   4   2   0

PORT

OIL FUEL BUNKERS P.&.S.

OIL FUEL BUNKERS

WT Bᴷᴰ   WT Bᴷᴰ

WT Bᴷᴰ

OT & WT Bᴷᴰ

Nᵒ 3 Sᵀᴰ

Nᵒ 4 PORT

Nᵒ 1 Sᵀᴰ

Nᵒ 2 PORT

O.T.Bᴷᴰ

O.T Bᴷᴰ

Fɪɢ. 2.—"Fʟᴏᴡᴇʀ" ᴄʟᴀss ᴄᴏʀᴠᴇᴛᴛᴇ, ʟᴀᴛᴇʀ ᴠᴇʀsɪᴏɴ. Pʀᴏꜰɪʟᴇ

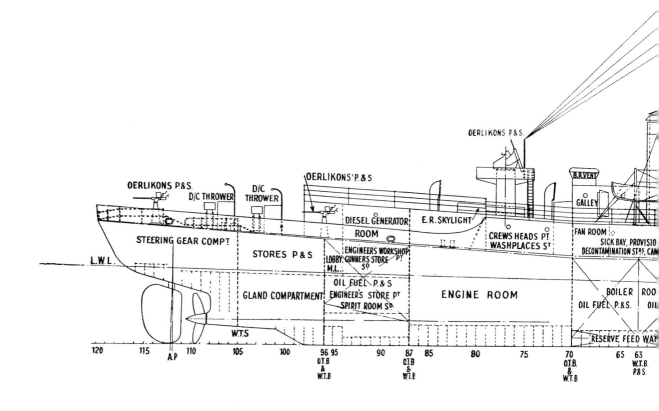

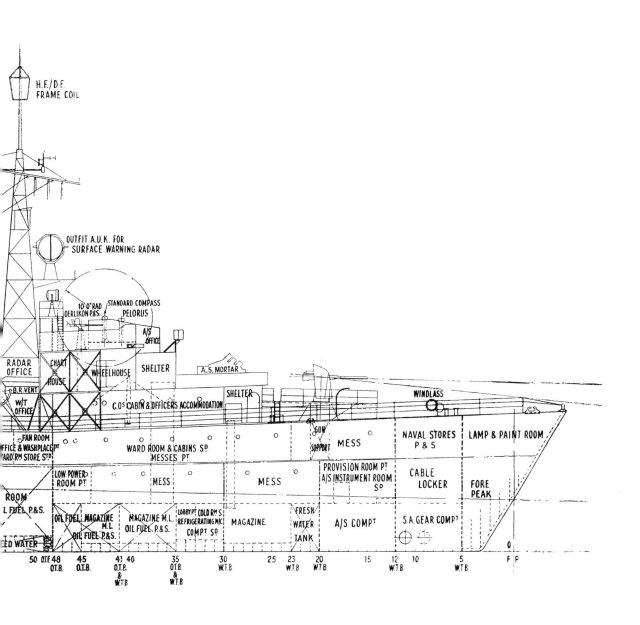

H.F./D.F.
FRAME COIL

OUTFIT A.U.K. FOR
SURFACE WARNING RADAR

10'·0" RAD
OERLIKON P&S

STANDARD COMPASS
PELORUS

A/S
OFFICE

RADAR
OFFICE

CHART
HOUSE

WHEELHOUSE

SHELTER

A.S. MORTAR

B.R. VENT

W/T
OFFICE

SHELTER

WINDLASS

C.Os CABIN & OFFICERS ACCOMMODATION

FAN ROOM

FFICE & WASHPLACE PT

ARD RM STORE STD

GUN
SUPPORT

MESS

NAVAL STORES
P & S

LAMP & PAINT ROOM

WARD ROOM & CABINS SD
MESSES PT

LOW POWER
ROOM PT

MESS

MESS

PROVISION ROOM PT
A/S INSTRUMENT ROOM
SD

CABLE
LOCKER

FORE
PEAK

ROOM

L FUEL P&S.

OIL FUEL MAGAZINE
M.L
OIL FUEL P&S.

MAGAZINE M.L.
OIL FUEL P&S.

LOBBY PT COLD RM S
REFRIGERATING MC
COMPT SD

MAGAZINE

FRESH
WATER
TANK

A/S COMPT

S.A. GEAR COMPT

ED WATER

50 OTE 48
OT.B.

45
O.T.B.

41 40
O.T.B.
&
W.T.B

35
O.T.B
&
W.T.B

30
W.T.B

25 23
W.T.B

20
W.T.B

15

12 10
W.T.B

5
W.T.B

F P

0

FIG. 3.—"CASTLE" CLASS CORVETTE DESIGN. PROFILE

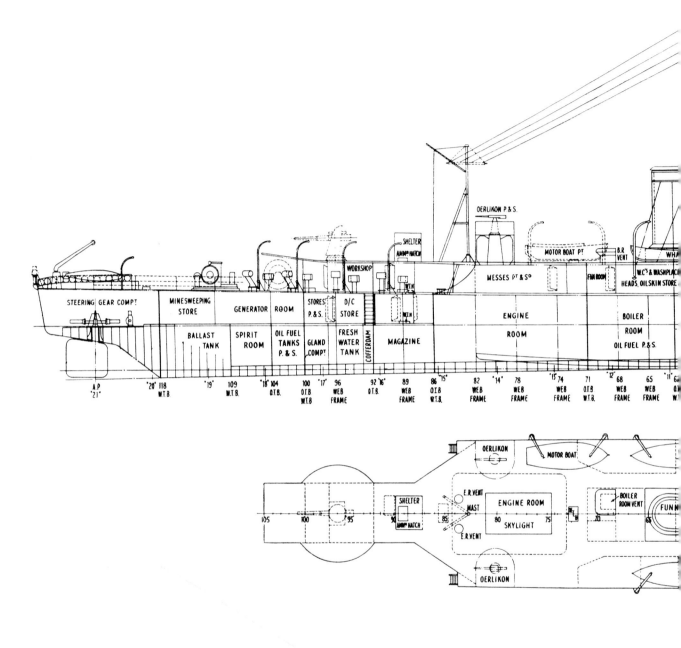

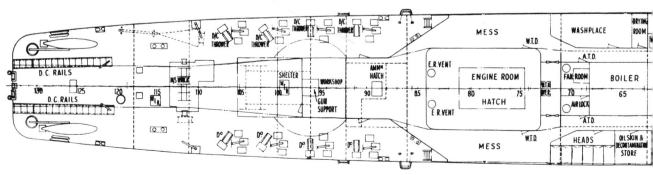

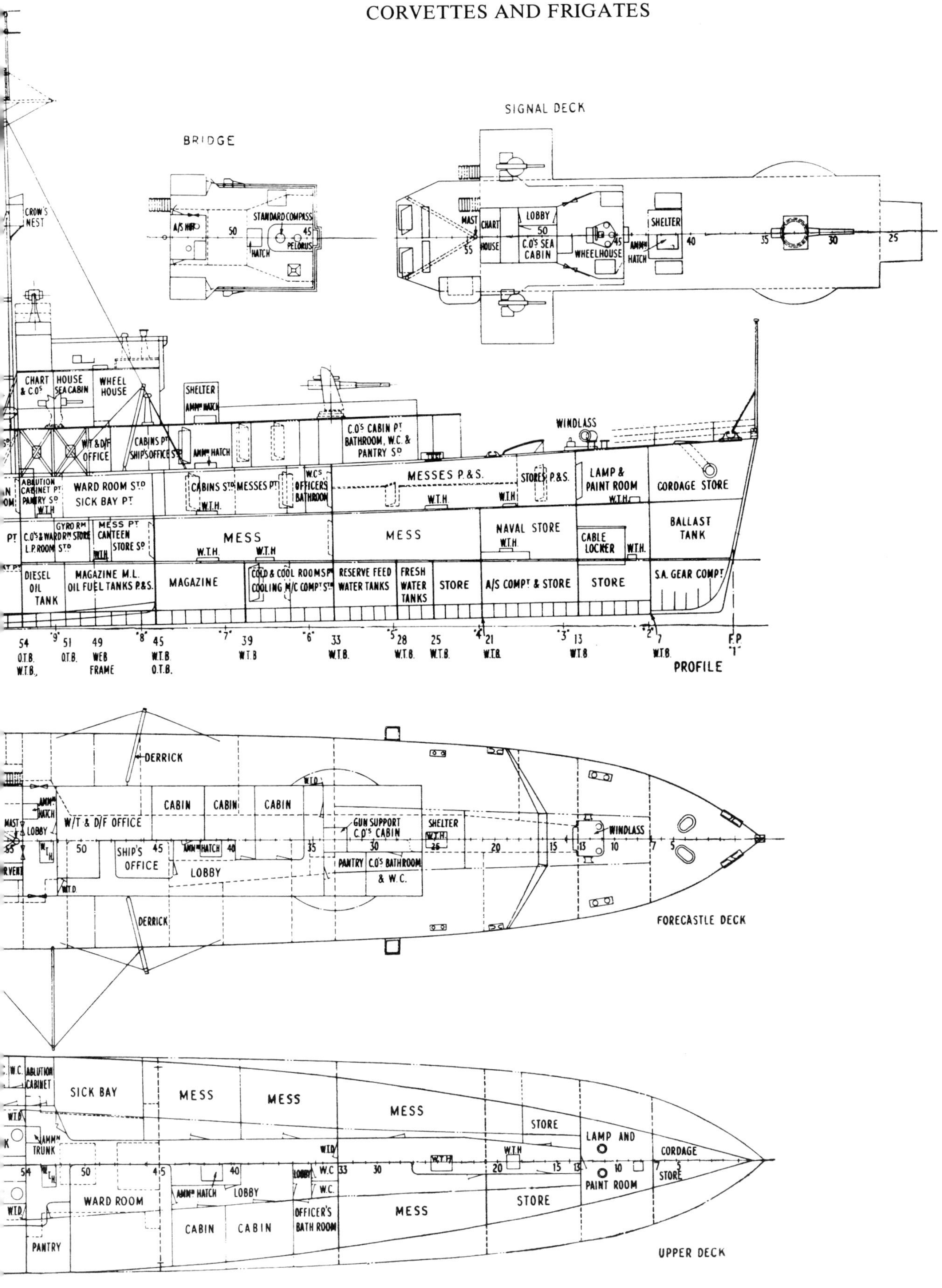

BRIDGE

SIGNAL DECK

PROFILE

FORECASTLE DECK

UPPER DECK

FIG. 4.—"RIVER" CLASS FRIGATE DESIGN. GENERAL ARRANGEMENT

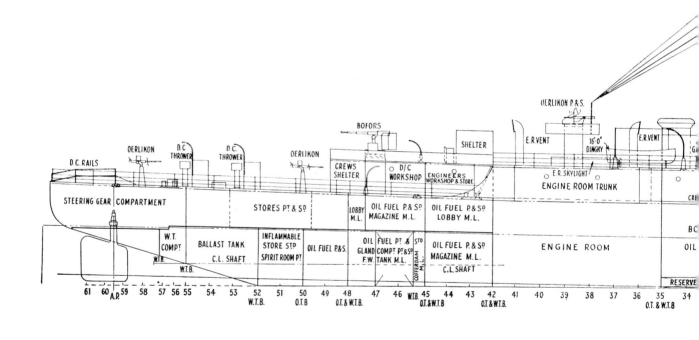

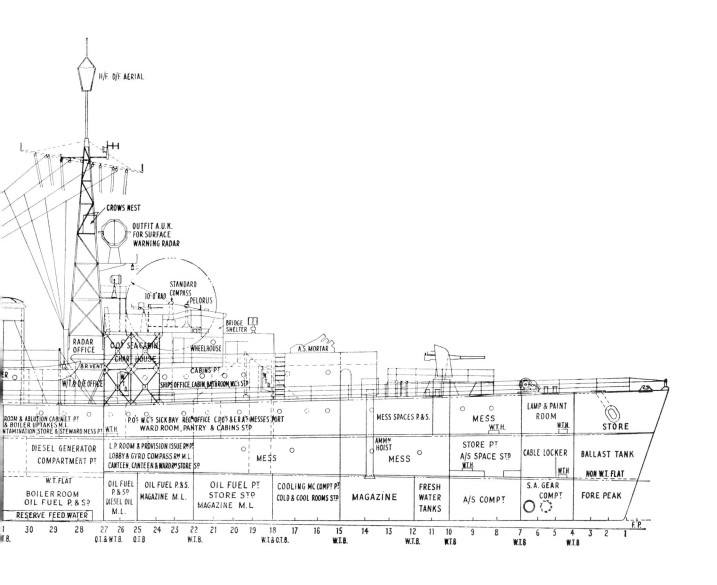

H/F. D/F. AERIAL.

CROWS NEST

OUTFIT A.U.K.
FOR SURFACE
WARNING RADAR

STANDARD
COMPASS
10'-0" RAD.   PELORUS

BRIDGE
SHELTER

RADAR
OFFICE

C.O.'S SEA CABIN

CHART HOUSE

WHEELHOUSE

A.S. MORTAR

B.R.VENT

CABINS P.

W/T.& D/F OFFICE

SHIPS OFFICE, CABIN, BATHROOM, W.C.'s STD

ROOM & ABLUTION CABINET PT
& BOILER UPTAKES M.L.
NTAMINATION STORE & STEWARD MESS PT

P.O.'S W.C.'s SICK BAY REG" OFFICE C.P.O.'S & E.R.A.'S MESSES PORT
WARD ROOM, PANTRY & CABINS STD

MESS SPACES P.& S.

MESS
W.T.H.

LAMP & PAINT
ROOM
W.T.H.

STORE

W.T.H.

DIESEL GENERATOR
COMPARTMENT PT

L.P. ROOM & PROVISION ISSUE RM PT
LOBBY & GYRO COMPASS RM M.L.
CANTEEN, CANTEEN & WARDR" STORE S.D

MESS

AMM'N
HOIST

MESS

STORE PT
A/S SPACE STD
W.T.H.

CABLE LOCKER

W.T.H.

BALLAST TANK

NON W.T. FLAT

W.T. FLAT

OIL FUEL
P.& SD
DIESEL OIL
M.L.

OIL FUEL P.& S.
MAGAZINE M.L.

OIL FUEL PT
STORE STD
MAGAZINE M.L.

COOLING MC COMPT PT
COLD & COOL ROOMS STD

MAGAZINE

FRESH
WATER
TANKS

A/S COMPT

S.A. GEAR
COMPT

FORE PEAK

BOILER ROOM
OIL FUEL P.& SD

RESERVE FEED WATER

F.P.

| 30 | 29 | 28 | 27 | 26 | 25 | 24 | 23 | 22 | 21 | 20 | 19 | 18 | 17 | 16 | 15 | 14 | 13 | 12 | 11 | 10 | 9 | 8 | 7 | 6 | 5 | 4 | 3 | 2 | 1 |

W.T.B.   O.T.& W.T.B. O.T.B   W.T.B.   W.T.& O.T.B.   W.T.B.   W.T.B.   W.T.B   W.T.B   W.T.B

FIG. 5.—"LOCH" CLASS FRIGATE DESIGN. PROFILE

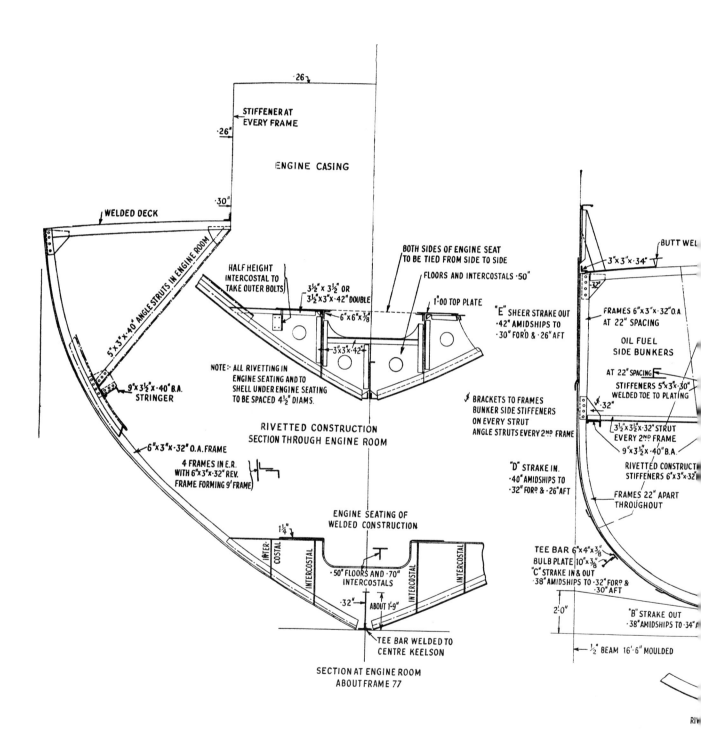

·26"

STIFFENER AT
EVERY FRAME

·26"

ENGINE CASING

·30"

WELDED DECK

BOTH SIDES OF ENGINE SEAT
TO BE TIED FROM SIDE TO SIDE

FLOORS AND INTERCOSTALS ·50"

5"x3"x·40" ANGLE STRUTS IN ENGINE ROOM

HALF HEIGHT
INTERCOSTAL TO
TAKE OUTER BOLTS

3½" x 3½" OR
3½"x3"x·42" DOUBLE

6"x 6"x⅜"

1"·00 TOP PLATE

"E" SHEER STRAKE OUT
·42" AMIDSHIPS TO
·30" FORD & ·26" AFT

BUTT WEL

3"x3"x·34"

·32"

FRAMES 6"x3"x·32" O.A
AT 22" SPACING

OIL FUEL
SIDE BUNKERS

AT 22" SPACING

3"x3"x·42"

9"x3½"x·40" B.A.
STRINGER

NOTE :- ALL RIVETTING IN
ENGINE SEATING AND TO
SHELL UNDER ENGINE SEATING
TO BE SPACED 4½" DIAMS.

STIFFENERS 5"x3"x·30"
WELDED TOE TO PLATING

·32"

6"x3"x·32" O.A. FRAME

4 FRAMES IN E.R.
WITH 6"x3"x·32" REV.
FRAME FORMING 9" FRAME

RIVETTED CONSTRUCTION
SECTION THROUGH ENGINE ROOM

BRACKETS TO FRAMES
BUNKER SIDE STIFFENERS
ON EVERY STRUT
ANGLE STRUTS EVERY 2ND FRAME

3½"x3½"x·32" STRUT
EVERY 2ND FRAME

9"x3½"x·40" B.A.

RIVETTED CONSTRUCTⁿ
STIFFENERS 6"x3"x·32"

FRAMES 22" APART
THROUGHOUT

"D" STRAKE IN.
·40" AMIDSHIPS TO
·32" FORD & ·26" AFT

ENGINE SEATING OF
WELDED CONSTRUCTION

1¼"

INTERCOSTAL

INTERCOSTAL

INTERCOSTAL

INTERCOSTAL

·50" FLOORS AND ·70"
INTERCOSTALS

·32"

ABOUT 1'·9"

TEE BAR 6"x4"x⅜"
BULB PLATE 10"x⅜"
"C" STRAKE IN & OUT
·38" AMIDSHIPS TO ·32" FORD &
·30" AFT

2'·0"

"B" STRAKE OUT
·38" AMIDSHIPS TO ·34" A

TEE BAR WELDED TO
CENTRE KEELSON

½" BEAM 16'·6" MOULDED

SECTION AT ENGINE ROOM
ABOUT FRAME 77

RIV

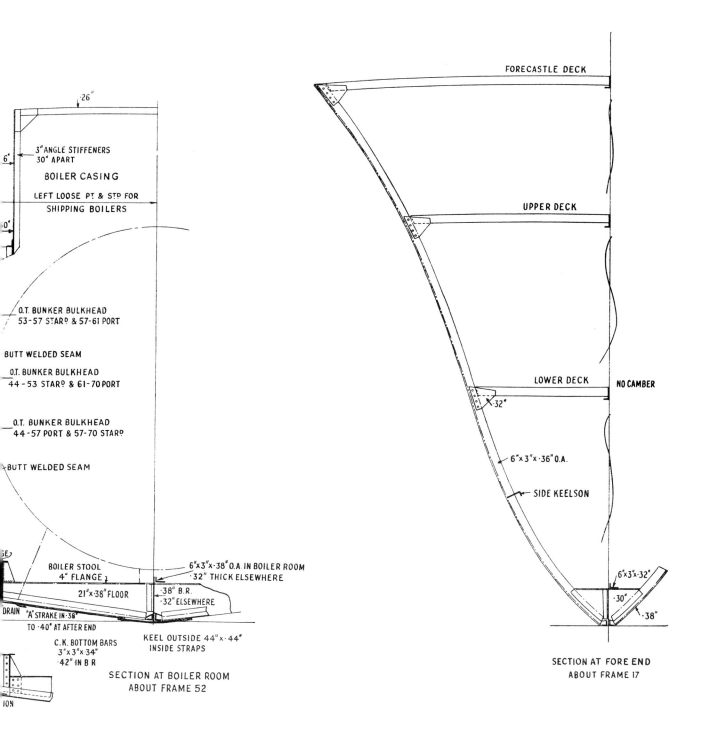

FIG. 6.—"FLOWER" CLASS CORVETTE DESIGN. STRUCTURAL SECTIONS

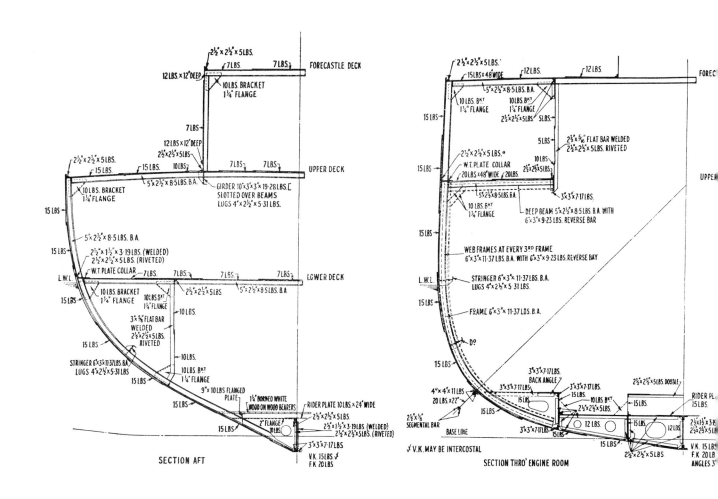

SECTION AFT

SECTION THRO' ENGINE ROOM

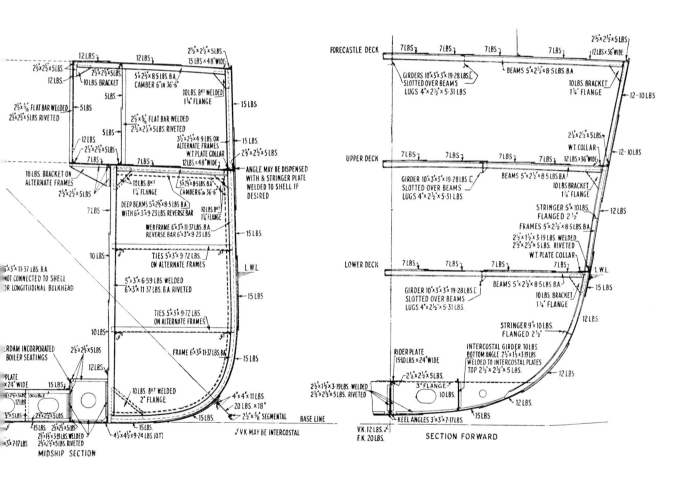

FIG. 7.—"RIVER" CLASS FRIGATE DESIGN. STRUCTURAL SECTIONS

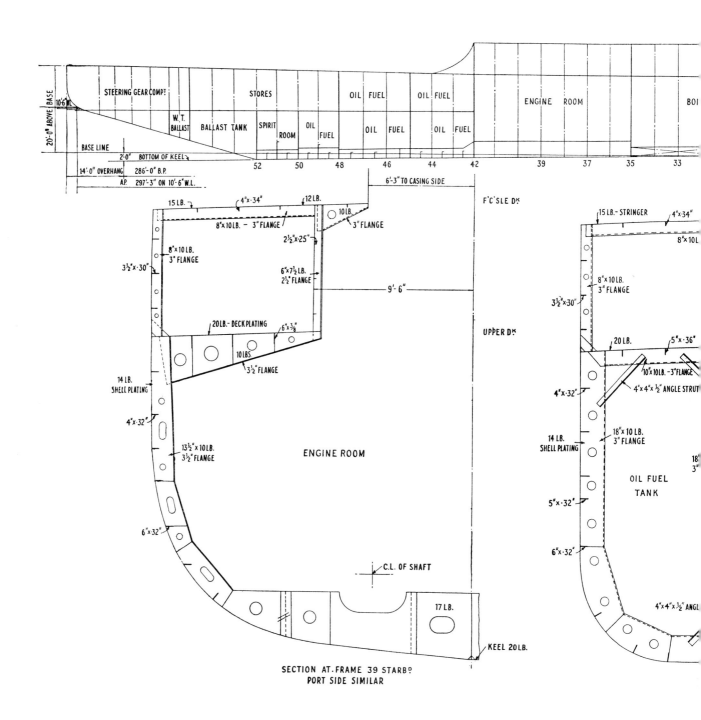

SECTION AT. FRAME 39 STARB?
PORT SIDE SIMILAR

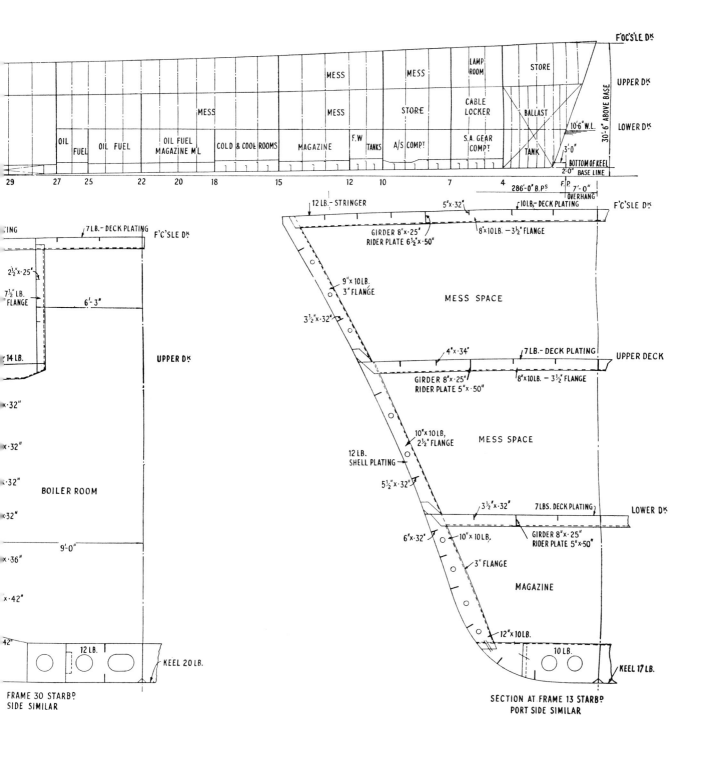

FIG. 8.—"LOCH" CLASS FRIGATE DESIGN. ARRANGEMENT OF STRUCTURE

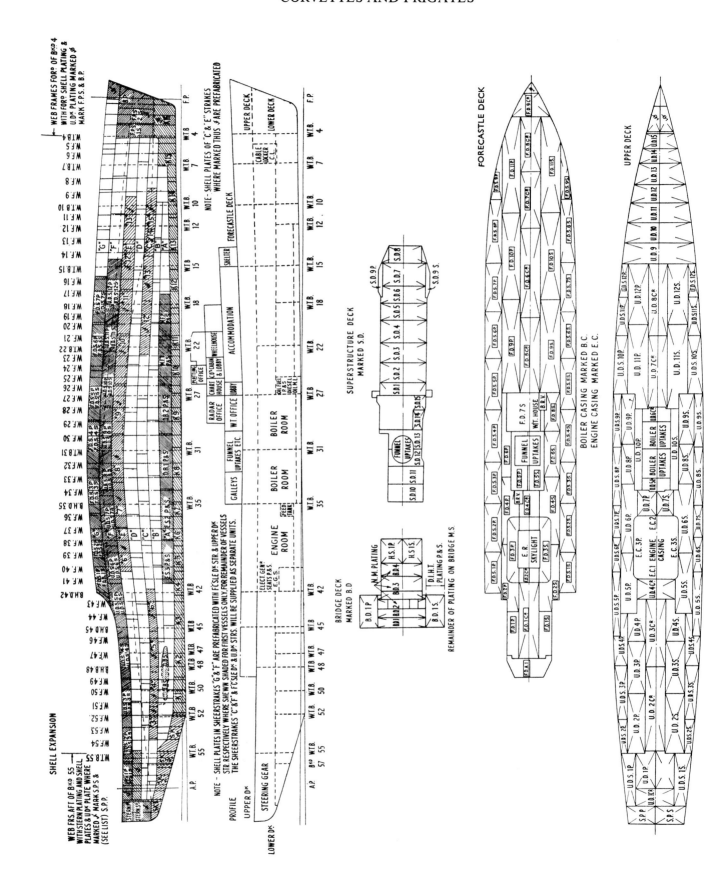

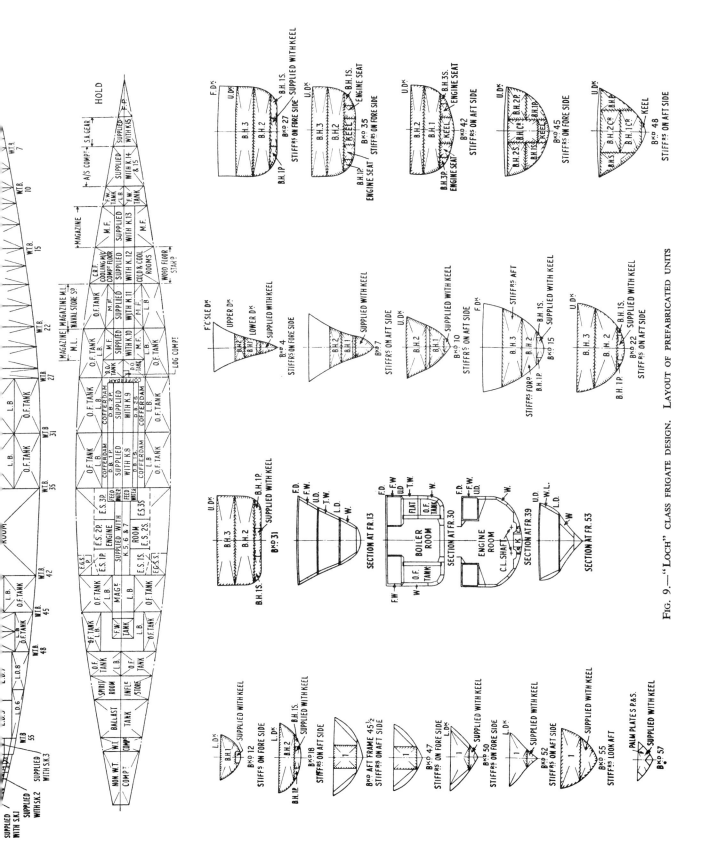

FIG. 9.—"LOCH" CLASS FRIGATE DESIGN.   LAYOUT OF PREFABRICATED UNITS

Fig. 10.—Erection of "Loch Fada," June 16, 1943

Fig. 11.—Erection of "Loch Fada," July 14, 1943

FIG. 13.—ERECTION OF "LOCH FADA," NOVEMBER 10, 1943

FIG. 12.—ERECTION OF "LOCH ADA," SEPTEMBER 15, 1943

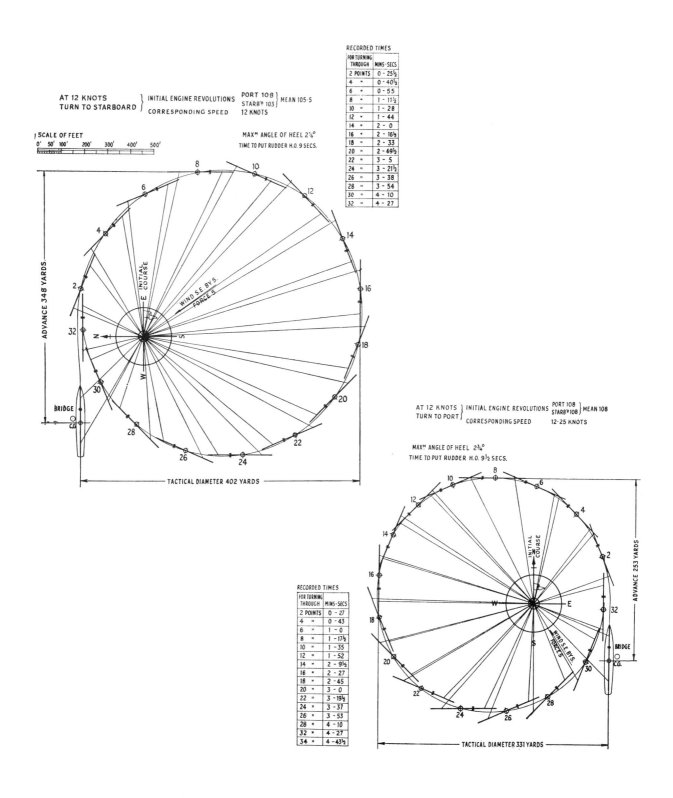

AT 12 KNOTS } INITIAL ENGINE REVOLUTIONS   PORT 108 } MEAN 105·5
TURN TO STARBOARD }   STARB'D 103 }
                   CORRESPONDING SPEED   12 KNOTS

SCALE OF FEET

0' 50' 100'   200'   300'   400'   500'

MAX^M ANGLE OF HEEL 2½°
TIME TO PUT RUDDER H.O. 9 SECS.

WIND S.E. BY S. FORCE 5

ADVANCE 348 YARDS

BRIDGE

TACTICAL DIAMETER 402 YARDS

RECORDED TIMES	
FOR TURNING THROUGH	MINS-SECS
2 POINTS	0 - 25½
4 "	0 - 40½
6 "	0 - 55
8 "	1 - 11½
10 "	1 - 28
12 "	1 - 44
14 "	2 - 0
16 "	2 - 16½
18 "	2 - 33
20 "	2 - 49½
22 "	3 - 5
24 "	3 - 21½
26 "	3 - 38
28 "	3 - 54
30 "	4 - 10
32 "	4 - 27

AT 12 KNOTS } INITIAL ENGINE REVOLUTIONS   PORT 108 } MEAN 108
TURN TO PORT }   STARB'D 108 }
                   CORRESPONDING SPEED   12·25 KNOTS

MAX^M ANGLE OF HEEL 2¾°
TIME TO PUT RUDDER H.O. 9½ SECS.

WIND S.E. BY S. FORCE 5

ADVANCE 253 YARDS

BRIDGE

TACTICAL DIAMETER 331 YARDS

RECORDED TIMES	
FOR TURNING THROUGH	MINS-SECS
2 POINTS	0 - 27
4 "	0 - 43
6 "	1 - 0
8 "	1 - 17½
10 "	1 - 35
12 "	1 - 52
14 "	2 - 9½
16 "	2 - 27
18 "	2 - 45
20 "	3 - 0
22 "	3 - 19½
24 "	3 - 37
26 "	3 - 53
28 "	4 - 10
32 "	4 - 27
34 "	4 - 43½

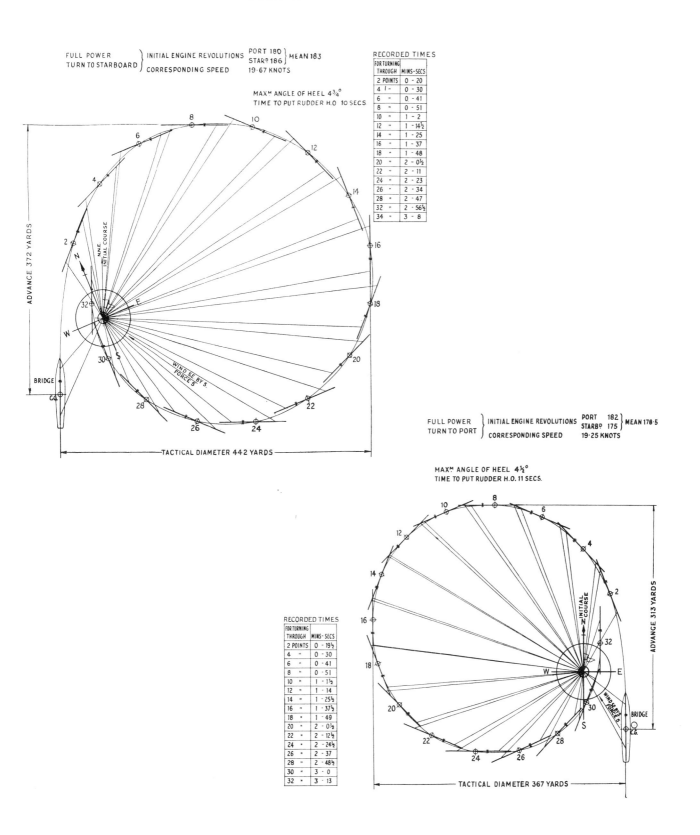

FULL POWER   } INITIAL ENGINE REVOLUTIONS   PORT 180 } MEAN 183
TURN TO STARBOARD }   CORRESPONDING SPEED   STARD 186
                                               19·67 KNOTS

MAXM ANGLE OF HEEL 4¾°
TIME TO PUT RUDDER H.O 10 SECS

RECORDED TIMES

FOR TURNING THROUGH	MINS-SECS
2 POINTS	0 - 20
4 "	0 - 30
6 "	0 - 41
8 "	0 - 51
10 "	1 - 2
12 "	1 - 14½
14 "	1 - 25
16 "	1 - 37
18 "	1 - 48
20 "	2 - 0½
22 "	2 - 11
24 "	2 - 23
26 "	2 - 34
28 "	2 - 47
32 "	2 - 56½
34 "	3 - 8

ADVANCE 372 YARDS

INITIAL COURSE N.N.E.

WIND S.E. BY S. FORCE 5.

BRIDGE

TACTICAL DIAMETER 442 YARDS

FULL POWER   } INITIAL ENGINE REVOLUTIONS   PORT 182 } MEAN 178·5
TURN TO PORT }   CORRESPONDING SPEED   STARBD 175
                                               19·25 KNOTS

MAXM ANGLE OF HEEL 4½°
TIME TO PUT RUDDER H.O. 11 SECS.

RECORDED TIMES

FOR TURNING THROUGH	MINS-SECS
2 POINTS	0 - 19½
4 "	0 - 30
6 "	0 - 41
8 "	0 - 51
10 "	1 - 1½
12 "	1 - 14
14 "	1 - 25½
16 "	1 - 37½
18 "	1 - 49
20 "	2 - 0½
22 "	2 - 12½
24 "	2 - 24½
26 "	2 - 37
28 "	2 - 48½
30 "	3 - 0
32 "	3 - 13

INITIAL COURSE N.

WIND S.E. BY S. FORCE 5.

BRIDGE

ADVANCE 313 YARDS

TACTICAL DIAMETER 367 YARDS

FIG. 14.—H.M.S.—"ROTHER." RESULTS OF CIRCLE TRIALS

of the light displacement of the River class vessels indicated a saving in weight of about 30 tons for the partly welded hull. When the Maritime Commission subsequently undertook the construction of a number of vessels to River class design for the United States Navy, an all-welded hull was adopted with still greater saving in weight.

§ 11

The new system was considered for the Castle class corvettes, but the shipbuilders concerned agreed that for speedy production the usual system of framing and erection at the launching berths was preferable, and avoided the possibility of a gap in deliveries of the corvettes, due to the greater time needed for preparatory work and for starting up a novel system. The construction of the Castle class is similar to that shown for the Flower class, except for some reductions of scantlings. To avoid jeopardizing speed performances, it was necessary to build the hulls as lightly as possible.

§ 12

The frigate structure arranged for prefabrication is shown in Fig. 8, and the scheme of assembly in Fig. 9. A longitudinal scheme of framing was adopted with deep transverse frames about 5 ft. apart, as proposed by Mr. J. L. Adam, C.B.E., Chief Surveyor of the British Corporation. In arranging the division of the structure into units for prefabrication it was necessary to limit the weight to $2\frac{1}{2}$ tons to suit the crane capacity at shipbuilding yards, and to limit the maximum dimensions of units to 29 ft. long, 8 ft. 6 in. wide, and 8 ft. 6 in. high, to suit rail and road transport conditions. About 80 per cent of the hull structure is prefabricated, and welding or riveted connections were adopted for manufacture of the units as best suited to the resources of the structural engineers employed. Riveting was mostly adopted for connecting the units together on the shipbuilding berths, and for the shell plating. The replacement of curved by straight lines for the prefabricated parts was an important consideration in facilitating the work of the structural engineers and the hull form was therefore revised in detail, especially above water. The water-lines forward were run as straight lines instead of slightly hollow, straight portions of considerable length were worked into the forward transverse sections, and the deck sheer was run in three straight portions instead of in the usual continuous curve. Model tank experiments at Haslar showed that the revisions produced little or no adverse effect on the resistance.

§ 13

It was considered advisable to press forward the construction of the first prefabricated frigate to obtain early notice of any difficulties encountered in erecting, fairing and joining the prefabricated units. The structural engineers were responsible for supplying units to correct overall dimensions, for marking guide lines for alignment of adjacent units and for correct details of connections to adjacent units. Messrs. Henry Robb, Ltd.,

laid off the form, undertook all scrieve board work, and were responsible for supplying full-size templates, moulds and other loft information where necessary.

Messrs. John Brown and Co., Ltd., undertook to build the prototype vessel named *Loch Fada* at Clydebank. Photographs of the prefabricated structure in course of erection on the launching berths are given in Figs. 10, 11, 12 and 13. No major difficulties arose, and the firms' experience gave promise of achieving a satisfactory reduction of time for assembly on the launching berth.

§ 14

Some notice may be taken of the scope of the drawing-office work involved in building the vessels in these war programmes. The number of shipbuilders engaged, the alternative riveted and welded construction, and the alterations authorized from time to time, all greatly added to the volume of this work. In addition, vessels were produced in Canada and in Australia, and the need for making a start in building operations overseas with the least possible delay, involved making special arrangements for the approval, reproduction and distribution of copies of working drawings, specifications and steel orders. Shipbuilders abroad required more information and in more detail than is usually supplied to shipbuilders at home, and additional technical information had to be reproduced for them. A system of reproduction of drawings by photographic means became of great help in facilitating transmission of information by air transport. The production of micro-films of plans, etc., was undertaken, and provision at the receiving end of equipment for viewing the films, and of apparatus for making enlarged reproductions of the micro-films. In 1942, when the planned programme and target date was adopted, it became necessary to press on the drawing-office work required for the Castle and Loch classes with the greatest energy and despatch. The prefabricated system of construction of the Loch class involved the preparation of many more than the usual number of detail working drawings and instructions. A temporary central drawing office was established in Glasgow for dealing with the frigates. It was manned by ship and structural engineering draughtsmen, and after the usual shipyard structural drawings were prepared, examined and approved as necessary, they were passed to the structural engineering side, for the preparation of many subsidiary working drawings complete with figured dimensions, suitable for the manufacture of the prefabricated units by structural engineers.

§ 15

Within the speed limits prescribed by production and other requirements, it was possible with the knowledge and assistance of the Haslar tank, to provide for good under-water forms having lengths and other characteristics favourable to low resistance.

The use of reciprocating engines, driving propeller shafting at comparatively low R.P.M. compared with turbines, enabled propellers of large diameter to be used,

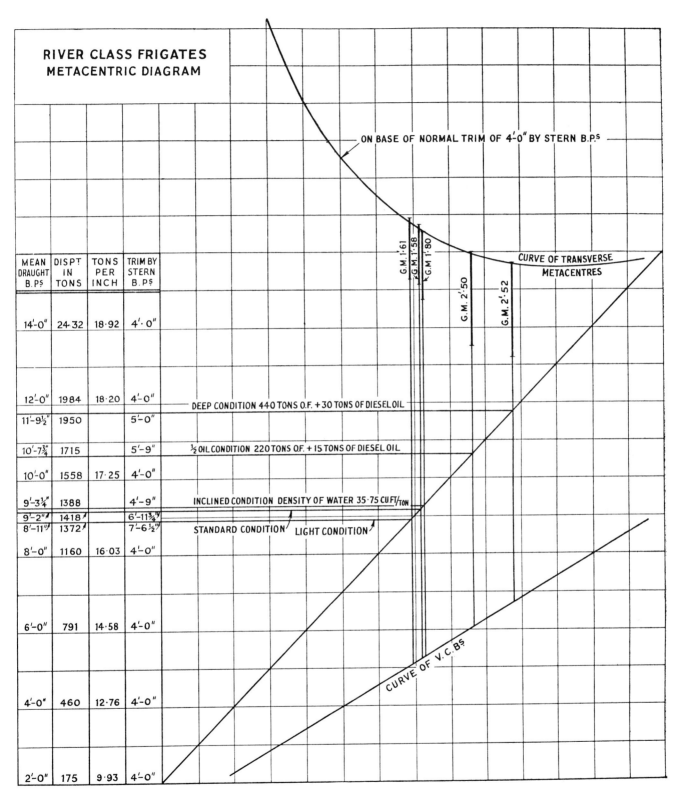

Fig. 15

favourable to high efficiency. All under-water forms were given large trim by the stern for the service conditions to obtain ample propeller tip immersion. On trial the first Flower class corvette obtained at full speed a propulsive coefficient related to I.H.P. of 0·535, and 0·50 was obtained for the twin-screw River class frigates.

§ 16

The provision of good manœuvring qualities was an important requirement for escort service, and a high standard was realized in all classes. This was obtained with an underhung balanced rudder of 86 sq. ft. area associated with the deadwood aft under-water well cut

§ 17

Design estimates of hull weights and centres of gravity in the service conditions were made with reasonable accuracy, and the beam of the load waterplane adjusted to provide adequate stability. A typical metacentric diagram and a diagram of G Z curves applicable to the River class frigates are given in Figs. 15 and 16. It is of interest to note the large effect on stability of the fuel load. A considerable increase of superstructure and weather deck equipment was required in the later stages of the war, raising the centre of gravity so much as to make adjustment of beam insufficient in itself to regulate stability. In the frigates the centre of gravity in the light condition was raised from 0·87 of the depth

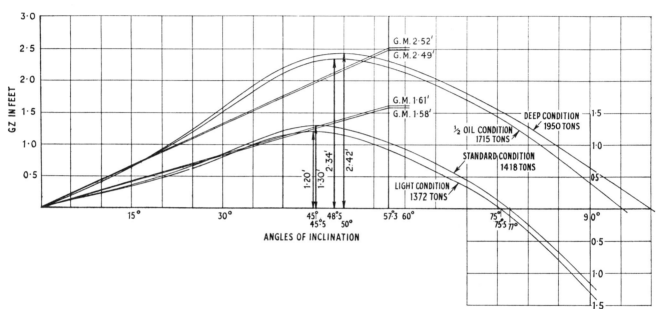

Fig. 16.—"River" class frigates. Curves of GZ

away, as seen in the profile views in Figs. 1–5. The steering trials of H.M.S. *Gladiolus* showed the Flower class to have exceptional powers for turning quickly and in a small space. At full speed ahead the rudder was moved from midships to hard over in 4½ sec. On turns at full speed the measured advance was 2·4 lengths and the tactical diameter 2·1 lengths. The corresponding times to turn through the first 16 and 32 points were 51 and 109½ sec. respectively. The maximum angle of heel was 3 deg. It was not to be expected that this result would be repeated in the longer frigates, but a very good performance was obtained with a rudder of the same area disposed in width to reach into the propeller races when hard over. The steering trials of H.M.S. *Rother* gave the time to put the rudder hard over from midships, at full speed, as 10½ sec. On turns at full speed the advance was 3·6 lengths and the tactical diameter 4·3 lengths. The time to turn through 32 points 190·5 sec. The maximum angle of heel on the turn was 4 deg. The results of the circle trials with this vessel are given in Fig. 14.

moulded in the River class to 0·90 in the Loch class, and from 0·71 in the Flower to 0·98 in the Castle class corvettes. In these circumstances it becomes necessary to regulate the stability when light by adding permanent or water ballast.

§ 18

The reports of behaviour at sea of the corvettes mentioned previously also indicated that, while the vessels' seaworthiness was satisfactory in the heaviest weather, many complaints of the lively motion experienced were made. This proved exhausting to personnel and reduced the efficiency of the asdic equipment, especially on ocean service which meant more frequent and more lengthy encounters with rough weather. The need for finding possible remedies was fully demonstrated, although it was realized that the main remedy of increasing the size of vessel must be excluded as a solution of the problem. Opportunity was taken to make some observations of roll at sea in typical small vessels, and the results are given in the following table:—

TABLE II

Name	Wind	Sea	Swell	Maximum Amplitude of Roll, Degrees	Maximum Half Roll, Degrees	Period, Seconds (Out to Out and Back)	Metacentric Height, Feet
Corvettes							
Heather	7–8	5	3	17	9	4·8 to 8·4	2·6
Salvia	4	3	2	16	8½	6·6 to 8·4	2·4
A/S Trawlers							
Northern Gem	4	2	0	14½	8	5·8	2·3
	4–5	3	1	18	11	7·5 to 8·1	
Stella	9–10	5–6	5	37	20	6·9 to 9	1·9
Capella	7–8	4	1–2	11	7	7·5 to 10·5	
Spurs	8	4	1	19	15	5·2 to 8·1	2·1
				21	11	7·5 to 8·6	
Whalers							
Southern Wave	3	2	0	10		3·5 to 4·5	1·3
Southern Spray	3	3	4	29	18	8·4 to 9	1·3
	3	3	4	24		8·4	
Southern Pride	4	4	3	14	8	5·8	2·0
	4	4	3	10	5½	7·3	
Southern Star	10	5	5	30	19	8·35 to 9·8	1·6
	10–11	5	5	24½	16½	8·3 to 9·7	

The table shows that the periods in the same vessel may vary considerably. One of the suggestions received from sea was that the paramount cause of the lively motion was the amount of metacentric height provided, so that a reduction, by its effect in lengthening the still-water rolling period would reduce liveliness to tolerable amounts. The suggestion, though plausible and possibly applicable to large ships with ample freeboard and range of stability, loaded to give small metacentric height, cannot be accepted as a remedy for the corvettes. The hull of this class already possessed all the characteristics favourable to easy motion at sea: large draught aft 16 ft. to 17 ft., propeller well immersed, ample freeboard, fine transverse sections well flared forward, and a long forecastle. The transverse sections below water had a large rise of floor and a large bilge radius offering low resistances to rolling, but the resistance to this motion was adequately provided by deep bilge keels. Stereoscopic photographs from which the contours of stormy sea surfaces may be derived often show a high degree of irregularity, and the corresponding forced motion of vessels in such stormy seas must also be irregular and difficult to predict. In these circumstances a convenient index of behaviour may be found by recording maximum acceleration at positions occupied by the personnel on duty. It has been stated that accelerations exceeding 0·1 g. will cause discomfort to passengers and some higher figure could possibly be allowed as the limit for seamen. Further investigations from this stand-point would be of general interest, and the type of investigation already made to improve the technique of forecasting sea, swell and surf in preparation for amphibious operations could well be extended to ocean routes concurrently with observations of accelerations in vessels of different sizes traversing these routes.

DISCUSSION

Sir Charles S. Lillicrap, K.C.B., M.B.E. (Vice-President): The production of this group of warships represented one of the major large scale shipbuilding operations of the late war, and equalled in scope and magnitude similar operations by our American allies and the enemy.

Success in this project was essential to our cause, and the fact that we are able to meet here to-day to hear this excellent paper is a measure of that success. Remembering those dark days, and the perils that beset us then, it is clear that a critical examination of the details, where available, must be of great value when similar projects have to be planned in the future.

There is no doubt that it is of great advantage to build and check the performance of prototype vessels, and to have detailed production plans ready for an emergency, although it was our experience with corvettes and frigates, that as the ocean conflict progressed, designs did not remain static; indeed, provision had to be made for the prompt incorporation of changes dictated by the operational and tactical pattern at sea, and the industrial situation ashore, with consequent modifications to vessels built and building and new design studies at headquarters.

The remarkable development of these types of ship during the war years has been described by Mr. Watson. Had the author been able to describe the parallel development in their armament, the paper would have given an even more complete survey of the problems with which the designers and shipbuilders had to cope.

The inception of the programme owes a lot to Mr. Reed, and its success to the efforts, not only of his firm, but to all the firms engaged, and to the co-operation of the classification societies.

Prior to 1933 the development of sloops in the

Admiralty was governed in the main by minesweeping considerations, but in that programme two new types made their appearance, the convoy sloop, a rather larger vessel than before, 280 ft. between perpendiculars, and the coastal sloop somewhat on the lines of the 1918 P.C. boat, and 220 ft. between perpendiculars. These vessels were the prototypes of A/S escorts, the larger for ocean work, the smaller for coastal service. Essentially both types met staff requirements and could carry the armament then expected to be of use against both submarines and aircraft. Both types relied on turbines for the main propelling machinery. By 1939 several ships of each class had been completed, and concurrently, plans and prototypes had been produced for the rapid conversion of trawlers for coastal A/S work, although all of them were deficient as regards speed.

The war came and with it the need for fleets of antisubmarine vessels: the coastal sloop was not suitable for rapid production by the smaller firms, in the main because of the machinery; and trawlers were recognized as being too slow. At this stage the whaler type filled the gap. The programme of coastal sloops, or corvettes as they were now called, lapsed; a programme of whaler type corvettes was substituted, and at the same time the convoy sloop programme was slowed down. So in the first years of the war the only considerable new deliveries of A/S ships were the Flower class corvettes. Meanwhile the submarine war became an ocean war, so these little ships had to fight all over the North Atlantic: in other words they had to do the work of the convoy sloop. The outcome was that, as stated by Mr. Watson, the original corvette came in for a lot of harsh criticism, much of which could only met by building larger ships. Larger ships were therefore designed as early as the end of 1940, and so started the River class; later on came the Loch class which might be described as glorified Rivers. These types are, in fact, of the same size and general capability as the sloops; they are to some extent sloops, simplified by using reciprocating machinery. Our American allies built large numbers of ships of about the same size.

It seems, therefore, that the pre-war naval staff were proved right as to the size and type of ship that would be required, but the number of ships required and the details of the ships themselves were not sufficiently correlated to the production effort, which such naval practice with its refinements and special requirements demands from the shipbuilding and marine engineering industries. Naval practice and naval requirements are even more elaborate to-day than before; in a future emergency we may not have time for a stop-gap to be efficient.

What then can be done to avoid a breakdown? It is not within the province of this Institution to take all the steps, but there are some which, with our great and detailed knowledge of the industry and productive capacity of this country and the Commonwealth, are peculiarly ours.

We must do our best, particularly in times of lean naval programmes, to keep naval thought, and particularly naval technical thought, in touch with the shipbuilders; we must encourage shipbuilders to look for and try new devices and processes, and more flexible production methods for every class of work, and we must foster the inception and acceptance of planned schemes of production in the industry.

Planned schemes of production are likely to differ according to the material and labour resources available. For instance in the war years there was a wide contrast between the procedure followed in the United States and in Britain on similar projects.

In each country there was a central organization for ordering and progressing supplies of materials, fittings, and equipment, but beyond this the systems differed.

In the United States new shipyards were created, and hitherto unskilled labour employed on a large scale. The new establishments were equipped to suit both the labour conditions and the type and size of vessel to be built. Workshops and assembly operations were fully detailed and arranged in time tables, and the training of workmen limited to particular tasks capable of supervision by a nucleus of skilled men.

At home, reliance was placed on utilizing existing shipyards and establishments, operated mainly with fully skilled workpeople, and on expanding them where possible without great changes in practice, culminating in the introduction of the prefabricated frigate.

Each of these systems, so peculiarly typical of the country in which it operated, produced good ships that did all that was required of them.

So let us go forward then in the spirit of co-operation that shows so clearly throughout Mr. Watson's paper with our great Institution providing the common means for discussion between the Navy, the shipbuilding and marine engineering industry, and the technical and scientific thought of the world.

Sir Stanley V. Goodall, K.C.B., O.B.E. (Vice-President): I wish to pay a tribute to Admiral Sir Roger Backhouse, who was First Sea Lord when the war clouds were gathering thick and fast and it was evident that the storm would break. He sent for me and said he was concerned about ships for anti-submarine duties. We must have great numbers. Of the types then on service trawlers were too slow, and escorts expensive to build in money and time. He wanted some sort of ship that was faster than the trawler, could be built rapidly, and would not need a big complement such as our escorts required.

About this time Mr. William Reed of Smith's Dock came to see me. He enlarged upon the properties of the whale-catchers of the *Southern Pride* class built to the British Corporation's classification. It seemed to me that ships with the characteristics of *Southern Pride* would meet the requirements outlined by Sir Roger Backhouse.

Mr. Watson tells the rest of the story of the development of the design into corvettes of the Flower class.

Production was quickly commenced as, at that time, many of the yards capable of building these small ships were not fully occupied, and their construction did not interfere with the rest of the warship programme. We are greatly indebted to Smith's Dock who supplied the plans for all builders including those abroad. To illustrate what was done it may be stated that Messrs. Harland & Wolff, Belfast, when fully in their stride, turned out corvettes at the rate of one a fortnight.

To say that these ships were cheap, simple to build, and required only a small complement is one way of expressing the fact that they lacked much of the equipment and amenities of the normal warship, and for this they were quickly criticised.

In 1942 when the enemy submarines were taking heavy toll of our shipping it was decided to build two hundred additional escorts as rapidly as possible. A meeting was called of shipbuilders, the British Constructional Steel Association, Lloyd's Register, and the British Corporation and two different designs were considered. One was for an improved Flower class corvette, the other was for a River class frigate re-designed in order that pre-fabrication might be undertaken by structural steel firms. It was decided to build to both designs. Some firms could not build the larger frigates. Moreover it was realized that the planning and organization necessary for pre-fabrication would require time and more escorts were desperately required as soon as possible.

The labour in the shipyards that was necessary for all this extra work was simply not there. By adopting pre-fabrication by structural steel firms for the Loch class a new source of supply became available. These firms entered into the scheme whole-heartedly and the standard of their work was high.

Much preliminary work had to be done before actual building commenced. A new and special drawing office was set up as well as a progressing establishment at Edinburgh, superintended by Mr. Paton, who we obtained with some difficulty from the Ministry of Supply. We knew, also, that while the structural steel firms and the yards could build the hulls, the latter had neither the capacity nor the labour for fitting the intricate armament and equipment, so we set up two fitting out bases, one on the Wear and one on the Clyde. Fitting out would have been our greatest problem. But the battle of the Atlantic was, in fact, won before the Loch class as a whole reached the fitting out stage, and after these ships lost their high priority it was a sad sight to see some of them complete as hulls lying idle at the fitting out bases.

One important matter in planning, a word that has become rather unpopular of late, is the psychology of the people called upon to carry out the plans. We have heard a great deal about prefabricated ships in the United States. There the shipyard labour was new and had to be trained so that the methods adopted were readily accepted. But in our case the prefabricated parts were assembled by men used to normal practice. They may vote progressive in elections but they are conservative in their work. It was very trying after all our efforts to see some work absolutely stopped because two unions could not agree which should put together the pre-fabricated parts to make a fair ship. Eventually, that difficulty was overcome but we lost some valuable time.

The last paragraph of the paper is of considerable interest. At one time I was, in all seriousness, pressed to put ballast on the upper deck of these corvettes. As Mr. Watson has pointed out, a little knowledge about stability may be a dangerous thing especially when small ships are the problem. I hope some of our students will read these lines, ponder over them, and give us the results of their thoughts, preferably reinforced with careful records of the behaviour of ships of this type at sea.

Mr. J. M. Murray, M.B.E., B.Sc. (Member of Council): The production of the corvettes and frigates detailed in this admirable paper was in many ways a remarkable achievement which reflected great credit on all concerned. Starting with the relatively simple Flower class corvettes, the complexity of the ships increased progressively, so that the latest Loch class frigates differed little from the type of ship built in naval yards. The gradual development of these patrol and escort ships enabled the merchant yards engaged in their construction to acquire experience of Admiralty practice by stages, but even making allowance for this it is remarkable that production should have proceeded as smoothly as in fact it did. From the structural point of view, the most interesting class was the prefabricated Lochs. Here the longitudinal scheme of framing proposed by Mr. Adam was extremely suitable for prefabrication, and the structural soundness was evident. Fundamentally, the scantlings and arrangements adopted in the Lochs were similar to those of the all-welded minesweeper *Seagull*, which has proved to be successful in service, but it should be borne in mind that the Lochs were rather larger ships than the *Seagull*. In the actual construction of the Loch class there were many difficulties to be overcome, and a tremendous amount of detailed planning to be worked out. The success of the venture was due, in a large measure, to the careful way in which the production was organized down to very small details by the various departments concerned. For the structure itself the various parts came together very well, and after having seen these ships in various stages of construction in different yards the outstanding impression made was the remarkably accurate way in which the erection of the parts proceeded. Perhaps the rate of production fell below estimate, but if it had turned out otherwise it would have been most unusual. The virtue of optimism always found its due place in the planning departments.

The construction of these ships was certainly expedited by the adoption of merchant practices in their construction, and perhaps more could have been done in this line. Nevertheless the Admiralty allowed considerable latitude as regards details, and modifications to meet yard facilities were always sympathetically considered. The use of welding was encouraged, and one yard completed River class corvettes with all welded shell plating. Here the end connections were butt welded, and the seams overlapped; an excellent job was produced in this way, and one which proved effective in service.

The author has drawn attention to the fact that while

in the Flower class corvettes the scantlings adopted were substantially those of the prototype whale catcher, those of latter ships conformed to Admiralty practice. These light scantlings can only be used in ships operating under certain conditions, and where the saving of weight is of paramount importance; they could not be adopted in merchant ships. Nevertheless they have become familiar to merchant shipbuilders, and to the classification surveyors through this programme, and must colour previous opinions of what are absolute minima in certain directions.

Structurally the ships gave little trouble, the only weaknesses revealed being a slight lack of strength against pounding which caused distortion at a point further aft than was usual in merchant ships, and a slight tendency of the ship to strain at the break of the forecastle. It was not difficult to cure these slight deficiencies. On this latter point it has often occurred to me that the design of the frigates would have been improved if the forecastle deck had been carried right aft to the stern. This would have improved the structure of the ship, provided more space internally, and given a drier ship aft. I was never in any of these ships in anything approaching heavy weather, but even in moderate seas it appeared to me that the after deck was too close to the stern wave for comfort.

Mention should be made of the association between the Admiralty and the classification societies on these ships. The scheme finally adopted whereby the latter concerned themselves with the hull structure and the normal classification requirements, leaving the rest to the Admiralty, was an extremely useful one, and led to very happy results. As with other aspects of the production of these ships few difficulties arose, and those that did were speedily adjusted. The D.N.C. department gave great help to the classification societies. The design staff headed by Mr. Watson and the production side under Mr. Hannaford, and later Mr. McCarthy and Mr. Hopkins were always ready to give sympathetic advice and encouragement.

Mr. R. W. L. Gawn, R.C.N.C. (Member of Council): It is thought that an account of some of the model investigations associated with the development of these small ships which played such a vital and arduous part in the war would be of interest. The conditions of the design favoured good speed performance in that there were very few circumscribing features to cause departures from the optimum form. In addition the proportion of beam to draught was less than for many classes of warship. As a result forms of a very high standard were evolved, closely approaching the optimum. The humps on the resistance constant curve were either absent or refreshingly diminutive.

The first models of the Flower class corvette were tested before the war in the late spring of 1939. The prismatic coefficient was favourably low namely about 0·54 and although the stern trim was large it was possible to arrange the centre of buoyancy in a satisfactory position. The rate of revolutions of the reciprocating

machinery was favourable and it was possible to fit a large propeller resulting in a good propeller efficiency of the order of 0·7.

We noted in the official report on the investigations that the length could be increased with advantage but this was precluded by the requirements of the first design. Following experience a longer ship was called for and in the Autumn of 1942, model experiments on the Castle class corvettes were put in hand. Although the displacement of the final design was 420 tons greater an increase of speed of $\frac{1}{2}$ knot over the Flower class was predicted largely as a result of increase of length of 37 ft. This striking improvement was confirmed by the trial results. The investigations on the Castle class reflect the pace of events in that critical period of the war. The first model was tested in October 1942. The design was subsequently modified, displacement, beam and length all being increased in different degrees. The final form was tested in January 1943, including inner drive screw experiments, and the recommended propeller design forwarded to Admiralty in February. The trials of the first ship of the class were completed within eight months. This speaks for itself as to rapid production, certainly for ships and propellers, and for model hulls and model propellers.

The frigates were also of a high standard. The first model of the River class tested in the Autumn of 1940 had the optimum prismatic coefficient and centre of buoyancy position for the designed full speed. At cruising speed the performance was also of high standard although a slight reduction in prismatic coefficient with a modification of centre of buoyancy forward would be necessary to obtain the last ounce of form efficiency at low speeds. Twin screws were fitted to each shaft, driven by the same machinery as for the single screw corvettes. The propeller efficiency was even higher namely 0·74, and the predicted speed was 4 knots greater. Displacement was 480 tons greater (i.e. 41 per cent) than the Flower class corvette and yet at the full speed for the Flower class, the effective horsepower was 20 per cent less, another indication of the advantage of increase in length, in this case 98 ft. We found this model so satisfactory with negligible change of resistance constant over a wide speed range that we used it as a standard model for correcting results for a number of years to scarph on to a new standard model then being made in brass.

The Loch class frigate form for rapid production produced two years later, was also of a good standard, but speed was reduced due to increase of beam and displacement. The final design showed a reduction of horsepower of 9 per cent at full speed and 4 per cent at cruising speed as compared with the initial model, the improvement being obtained by reduced eddy making consequent on stern modifications.

An interesting design tested as an alternative to the Flower class corvettes in 1940 was of straight line section for rapid production. The hull resistance proved excessive which is not surprising in view of the favourable form of the corvettes. In calm water the straight line form required about 14 per cent more horsepower than the round bilge at 15 knots and 6 per cent more at cruising speed. This disadvantage was rather masked in heavy seas. Model experiments suggested that the speed of each type would be reduced to about 13 knots under extreme conditions, allowance being made for loss of propeller efficiency as well as additional hull resistance.

Rolling experiments indicated that the extinction at 10 deg. was about $2 \cdot 0$ for the round bilge form and $1 \cdot 2$ for the straight line form, but at high speed there was little to choose, the extinction being $2 \cdot 8$ for each form at 16 knots.

The conception of acceleration as a yardstick for ship motion introduced by the author is most useful. It correlates the separate and combined effects of pitch, heave, and roll both as to amplitude and period. It gives a ready assessment of the effect of different motions on fighting efficiency, both as regards personnel and material.

Records of pitch and heave during the rough weather model experiments indicated that under the most severe conditions of synchronous motion in steep seas the extreme acceleration might approach $\frac{3}{4}g$ at bow and stern, the amplitude of pitch being about 5 deg. and heave about 6 ft. In moderate conditions the motion is greatly reduced but the figures speak for themselves as to the severity of movement of small ships in the Atlantic forced, by war conditions, to maintain course and speed on convoy duty in all weathers. Sustained accelerations of only about $1/10$ of g especially when irregular and changing rapidly are uncomfortable and $1/5$ g distinctly so. The extreme rolling acceleration on deck side amidships is about one half that associated with pitch and heave, but fortunately while heavy rolling and heave may occur together they are not ordinarily associated with heavy pitching movement.

Mention may also be made of propeller singing which proved a nuisance as the number of corvettes on service increased. A large number of ships of the class were free, but singing of a borderline character occurred in a proportion of the ships generally with maximum intensity at about one third full power revolutions. Since the after lines were fine and the wake moderate and therefore not unduly mixed, it was clear that the trouble was inherent in the propeller design. The persistence of a unique singing note was a menace in that it would lead to detection of the corvettes and the convoy. The propellers were quickly modified to designs produced at Haslar, with satisfactory results.

We are most indebted to the author for an excellent paper which puts on record the main characteristics of the designs and considerations which governed them.

Rear-Admiral (E.) G. H. H. Brown: This paper deals with the subject entirely from the shipbuilder's angle and refers only briefly to machinery. A few remarks on the machinery aspect of the work will, therefore, not be out of place.

The design of the original Flower class corvettes, based on the whale-catcher *Southern Pride* designed and built by Messrs. Smith's Dock Co., Ltd., Middlesbrough, embodied four-cylinder triple-expansion reciprocating engines and cylindrical marine type boilers. The urgency of the situation demanded machinery capable of rapid production, and as the ships were to be manned by personnel drawn largely from the fishing industry it was necessary that the machinery should be of a type with which they would be most familiar.

Whilst the choice of cylindrical boilers for this service was open to criticism on the score of want of flexibility, the lack of capacity for manufacture of water tube boilers of the type usually fitted in warships decided the issue.

Some difficulty was experienced in ships of this class in meeting the frequent and large changes of speed required when employed on convoy escort duty and when attacking submarines, but, in general, the ships gave excellent service, and having regard to the severe operating conditions to which they were often exposed, maintenance of the cylindrical boilers did not prove to be an insuperable problem.

Howden-Johnson type boilers were fitted in a number of ships built by Messrs. Harland & Wolff, Belfast, and also gave excellent service.

In later ships Admiralty 3-drum type water tube boilers were installed, arranged in separate closed stoke-holds, and this type was adopted for the River and Loch class frigate and the Castle class corvettes. This change introduced the necessity for increased stowage of fresh water and distilling plant of greater output than that fitted in the original design.

Working drawings of the machinery and boilers designed by Messrs. Smith's Dock Co., were circulated to a large number of engineering firms in Britain and Northern Ireland, and to Canada, Australia, and the U.S.A.

To assist the rapid production of machinery for the twin screw frigates, the corvette four-cylinder, triple-expansion engine was retained for these ships, modified by the addition of a coupling to the forward end of the crankshaft so that the engine could be turned end for end to suit either a port or starboard position. In these twin screw installations each engine was arranged as an independent unit with separate condenser and circulating water systems.

Whilst for the Flower class corvettes and River class frigates the machinery was contracted for by the individual builders, for the prefabricated Loch class frigates and the Castle class corvettes it became necessary to introduce a system under which the Admiralty placed bulk orders for boilers, main and auxiliary engines, shafting, propellers, etc., the various items of machinery being allocated to shipbuilders for embodiment in the hulls as required to meet the progress of work of fitting out.

This procedure involved the setting up within the department of the Engineer-in-Chief of a special planning and progress section to handle the work of placing orders and allocation to the shipbuilders.

In spite of some preliminary difficulties the system

worked well, and delays in completion of ships that might otherwise have occurred were obviated thereby.

In addition, pipework for the Loch class frigates was fabricated from sketches made by the parent firm and the pipework carried out by firms specializing in this class of work, completed pipes being allocated according to the needs of the various firms fitting out the vessels.

A total of approximately 1,150 engines was built between January 1940, and December 1944, to the design originally supplied by Messrs. Smith's Dock Co. To obviate any possibility of vibration likely to arise at critical speeds of the engines special trials were carried out in one ship with the engines uncoupled from the line shafting. Lloyd's representatives were called in to assist in this trial, the results of which were satisfactory.

All the machinery and boilers were built to the standard requirements of Lloyd's Register and British Corporation and under their supervision.

In order to avoid delays at certain shipyards with limited accommodation for fitting out, arrangements were made by the Admiralty for some hulls to be transferred after launching to fitting out basins at Hendon Dock for the Tyne Area, and Dalmuir Basin for the Clyde, for installation of machinery and completion for service. At the former the work was carried out by Messrs. North Eastern Marine Engineering Co., in association with Messrs. George Clarke & Co., Ltd., and at the latter by Messrs. John Brown & Co., and other firms.

In the foregoing remarks I have touched only on the principal features of this project, which might well form the subject of a separate paper. That such a programme could be carried out without encountering any major difficulty reflects the greatest credit on all those concerned, who worked together most harmoniously and contributed, to no small extent, to the destruction of the U-boats and the ultimate defeat of the enemy.

Mr. T. C. Grisenthwaite: In the first place, I should like to thank you for allowing me the privilege of contributing to this discussion.

I shall confine my remarks to that part of the paper dealing with the Loch class, on which I was responsible under the British Constructional Steelwork Association for the preparation of the constructional steelwork drawings, and that part of the shop inspection dealing with the accurate fitting together of the components of the prefabricated units.

The project was a team job involving co-ordination between the Admiralty, classification societies, shipbuilders and constructional engineers, and all these parties worked in the closest collaboration with each other at all times.

The scheme was started towards the end of 1942 when the German submarine menace was one of the most important problems facing the country.

It will be realized at the outset that the methods adopted were only a feasible and economic solution where a large number of similar vessels were required to be built, and where the prefabricated units had to be made by firms with little or no experience in shipbuilding. Furthermore, these units had to be spread over a large number of contractors in different parts of the country, with widely different plant capacities and workshop methods.

The scheme involved, as the author has pointed out, the formation of a central drawing office in Glasgow of both shipbuilding and constructional draughtsmen. This was the preliminary set-up, but a large amount of work was necessary in the co-ordination of the drawing office work with the production of templates, the ordering of material, placing orders for units and progress work with the various contractors, so as to ensure that the finished units were delivered to the shipyards in a proper sequence.

There are many differences in the technique of work between shipbuilders and constructional firms, particularly in the type of drawings and templates used. Previous schemes of prefabricated ship work had been carried out, but these usually consisted of single plates or built-up sections, made from fully dimensioned drawings on which the position of every rivet hole was accurately determined.

It was soon apparent that the vast number of drawings required could never be produced in an adequate time if this method were adopted.

Messrs. Henry Robb of Leith undertook the manufacture of all the necessary templates from the drawings prepared by the constructional engineers. No praise can be too high for this important work carried out by Messrs. Robb. In addition to the actual production they were most helpful in every way in explaining the templates to the engineering firms—many of whom were at that time unfamiliar with such terms as "frame line," "mould line."

Another difficulty soon arose when several firms in different parts of the country were engaged on the production of similar units, and duplication of templates was necessary.

Here again, the interchange of information between firms was very marked; in many cases firms pooled their experience in the manufacture of jigs and the most suitable methods of welding to prevent distortion.

The constructional side of the drawing office was commenced in January 1943, and in two months had grown to 25 draughtsmen with an equal number of shipbuilding draughtsmen working alongside.

The preparation of the detail drawings probably took longer than the original forecast, but it was scarcely realized at the commencement that all fully detailed drawings would be necessary. In about six months these drawings were produced, sent to the template loft and to the various contractors. Actually, there were 1,360 prefabricated units for each vessel, and altogether nearly 100 contractors were engaged in the programme —apart from those portions of the work supplied by the shipbuilders.

Bulkheads were fitted complete with watertight doors, ladders, etc., and deck units with hatches, and deck treads welded on. The sloping keel section had the rudder bearing incorporated in the unit.

In passing, it should be mentioned that the production of the units—which were largely of welded construction —necessitated the construction of substantial jigs, particularly for the keel sections. Although every unit had to be accurate to the dimensions and connections shown on the drawings, a certain amount of latitude was allowed in the detail construction to suit the plant of each firm. For instance, deck beams were generally of flanged L section, with the toe welded to the deck. Firms who could not cold flange the plates made up an L section of two plates welded together.

As the work proceeded it became evident that some organization was necessary to ensure the accuracy of adjoining units. Experienced men from the drawing office were sent out as inspectors, and located in Glasgow, Newcastle, Manchester, Birmingham, and Bristol. These inspectors were responsible for the connections of adjoining parts, arranged for the transfer of templates, correct marking of guide lines, etc. In some instances, where the distances between adjoining firms were not too great, connecting units made by different contractors were proved before being sent to the shipyards.

As the author has pointed out, the conflicting requirements of operational authorities and the necessity for rapid production had to be nicely balanced. It will readily be appreciated that even minor modifications required alterations to many drawings, templates, and notification to many contractors involving delays in production.

It was only natural that in a scheme of this magnitude, carried out under such conditions, mistakes were bound to occur. A careful record of all mistakes was kept, and interested contractors were notified immediately to prevent repetition of the error. Such errors were of a minor character which were readily rectified at the shipyard.

A system of guide lines was chiselled on bulkheads, deck units, etc., showing their relation to the centre line of vessel or height above keel mould line, as the case might be. These lines were of great assistance in the correct "fairing" up at the shipyard.

In the light of the experience gained on this project certain improvements might be effected should it ever be necessary to carry out again a similar undertaking:

1. Central Drawing Office, template loft and building of prototype to be at one site.
2. Absolute uniformity of frame spacing throughout the vessel.
3. All units not to exceed dimensions of the usual type of railway wagons available. Outsize units require special wagons involving delays in transport.
4. Absolute minimum number of thicknesses of plates and sections, consistent with weight requirements.
5. Plates to be of same width in as many cases as possible to relieve delays and sorting out at steel mills.
6. Work on actual construction to be delayed at shipyard until adequate supplies of units available.

7. Light partitions and minor bulkheads of a flimsy nature are unsuitable for railway transit, and can best be made at shipyards.

In conclusion, I would apologize for the length of my remarks and ask your indulgence of the audacity of a constructional engineer in addressing to naval architects the views of one who made such a brief venture into shipbuilding.

The President: I should like to propose that we give a hearty vote of thanks to Mr. Watson for a most interesting paper. I am sorry that owing to the time difficulty, it has been impossible for others to take part in the discussion; there really is no time for people to read a typewritten script in these discussions—it is much better for people to speak extempore—they can always send in later a fuller contribution to the discussion and it will be included in the TRANSACTIONS.

Written Contribution to the Discussion

Admiral Sir Percy Noble, G.B.E., K.C.B., C.V.O.: The submarine of the future will have a far higher speed— in fact I have heard "25 knots under water" mentioned! If this be so we must have much faster escort vessels.

Mr. W. Reed, O.B.E. (Member): The author is to be commended on writing this paper, giving so much information, showing designs, and the many details which are so important.

It may be of interest to the Institution to describe how the corvette has been developed over a long period.

When chasing the submarine, it is essential to obtain the greatest speed, rapid turning, and ability to "get off the mark" quickly.

Early in 1915, the Admiralty were devising ways and means of dealing with the German submarine campaign, which was then becoming a serious menace. The Admiralty at that time placed with Smith's Dock Co. the building of small vessels, namely "Z" whalers, as they were then of the opinion that the war was largely one necessitating mosquito craft to combat the submarines.

It would have taken too long to build vessels of the destroyer type. It was then decided to place with the company the building of 15 boats with a draught as light as possible to pass over the minefields, and with the greatest speed. These 15 vessels were built and named "Z" whalers, having a speed of 14 knots on a draught of 9 ft. They were to be based on the British ports and were not required to work long distances, not more than say three or four days full speed.

The hunting of submarines was described then as being very similar to that of hunting whales, as it was not known what part of the circle the submarine would come to the surface.

Many of these vessels were intended to be built as long as the German submarines operated round Great Britain, but should the Germans operate in the Atlantic,

CORVETTES AND FRIGATES

it was decided that larger vessels would be built. The average time taken to complete these vessels was 14 weeks. They were about 125 ft. long, having a beam of 25 ft., fitted with triple-expansion engines, coal fired, and two water tube boilers.

These vessels, running under full speed, were able to turn a half circle in a little over half a minute, and a full circle in 1¼ min.

Following this, many trawlers were built throughout the country for convoy work, minesweeping, etc.

In 1917 the Admiralty then decided on the building of larger boats, as the Germans were at that time operating in the Atlantic. It was proposed to build vessels of, say 17–18 knots speed, and it was suggested that they should have oil fuel burning, water tube boilers. Apparently, however, there was insufficient oil in the country and there was not the necessary personnel for the control of water tube boilers. It was then decided that the company should build 37 boats, having Scotch boilers, coal burning, and they were named *Kil* boats. The contour of these vessels was such that the stern had the same sheer and shape as the bow, so that at a long distance it was difficult to discern which way the vessels were operating.

It will be appreciated that the adoption of Scotch boilers and coal burning, as against water tube boilers and oil fuel, necessitated a fuller model, due to the greatly increased weight than would otherwise have been the case. Therefore the speed obtained was only 14 knots.

The first *Kil* boat was built within a period of 4½ months, and they were afterwards completed at the rate of two per month.

The corvettes built for the last war, i.e. 1939–45, were those proposed to be built at the end of the 1914–18 war, having oil fuel burning and water tube boilers. It was then intended to use these corvettes solely around the United Kingdom and the Western Approaches.

The first of the Flower class corvettes (prototype) was completed in 5½ months, and the following Flower class vessels were completed at intervals of 3½ weeks. The total number of these built by the company was 19.

At that time the Navy had the co-operation of the entire French fleet, but after the fall of France in 1940 there arose an acute shortage of destroyers, and the Admiralty felt it necessary to use the corvettes for convoy work across the Atlantic. It was therefore suggested that the Flower class corvettes be lengthened by about 30 ft. to enable them to carry additional bunkers for the Atlantic service, and this would also improve the vessels' sea qualifications for that service, but it was decided not to make any further alteration in introducing these modifications as it might have caused serious delay in production, not only in Great Britain, but also in Canada.

It may be of interest to note that at that time, when the corvettes were transferred to convoy work across the Atlantic, some adverse reports were made in regard to their excessive rolling. However, the rolling was reduced considerably by increasing the width of the bilge keels. It was nevertheless apparent that these vessels were really too small for operating in the Atlantic,

for the reason that in small ships the period of roll is not the natural period for smoother water conditions, but varies considerably with the size of the waves encountered. In other words, the energy these waves can impart is very great compared with the inertia of the ship, and causes heavy forced rolling which can only be reduced by increasing the size of the ship so that the length is equal to, or greater than, that of the longest wave to be encountered.

As will be seen later, it has been proved an advantage to increase the length of the vessel, as in the case of the *Hadley Castle* and sister ships, from 205 ft. overall and 190 ft. between perpendiculars, to 252 ft. overall and 225 ft. between perpendiculars.

The *Hadley Castle* type was suggested for the Atlantic service, as more of these vessels could be built in the smaller yards as compared with the twin screw vessels. Moreover, this would reduce the number of engines to be produced and there would be a corresponding reduction in the number of personnel required.

The first of these lengthened corvettes (prototype *Hadley Castle*) was built in 5½ months from the date of laying the keel to completion.

From the paper which the author has very ably given, it will be observed that the original corvettes, 180 ft. between perpendiculars and 33 ft. beam, with oil fuel storage having 200 tons capacity with a load displacement of 1,170, 2,750 I.H.P., gave a speed of 16 knots. The Castle class, which was a development from the original corvette, increased in length to 225 ft. between perpendiculars, with a beam of 36 ft. 6 in., having oil fuel storage for 480 tons with a displacement of 1,580, and with the same machinery as the corvettes, namely 2,750 I.H.P., gave an increased speed to 16½ knots. These vessels were found to be more suitable for the Atlantic service.

Since the inception of the Flower class, the amount of fighting equipment added to the *Hadley Castle* type to make these ships suitable for their very extended and arduous duties, was very considerable, and necessitated a much larger vessel. This equipment in turn necessitated an increased number of crew—three times more than the original corvettes, and to obtain the extended endurance, the capacity of the oil fuel bunkers was over 100 per cent greater (from 200 tons increased to 480 tons).

It appears to be unnecessary to make any comments on the frigates, as the author has described these vessels very fully.

Mention may be made that the plans for the corvettes and *Hadley Castle* type were all produced by Smith's Dock Company and supplied to all British shipbuilders, and, in addition, to Canada and other countries.

Smith's Dock Company's Engineer, Mr. A. Warley, is contributing a full description in detail of the machinery which was built for all corvettes and frigates.

Mr. A. Warley: At the beginning of the 1939–45 war, faced with the sudden impact of Germany's well-prepared submarine warfare, some form of anti-submarine vessel was needed, and that very urgently.

118

Smith's Dock Co., Ltd., as pioneers in the design and building of Catcher vessels for the whaling industry, pointed out to the Admiralty the great similarity which existed between the methods adopted for hunting whales and those which could be applied for use in hunting submarines. This firm was then given the responsibility of designing such a vessel, the first type and design being the Flower class corvette, or as they were originally called patrol vessels—whaler type.

The urgency of the situation demanded that the vessels with the machinery should be capable of quick production, and as they were to be manned by personnel largely taken from England's great fishing fleet, it was necessary that the machinery should be of a type with which they would be most familiar. Accordingly it was decided to instal in these vessels two large cylindrical smoke-tube type boilers, and reciprocating steam engines of the 4-cylinder triple-expansion type, there being many engineering firms in this country with suitable plant for the manufacture of such machinery.

The ship was designed by Smith's Dock Co.'s shipbuilding department, and the main engines by the engine works department of the same firm.

The two main cylindrical boilers were placed in line in the vessel one forward of the other with a common stokehold between them. They were of the usual merchant practice design, 16 ft. 6 in. internal diameter, 12 ft. 6 in. long, and each fitted with three Deighton corrugated furnaces arranged to burn oil fuel under Howden's system of forced draught. The working pressure was 225 lb./sq. in., and saturated steam conditions.

The main engines were of the 4-cylinder triple-expansion 4-crank type, balanced on the Yarrow Tweedy Slick system, the cylinder sizes being as follows:—

H.P.	..	..	..	$18\frac{1}{2}$ in. diameter
M.P.	..	..	..	31 in. ,,
Forward L.P.		..	..	$38\frac{1}{2}$ in. ,,
Aft L.P.	..	..	..	$38\frac{1}{2}$ in. ,,
Common stroke		..	..	30 in.

The piston and slide valve rods were all fitted with patent metallic packings to the stuffing boxes and all pistons fitted with patent packing rings and springs. The H.P. slide valve was of the piston type whilst the M.P. and L.P. slide valves were of a patent balanced type.

On the original design, reversing of the main engine was operated by a separate steam reversing engine of the "all round" type, but as quick manœuvrability of the ship and engines became of ever greater importance in the hunting of the U-boat, it was decided to fit a steam operated hydraulic reversing engine of the direct "push" type, and this latter type was incorporated in all the later built engines.

The main engines were designed to be capable of developing 2,750 I.H.P. at 185 revolutions per minute continuously in service.

These revolutions per minute were the maximum for an open engine of this size when not fitted with forced lubrication.

The first vessel of this class was H.M.S. *Gladiolus*, and the class was then known as the Flower class corvette.

The vessel ran her official Admiralty trials at Spithead on April 14 and 15, 1940. The machinery easily developed its power and revolutions.

The working drawings for this machinery were circulated to a large number of engineering firms in Britain and Northern Ireland, also to France, and at a later date to Canada, Australia, and the U.S.A.

Later Flower class corvettes were designed and built in which Admiralty 3-drum type water tube boilers were installed.

Howden-Johnson boilers were also fitted in a number of Flower class corvettes.

With the introduction of the water tube boiler came the necessity for purer fresh water and larger fresh water storage, and the necessary evaporating and distilling plant was then added in the engine-room to meet this requirement.

The next stage in the development of this class of vessel was the River class frigates, and later the Loch class frigates. These vessels were of the twin screw type and at the commencement were known by various titles such as—Flower class corvettes (twin screw), new twin screw corvettes, fast corvettes, before settling down to the Admiralty title of River class frigates, and the later vessels Loch class frigates.

The boilers in the frigates were of the Admiralty 3-drum water tube type, working pressure 225 lb./sq. in. saturated steam with the closed stokehold.

To assist in the quick production of the propelling engines, the corvette 4-cylinder triple-expansion engine was maintained in the frigates. This engine was slightly modified so that the steam engine was suitable for a single- or twin-screw vessel.

The great advantage of this is obvious considering that the engines were being built all over the country and many by "inland" engineering firms.

Due to the design of the 4-cylinder engine the modifications were very simple, a shaft coupling was added to the crankshaft at the forward end. This meant that the engine could be turned end for end to suit either a port or starboard side engine.

The forward L.P. engine on a port side engine when reversed would become the after L.P. engine on a starboard side engine. This difference was immaterial as both the L.P. engines were identical.

In the twin-screw installations the arrangement was that each main engine (port and starboard) was fitted as an independent unit with separate condenser and cooling water circulating pumps for each, a distinct advantage should one engine be put out of action.

All the machinery for the River class frigates was contracted for by the respective builders, but for the later Loch class vessels, the Admiralty placed bulk orders for all the machinery.

For example, manufacturing firms received orders for the maximum number of engines they had capacity to build. These main engines were then allocated according to their completion delivery dates to any ship's hulls requiring main engines at the same date.

The same procedure was adopted for boilers, auxiliary machinery, shafting, propellers, etc.

In spite of some preliminary difficulties this allocation worked satisfactorily. As prefabrication was the order of the day at this period, all the pipe work for the Loch class frigates was fabricated from sketches made by the parent firm, and the pipe work carried out by, and sublet to, firms specializing in this class of work, and the completed pipes were allocated according to the need of the various firms fitting out the vessels.

At the same period as the Loch class twin-screw frigates were being built, a demand was received for a small number of single-screw corvettes with Admiralty type water tube boilers, these were known as the Castle class corvettes.

A total of approximately 1,150 engines were built off this one design between January 1940, and December 1944, and it will be appreciated that with such a large number of engines to the same design, the Admiralty was apprehensive of any troubles which might arise due to vibration periods at various critical speeds of the engines. To obviate any such possibilities it was decided to investigate this aspect thoroughly and Lloyd's representatives were called in to assist.

A test was then arranged to be carried out to ascertain the critical vibration periods on the main engines of a single-screw Castle class corvette which was available at the time. The main engine was un-coupled from the line shafting and run free at full revs per min. Lloyd's representative's instruments were placed in position and vibration diagrams taken in the presence of the Admiralty representatives. The results were very satisfactory, as the diagrams showed practically a straight line, the instruments not being able to register any appreciable vibrations.

Previous to the test, a disc had been made with changeable weights on it for bolting to the forward coupling of the crankshaft so that should vibrations be excessive, some trial and error experiments could be tried to improve it. This gear, however, was never used as the above test had proved so satisfactory.

History now tells of the unqualified success of the corvette and frigate machinery, actual performance during the war proving their reliability under all extreme conditions of service and satisfying the Admiralty's most exacting requirements, They steamed the seven seas the world over and endured winter seas and hurricanes escorting convoys across the Atlantic, and it can well be claimed that the success and reliability of the machinery contributed in no small way to the crushing destruction of the U-boat and the ultimate defeat of the enemy.

Mr. C. J. W. Hopkins, M.B.E., R.C.N.C. (Member): The author's interesting paper generally covers the design side of what was really the Admiralty's first effort at mass prefabricated construction.

As stated in the paper, this involved the use of many firms strange to shipbuilding, and it also involved the use of many firms outside the usually recognized Admiralty firms for the supply of large quantities of fittings, etc.

The whole programme was planned on an ambitious scale.

Supply of steel, etc. to the various fabricators reached a maximum of over 500 tons per week.

Among the items supplied to shipbuilding contractors by the Admiralty were:—

Rudders, shaft brackets, propeller posts, propeller tubes, W/T office complete, R.D.F. and asdics office, mast tubes and lattice masts, depth charge rails and chutes, squid equipment, S.A. gear, bollards and fairleads, davits, pumps, electric bollard hoists, clear-view screens, watertight doors and hatches, side scuttles, pumping, flooding and draining valves, ventilation valves, steering gear, anchor and cable gear, cooking ranges and gear, hot cupboards, cabin doors, steel furniture, chests of drawers, desks, book shelves, toilet cabinets, secretaires, blocks, windlasses, bell cabinet, asbestos lagging, mattresses and accommodation fittings, A.L.O. sights, deck sockets and scuttles, spurling pipes, hawse pipes, windscreens, firework fittings, hose couplings, etc., steering indicators, light excluding ventilators, signal lockers, mess racks, fans, bottle rack stowage, ammunition lockers, kit lockers, seat lockers, first-aid lockers, depth charge lockers and many others.

The numbers dealt with were often large with a high rate of production. Some typical monthly rates were:—

Pumps	55
Electric bollard hoists	30
Watertight doors	240
Valves	2,000
Side scuttles	650
Bottle rack stowage	2,960
Ammunition lockers	990
Depth charge racks	360
Bollards and fairleads	512
Kit and seat lockers	1,500
Fans	150

Supplies generally were planned to work up to a steady delivery rate for 12 ships per month.

It will be realized that to meet such outputs it was necessary to go to a large number of firms, many of whom had no previous experience of Admiralty work, and great credit is due to these firms in making a success of the whole scheme. This is particularly so when it is realized that the time allowed to get into production was a matter of months, much too short for such a proposition without a prototype.

It is interesting to recall that in 1914–18 a similar call was made for a large number of convoy and submarine destroyers and if I recollect rightly Lord Fisher expressed his view of simplicity as "Something which would last six months and could be driven by the man in the street." The Flower class sloops were the result, and I think the late Mr. J. H. Narbeth gave an account of these vessels to the Institution. Some development of this type took place in the between war years.

In 1939–45 the call again came for vessels to serve a somewhat similar purpose and once more we had to start all over again.

It remains to be seen whether we shall lapse again and have to make another fresh start in the event of another emergency arising.

Twice we have had to rely largely on help from outside the Empire for our ship requirements and no doubt we should have to again in the future, but it does seem essential that research and experiment should be pursued in peace-time to devise means of greatly increasing the output of small ships from our limited number of slips.

Prefabrication and standardization seem to be the key to this problem and it is to be hoped that this practicable side of research will not be lost sight of in the days of peace.

Mr. L. Woollard, M.A., R.C.N.C. (Vice-President): The remarks at the end of this paper on the behaviour of corvettes and other small vessels at sea are of interest, and I agree with the author's view that small metacentric height is not a remedy for liveliness in the circumstances mentioned.

These ships, designed for coastal patrol, were used on open seas where they were exposed to the action of large waves and ocean swells. Their dimensions are small in relation to those of the waves encountered, and they must perforce partake in large measure of the orbital and other movements of the water. These motions alone render them lively. If they could with safety have been given very small metacentric heights, they would possibly have rolled a little less, but the reduction in their total acceleration would hardly have been noticeable.

I agree also that further investigations including observations of accelerations in ships at sea would be of great value.

Mr. J. L. Adam, C.B.E. (Vice-President): A documentary of this order is always useful and when it includes so much valuable detailed information and explanation it is very useful indeed.

I personally am very interested because, for many years, we have been associated with the building of the whalers at Smith's Dock, the consumation of which, before the war, was the *Southern Pride*.

The Flower class corvette is, as will be seen, a substantially built ship with scantlings according to merchant ship practice. Structurally I believe they have been absolutely trouble free and it will be seen that the structural arrangement incorporates a number of features which have great advantages from certain points of view. For instance, in the engine-room wide spaced deep frames are fitted, that is reverse frames fitted on the ordinary framing at four frame spaces apart and a distributor in the form of a heavy bulb angle fitted inside of the frames and clear of the shell. A similar construction is adopted in way of the oil fuel side bunkers, and long experience has shown that where the shell is of substantial thickness this is a very effective way of providing proper distribution, and has the advantage that normal bumping causes no disturbance through the shell.

The Loch class fabricated frigate, with which the author has been good enough to associate my name, is probably the most interesting of the series in many respects. I very well remember a meeting at Whitehall, to which Sir Stanley Goodall referred, when we discussed the system of construction and visualized the prefabrication arrangements by means of models. Models, incidentally, have proved very useful, not only in this country, in dealing with proposed pre-construction arrangements.

Mr. Watson asked me some time ago whether in the same circumstances I would put forward the same proposals and my reply was that in the same circumstances I *would* put forward the same proposals.

The principal value of a paper, however, is the use that we make of it in the future, and from this aspect I think we might gain much from the experience with the fabricated frigates.

There is no doubt that the limit of $2\frac{1}{2}$ tons lift and 9 ft. in width or depth and a limit in length, so that special railway trucks would not be required, was a great handicap. If, however, in the future it is considered necessary to produce these or similar craft as quickly as possible and with the minimum of manpower it is suggested a rather different procedure might be adopted. For instance, if the "lift" could be increased to even 5 tons and auxiliary prefabricating structural works could be established in such a position in respect of the shipyards that the sidings did not have to pass under bridges, the majority of the sections could be from 20 ft. to 24 ft. in width and up to 30 ft. in length, and only a few would require to be less. These prefabricated sections might all be welded and either assembled by means of riveted longitudinal joints or overlapped welded joints. It will be obvious from the paper that if the alternatives of welding or riveting be permitted, a great deal of time is spent in the preparation of drawings, and I know from what I have seen in the United States that, with light craft of this order, assembling of long sections is much easier if overlapped welded joints are permitted. I do not think we should allow our judgment to be upset by making a fetish of the butt weld as being the only efficient joint. Efficiency in ship construction is definitely a compromise.

Under such conditions as have been indicated, the number of parts to be assembled would be approximately one-quarter of those actually prepared for the prefabricated frigates. So far as can be judged from the information and knowledge available such an arrangement would permit of the use of non-shipbuilding labour to at least as great a degree as with the fabricated frigates, and with very much less labour than was necessary with the U.S. method of prefabricating in large transverse sections. It was, of course, obvious during the discussions that such methods could not be adopted in the prevailing circumstances, but it is suggested that the powers that be might look into the question of whether we should not now indulge in some "planning," since this is the favourite word to-day, and encourage the development of structural works, suitably positioned, for use in an emergency. More than that, it is possible that these might be of the greatest value in the meantime in the production of economical merchant ships. The Shipbuilding Conference, with the encouragement of the Admiralty, might find that this was one method of arriving at a very much desired end.

The author and others have referred to the degree of co-operation that was shown in producing these frigates, and this I most heartily corroborate. With the Admiralty production and correlating staff, with the central drawing office established in Glasgow, Lloyd's and the British Corporation technical staffs in Glasgow dealing with the plans produced by Mr. Cairns "on the spot"—so that there was no waste of time in correspondence nor possibility of misunderstanding—and the rapid approval thus obtained being correlated by Mr. Grisenthwaite into structural engineers' drawings, and with the division of the inspection of fabricated units between the classification societies by agreement, there was possibly never a greater example of co-operation without friction.

Structurally, both the River class frigates and the Loch class frigates would appear on the surface to be greatly different from merchant practice but I suggest that it is mostly on the surface. True in the case of the River class frigates the shells are lighter, but are substantially and effectively—even if expensively—reinforced by the welded stringers which perform a dual function of distributors to the internal structure and reinforcement to the shell.

In the case of the Loch class frigates the system of longitudinal framing provides adequate strength to the structure generally and reinforcement to the relatively thin shell. In addition, in all of these ships there are so many longitudinal bulkheads that it is not surprising to find that they are effective structures and only show trouble in minor details, and there only where there has been some departure from the approved plans. Many of the corvettes have been converted into useful merchant ships, and with their robust scantlings few precautionary measures have been necessary. Ships of the River class frigate type have also been converted to merchant ships, and while it has been necessary to provide some more or less local stiffening of the shell for general service purposes, the actual question of structural strength has not arisen.

While it is perhaps outside the scope of the author's paper, it would have been of great interest and, I think, of value, if he had been able to include drawings of the very successful rudders that were developed by Smith's Dock and manufactured by the score by structural works such as Colville Construction Co., and if he had been able to illustrate that exceedingly fine piece of fabricating work represented by the propeller boss post in the corvettes.

Mr. H. J. Tabb, R.C.N.C. (Member): The author's paper has interested me for two reasons. Firstly, I was for a time concerned with corvettes and frigates in the Naval Construction Department under Mr. Watson's direction, and secondly I was privileged to go with him to the U.S.A. at the end of 1942, to examine methods of building similar craft.

I should like to emphasize what the author has said concerning the increased complexity of the ships which became more and more apparent as the war progressed. The changes were such as to make the profile of the later ships almost unrecognizable to anyone familiar only with the earlier vessels. It is an unfortunate fact in most warships that increased requirements for new devices and weapons can only be made available by encroaching on space originally allocated to the crew, whilst in addition, more personnel with special training are needed to operate this equipment. Habitability thus suffers in an exaggerated degree from such changes. Fortunately, in the Flower class corvettes it was possible to extend the forecastle and so provide some increase in accommodation, but such a course is not always practicable in a vessel designed with a normal margin of buoyancy and stability.

The methods of building vessels of similar type in America were not generally applicable in this country for reasons which are well known. My experience, however, suggests that it would be generally to the advantage of British shipbuilding if more of the American methods were adopted. The setting up of a single drawing office, with draughtsmen drawn from the different firms employed on building the vessels has been mentioned by the author and was found to be a great advantage. It follows to some extent the American practice of handing detail design over to design agents, such as Messrs. Gibbs & Cox. The present practice of arranging a demarcation of drawing office work amongst three or four builders is not nearly so satisfactory and causes much overlapping and many inconsistencies. The approval of plans is also much easier if frequent visits can be paid to one drawing office by the constructor in charge of the design. A further change I should like to suggest is the general use of standardized plates. Eight, or perhaps twelve, different sized plates should be adequate and would save much time in the yard, since plates are merely stacked according to size and thickness and it is not necessary to identify particular plates and to use them only for given positions. Surely this would greatly simplify the steel-makers' task, especially with new types of mill machinery producing standard widths of plate. It is also possible by this method to place orders for steel well in advance of the completion of drawings.

Pipe work was a factor specially noticed in the U.S.A., where the general prefabrication of structure permitted similar methods for pipes, and in some cases up to 90 per cent of the pipework was completed prior to assembly and only closing lengths made to template. A greater proportion of pipework details should be carried out in the drawing office to enable as much of the shipwork as possible to be done early in the life of the ship. It is believed to be not uncommon in this country for a great mass of pipework to be fitted very late in the construction of the ship, and this delays final testing and completion.

Several papers have been written recently concerning the necessity for more up-to-date planning and progress control in British yards, which still rely for their efficiency on the experience and personal contacts of one or two persons in a yard who carry out the duties of shipyard managers. Much more should be done to introduce a system which provides clearly, *in advance*, notice of possible shortcomings. The system, however, must be simple and straightforward and operated by the minimum of personnel.

The drawing office can be responsible for much of the planning and could show more imagination in departing from methods which have become out-of-date. Simplification and the introduction of modern ideas must take place from the inception of a design and not as afterthoughts or modifications grafted on to existing schemes. The fillip given to electric welding by war-time construction should be used to the maximum possible extent to reduce weight and build more efficient structures.

Mr. F. C. C. Rogers, R.C.N.C. (Associate-Member): As would be expected these vessels, during the course of the war acquired many additions, and in many cases fairly large amounts of compensating ballast were added. There were, however, no serious structural troubles within the experience of Devonport Dockyard officers and the most frequent troubles there dealt with were oil fuel leaks and occasional loose outer bottom rivets, due to the lightness of the construction of the vessels and the shock of depth charge explosions.

The Flower class, in particular were very congested owing to the repeated additions made, and it is surprising that the crews accepted the conditions without complaint.

The metacentric diagram for the River class shows that the designers had profited by the experience of the last war and had allowed for adequate stability accepting possibly a risk of increased rolling.

The turning trials indicate that the River class frigate's turning powers are about the same as those of the destroyers referred to in Mr. A. P. Cole's paper of 1938 at the same or corresponding speed, notwithstanding that the frigate has about 20 per cent more rudder area. No circles are given in Mr. Cole's paper so that the figures for the destroyers have had to be taken from the curves in the paper and are averages. The increased rudder area is presumably due to the greater draught and projected area of submerged profile of the frigates as compared with the destroyers, which are longer but of less draught.

It is noteworthy that the difference between the starboard and port circles is very considerable, the starboard circle being much the larger. It is quite usual to find a difference between the two circles in similar vessels, and sister vessels will behave differently in this respect; but the difference is not usually so large as in the case of *Rother* and it would be interesting to know if the author knows of any cause for this large difference.

As regards the Loch class frigates the midship section shown does not appear to be any great advance on that of the *Seagull* (Nicholls, TRANS., I.N.A. 1939) nor does prefabrication in large units appear to have been undertaken, but the necessarily small scale of the drawings makes it difficult to see exactly what was done: in particular the amount of riveting employed is far from clear. The small lifting power of available derricks was undoubtedly a severe limiting factor as it was in the case of *Seagull*.

The addition of particulars, for comparison, of the Captains class of frigates, built in the U.S.A. and entirely welded, together with some details, if available, of the method of construction of these vessels would increase the value of the paper, which is largely historical. Comparative figures for the pre-war design of escort vessels, many of which did some very good work, would also be of value.

Mr. W. J. Holt, R.C.N.C. (Member): I made no contribution to the design of the corvettes but was well placed to obtain a good onlooker's view of the design.

Sea opinion, generally, was that the Flower class corvettes were lively craft in a seaway. It seems desirable to outline the distinction between (*a*) quietness (i.e. absence of liveliness) on the one hand, and (*b*) seaworthiness on the other.

(*a*) It is possible to design a small ship having low freeboard, no top hamper, deep draught and small stability, which will prove a very quiet ship in a small seaway.

On the high seas, in other than light weather, this ship will wallow and labour in the sea, and her decks will be continually swept by green seas, more or less like a half-tide rock.

This ship will be neither seaworthy nor worthwhile operationally.

(*b*) On the other hand, a ship may be designed having good freeboard and sheer of decks to keep the green seas off the deck, good range of stability, and such top hamper as is dictated by operational requirements. This small ship will certainly prove livelier than its low freeboard alternative but will, nevertheless, be a much more seaworthy craft and a good fighting ship.

Judged on their operational function, their comparatively small size, and the zones of ocean in which they saw service, it is my opinion that the small corvettes were not more lively than would be dictated by good design.

Other things being equal, liveliness is largely a function of ship's size in relation to the seas encountered; it is also very much a function of speed. Usually liveliness can be reduced by increasing the size of ship, and by decreasing the speed in a seaway. The corvettes were remarkably small vessels to undertake convoy escort on the great winter seas of the North Atlantic. They were also relatively fast craft and inevitably their crews experienced a tough time. To drive home the argument on the effect of size and speed in relation to liveliness, it can be pointed out that starting from the corvette and going down the scale in size and up in the scale of speed, we arrive at coastal force craft. Whatever may be said of the lively motion of a corvette, I speak from personal experience in stating that the motion of a corvette in a seaway is positively stately in comparison with the motion of a coastal force craft in the same seaway.

It appears to me that slight criticism of the early Flower class corvettes was as follows:—

(i) They were rather deficient in sheer and rather lacking in flare of lines forward. This tendency to lack of sheer and appearance of being "down by the head" was aggravated by the evolution of, and necessity for fitting, anti-submarine attack weapons forward of the bridge.

(ii) The short forecastle encouraged any green seas which came over the bow to charge over the rear end of the forecastle down on to the well deck forward; a menace to everything in its path.

In a small warship intended for ocean service there is much to be said in favour of the scheme of plating over the forward well, i.e. providing the craft with a forecastle which is half- to two-thirds the length of the vessel.

As stated by the author, in later Flower class corvettes and in the enlarged Castle class corvettes these defects were remedied.

I had some sea experience of the frigates; they impressed me as being very good sea boats; their motion was easy, and they re-awakened in me memories of the motion of British destroyers of the early 1930's.

In concluding these notes I would like to add that throughout the war, and with great singleness of purpose, the author of this paper devoted his energies to the advance of the design and production of corvettes and frigates. His efforts, together with the efforts of his design constructor—Mr. Kimberley—deserve very high praise.

Sir Wilfred Ayre (Member of Council): It is well that the author has recorded particulars of the corvettes and frigates which were built mainly by shipbuilders not usually engaged in warship construction. This left the larger firms normally engaged in the construction of naval craft of all sizes and types free to concentrate on heavy capital ships and other specialist types. When the urgent need came for the building of 200 frigates of the Loch class in the autumn of 1942 it was decided that, in order to expedite delivery to the fullest extent, the design and construction should follow as closely as possible modern principles of prefabrication and mass production, as had been seen by the author and the writer in the U.S.A. on comparable types of war vessels. There was not, however, any drawing office capacity available in the Admiralty at that time for the preparation of the necessary general and detailed drawings. At the request of the Controller of the Navy the writer undertook to organize a central drawing office in Glasgow for this specific purpose. This was staffed by about equal

numbers of ship and constructional engineering draughtsmen. Many shipbuilding and engineering firms willingly agreed to lend experienced draughtsmen for certain periods and these were replaced by subsequent relays made available by other shipbuilding and structural engineering firms. The essential drawings were prepared in a remarkably short space of time by the shipbuilding side of the drawing office, and were then transposed by the structural engineering side in appropriate manner for submission to a large number of structural engineering firms situated in different parts of England and Scotland which had been entrusted with the work of fabrication. The experiment was unique and it was successful. It was carried through with enthusiasm by all concerned and it is a remarkable feature that the degree of accuracy attained in the hundreds of prefabricated parts, when assembled, in no case disclosed errors or involved alterations on site. The central drawing office was operated under the aegis of the Shipbuilding Conference and every possible assistance was afforded it by the helpful interest displayed by the Director of Warship Production as well as the author and other officers of the Admiralty. The experience in mass-production technique gained from the Loch class frigate programme fully justified the wisdom of the experiment in the circumstances prevailing in a time of stress.

Mr. J. M. McNeill, M.C., LL.D. (Member of Council): It was my privilege to be associated with the author in the arrangements for the construction of the prototype vessel, *Loch Fada*.

The methods whereby parts for 80 per cent of the hull structure were welded and assembled in various parts of the country by structural engineering firms, and were then successfully faired, erected, and worked into the structure, gave very satisfactory results. This was, in large measure, due to the excellent work performed in the central drawing office in Glasgow, and to the close liaison maintained between the Admiralty departments, the structural engineering firms, and shipbuilders concerned.

For a programme of construction of the nature involved in building Loch class frigates, the departure from the orthodox methods appears to have been completely justified. Had the necessity for pressing on with such a programme remained, the results achieved would have been all the more satisfactory and the methods used should be kept in mind should ever a like emergency again arise.

The information on stability and rolling given by the author also calls for favourable comment. The long range of positive G Z curves amply justifies the design as evolved for the Loch class, although the continuation of the forecastle deck further aft might have still further improved not only the habitability but also the safety of the vessels.

It is interesting to note that the maximum angles of roll are reasonable in amplitude. They agree closely with measured values in other ships of a similar build and should discount the exaggerated accounts sometimes given of the rolling of vessels in a seaway.

In the writer's opinion the Loch class frigates were outstandingly successful in design, construction, and performance, and the methods employed in carrying out the programme of construction reflect the greatest credit on the author of this paper and all who were associated with him.

Author's Reply to the Discussion

The comments of my present and late chiefs, Sir Charles Lillicrap and Sir Stanley Goodall bring out many aspects of the development of major war shipbuilding programmes. Sir Charles does well to direct attention to the study of problems that will arise when the rapid production of warships of increasingly complex types is undertaken. With regard to the future prospects of prefabrication a reference to costs might be added. It is to be expected that prefabrication should lead to quickened output and that sufficient gain in time would justify increased cost. Provided the number of prefabricated items required involve an adequate volume of repetition work, individual vessels so constructed should not necessarily cost more. But as Sir Stanley remarks "fitting out" was the greatest problem in the Loch class scheme, and the costs of setting up new fitting out establishments may have to be allowed for.

Mr. J. M. Murray refers to the very useful association between the Admiralty and the classification societies. His own contribution was a major factor in its success. He was stationed at Bath during the war, and we were able to refer to him all structural difficulties as they arose. We quickly found we could rely on his unstinted help and advice. His suggestion to extend the forecastle deck right aft in the frigates is deserving of consideration but the tendency to strain at the break of the forecastle was not considered sufficient to justify extension, and suitable stiffening was fitted. A note on warship conditions applicable to his suggestion may, however, be of interest. In arranging superstructure a low silhouette giving reduced visibility is important and is easier to protect where this is necessary in action. These considerations make it desirable to limit the extent of superstructure strictly to essential requirements, i.e. for enclosed spaces above water, for adequate reserve of buoyancy and a working platform at sea.

Mr. Gawn's remarks on the model tank investigations that are his special province, illustrate how the foundations of speed performances were laid. His accurate predictions which incorporated all favourable factors were borne out on trials, and his work was largely responsible for the excellent results that were achieved.

The remarks of Rear-Admiral Brown and Mr. Warley are very welcome. I fully agree with Admiral Brown that the subject of propelling machinery deserves a separate paper. Mr. Warley raises the question of vibration. With higher speeds always before us as a target, involving lightly built hulls, it was a courageous step on the part of the Engineer-in-Chief to adopt reciprocating instead of turbine machinery for these designs, bringing the possibility of difficult vibration problems, arising from the relationship of the natural periods of hull vibration, the speed of the engines, and the balance of their reciprocating parts. No sensible vibration was in fact experienced in the Flower and River classes, but when the Castle class corvettes were approaching completion it was anticipated that their increased length, involving lower natural frequencies might result in resonance with any engine unbalance occurring at full speed. The investigations described by Mr. Warley gave satisfactory results and no trouble on this score was experienced. This is not to conclude that the installation of over 1,000 reciprocating engines passed off without incident. Mysterious vibrations of a temporary character did occur occasionally, which, as often happens, aroused in engineers the urge to study engine bearers, and in shipbuilders an equally strong urge to study the alignment of crankshafts.

Mr. Grisenthwaite's remarks add very much of value to the information given in the paper concerning the prefabricated construction of the Loch class. He himself took a leading part in the activities of the constructional engineers and his suggestions for improving the technique of shipbuilders and constructional firms will be borne in mind for future joint undertakings.

Admiral Noble, under whose command so many of the vessels described saw service, indicates the need for faster vessels in future. I feel sure the corvette shipbuilding group and their associates will find a way to meet the challenge if called upon.

Mr. William Reed's remarks deserve special attention because of his long association with the design and building of the vessels described, and also with similar types built for the 1914-18 war. His energy, enthusiasm, and great ability were applied to design work, to the extra work of leading shipbuilder, responsible for the production and distribution of working plans, and to advancing the completion of the first Flower class *Gladiolus*, the first River class *Rother*, and the first Castle class *Hadleigh Castle*, so that early confirmation of performance of these classes was obtained, so important in dealing with large programmes. This vast contribution deserves the highest praise. Mr. Reed's observations on the behaviour of the corvettes in the Atlantic are confirmed by the results given in Table II which indicate larger minimum angles of roll in the smaller vessels with varying periods of roll in all types.

Mr. Hopkins' remarks on the production of steel and equipment give a good indication of the extended range of supplies arranged by the Admiralty for the shipbuilders and constructional engineers. His suggestion that attention should be given to production problems in peace is of great importance if the country's resources are to be allocated to best advantage when a state of emergency arises.

I am glad that my colleagues Mr. Woollard and Mr. Holt, both of whom have a wide experience of the behaviour of ships at sea, have commented on the question of liveliness and its origin, also referred to by Mr. Gawn, Mr. Reed and Dr. McNeill. It seems evident that a scale of liveliness based on acceleration measurements is well worth further study. Mr. Holt's final remarks are much appreciated. I would like to give full support to his reference to Mr. Kimberley who as constructor in charge of designs, bore heavy responsibilities, which he discharged with conspicuous ability and success.

Mr. Adam's remarks, like those of Mr. Reed, deserve special attention because of his close association with all the designs and his special knowledge and authority on structural matters. I agree with him that in planning future preconstruction arrangements the question of auxiliary prefabricating structural works, as well as of new "fitting out" establishments should be considered, especially if they are likely to lead to the adoption of larger prefabricated sections and result in a reduction of erection work on the launching berths.

Mr. Tabb draws attention to the shipbuilding methods adopted in U.S.A. which we had the great privilege of examining together during the war. I think his suggestion to give more consideration to American methods is a good one. Sir Charles Lillicrap mentions the wide contrast between the procedures followed in British and American shipyards, while noting that both procedures produced good ships. In examining alternatives, therefore, it must not be forgotten that the target scheme, as organized for the Loch class generally, maintained the individuality of the shipbuilders and their associates, as more suited to British temperament and methods, than a highly centralized scheme organized for operating with large-scale establishments.

Mr. Rogers refers to the difference in the port and starboard circles of *Rother*. I am not certain that this is beyond the limits of error made possible by trial conditions. The recorded times in Fig. 14 for a given amount of turn are in much closer agreement than are the positions as plotted. In using the results for making a comparison of turning powers with those of other classes it appears satisfactory to use a mean of the port and starboard results.

Sir Wilfred Ayre's comments on the scheme for building the Loch class are noted with much interest. A committee of shipbuilders under his chairmanship was associated with the design at the outset, and were responsible for organizing and encouraging all appropriate steps required to obtain the maximum and most expeditious production. Mr. Griesenthwaite has already remarked on the work of constructional engineers in the central drawing office in Glasgow, and in confirming Sir Wilfred's tribute to the speed of preparation of essential drawings in that office, I should like to mention the work of Mr. J. W. Cairns, who was, fortunately, available to undertake the management of the office at the outset. He had recently retired from the post of General Manager and Naval Architect with Smiths' Dock Company, and his special knowledge of the corvette and frigate designs was invaluable.

Dr. McNeill's comments are also noted with great interest. His help during the building of the prototype *Loch Fada* was always freely given, despite the great pressure of other important warship work. He advocates a longer forecastle for the frigates, and I have already dealt with this proposal in replying to Mr. Murray.

In conclusion, may I say how much I am indebted to all who have taken part in the discussion, for their remarks and personal references. In preparing this paper, intended to give a comprehensive but concise account of the group of warships described, I was only able to outline activities associated with design and construction, indicate the course of events, and illustrate the account with leading particulars of the designs. Contributions to the discussion on a paper of this kind greatly increase its future value to those interested. Some contributors have asked for additional information which deserves compliance, but must be left for a separate paper.

Coastal Force Design
by W J Holt RCNC, MINA

Originally published in *Transactions*, Volume 89, Number 3, July 1947, pages 186-217

COASTAL FORCE DESIGN

By W. J. HOLT, R.C.N.C.,* Member

(Read at the Spring Meeting of the Eighty-eighth Session of the Institution of Naval Architects, March 27, 1947, Admiral of the Fleet the Right Hon. Lord Chatfield, G.C.B., O.M., K.C.M.G., C.V.O., President, in the Chair, which was subsequently taken by Sir Stanley V. Goodall, K.C.B., O.B.E. (Vice-President).)

Introduction

The range of designs of M.L.s, M.T.B.s, M.G.B.s, and so on, developed immediately before and during the 1939–1945 war, covers so wide a field that it is difficult to do justice to the subject within the scope of a single paper. What follows is an attempt to outline the designs and the thoughts involved in their development, to form a record in the TRANSACTIONS.

The designs of Coastal Force craft in service during the war were mostly original conceptions. They had little in the way of ancestry, and could not, therefore, be based on experience of a type over a period of years.

Coastal forces fall naturally into two main groups. The first group comprises the M.L.s, moderate speed craft, the original function of the designs being anti-submarine patrol and convoy escort work. The second group includes the high-speed offensive craft, such as the motor torpedo boats and motor gunboats. In this paper it seems desirable to follow the progress of the two groups separately.

MOTOR LAUNCHES

History of M.L.s in 1914–1918 War

80-ft. M.L.s

In the early stages of World War (1914–1918) the success of the German submarine attacks in coastal waters led to a demand for anti-submarine motor launches. The requirement was met by the production of about 600 motor launches, by the Electric Boat Company of Bayonne, New Jersey, for shipment to United Kingdom. Early boats of this series were 75 ft. in length, but later deliveries were 80 ft. in length. Particulars were as follows:—

Length: 80 ft.
Beam: 12 ft.
Draught: 4 ft.
Displacement, fully equipped: 42 tons.
Fuel, paraffin and petrol: 6·6 tons.
Engines: Two sets of six-cylinder petrol engines, each 220 B.H.P., R.P.M., 460. These engines were afterwards converted to run on paraffin with petrol starting.
Speed (on trial): 19 knots.

*Chief Constructor, Naval Construction Department, Admiralty.

Endurance judged from trials: 1,000 miles at 15 knots.
Stability: 1·38 ft. metacentric height.
Armament: One 3-pdr. gun. Some boats carried a Lewis gun to deal with aircraft. Ten type "D" depth charges.
W/T: The flotilla leaders were fitted with W/T.

Fig. 1 shows the 80-ft. M.L. in outline.

The 80-ft. M.L.s were very similar to the sheltered-water type of motor cruiser popular in America. They were not well suited to the open-water conditions around the coasts of Britain, being very wet in a seaway. They were of limited operational value.

At the end of the war the 80-ft. M.L.s were sold out of the service.

From time to time during the period 1918–1938 stray proposals for M.L.s were received from outside designers, but no money was applied to building craft of the type.

1939–1945 War M.L.s

"A" Type M.L.s (Fairmile)

At the outbreak of war no M.L.s were in service, but a start had been made on the building of the first "A" type M.L.

The Fairmile organization approached the Admiralty, some months before war broke out, with a scheme for the mass production of a large hard-chine motor launch. The form of the design was an enlargement on an existing motor yacht. No armament was indicated in the proposal. The scheme put forward was that the framing, keels, stem, etc., should be prefabricated by saw-mills and furniture makers in London and, after prefabrication, sent out to selected yacht builders for assembly of the hulls on the building stocks.

The scheme of prefabrication involved the use of widely spaced transverse frames, sawn to the transverse sectional shape of the M.L. out of large sheets of waterproof bonded plywood—in effect the frames were fretwork on a large scale. The plywood transverse frames were notched at intervals around their peripheries to receive longitudinal stringers. The keel pieces, stem pieces, stern pieces, deadwoods, bulkheads (sawn from plywood sheets), and transom were all shaped, scarphed, etc., by the London prefabricators, ready for assembly

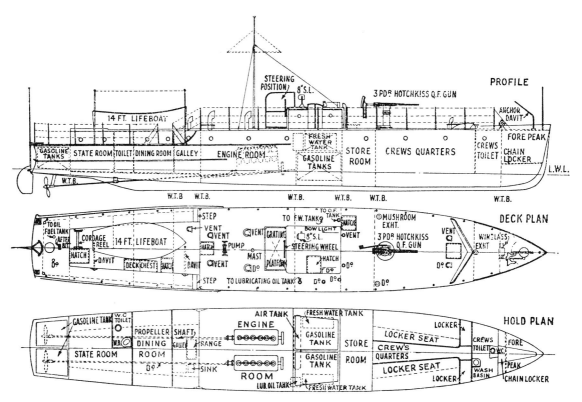

FIG. 1.—OUTLINE OF 80 FT. M.L. (1914–18) WAR

by the yacht yards. At the yacht yards the sections of the keels were brought together on the building blocks, and the bulkheads, transverse frames, stem pieces, etc., assembled on the keel in their proper relative positions. The longitudinal stringers were then fitted in the notchings of the transverse frames and secured to the frames. This gave a rigid skeleton of the M.L. ready to receive the planking. The timber for planking was sawn to size and planed by the prefabrication firms, and then delivered to the yacht yards ready for fitting. The photograph (Fig. 30) shows a prefabricated assembly.

After discussion between representatives of Admiralty departments and the Fairmile organization, the Board of Admiralty approved to place an order for an M.L. with Fairmile and detailed the armament to be fitted.

Fairmile agreed to strengthen the deck of their design and to use double skin bottom planking, instead of the single skin planking they had proposed. The first M.L. was laid down at Woodnutt's Yard, Bembridge, Isle of Wight, and was styled the "A" type Fairmile M.L. The progress of construction of this boat was kept under close observation by Admiralty departments.

General particulars of the "A" type Fairmile M.L. were as follows:—

Length overall: 110 ft.
Beam: 17 ft. 5 in. over rubbers.
Draught forward: 4 ft. 6 in.
Draught aft: 6 ft. 0 in.

The hull was constructed of African mahogany planking. The ring frames of 1 in. birch plywood were approximately 4 ft. 6 in. apart, with four intermediate bent timbers.

As originally designed, the craft was engined with three Hall Scott Defender engines, each giving a B.H.P. of 600 at full power. The fuel stowage was 1,200 gallons.

The armament was one 3-pdr. gun, two Lewis guns, and twelve depth charges.

Asdic was fitted.

Accommodation was provided for two officers, two petty officers, and twelve ratings.

Trials indicated about 25 knots maximum speed and 22 knots maximum continuous speed, on a displacement of 50 tons. The trials were not run at full-load displacement.

In all, twelve "A" type M.L.s were built.

The M.L.s were converted to minelayers early on in their service.

Origin of the "B" M.L.

In late 1939 it was clear that there was an urgent requirement for a great number of M.L. type of craft. The production of the "A" type M.L. had served to show that the scheme of prefabrication was sound. On the other hand, the "A" type fell short of requirements in important particulars—the fuel tank capacity was about half that required. Due to the hard-chine form, the boat was very resistful at cruising speeds, and the bow was inclined to throw up light spray and to pound in a seaway. The accommodation was awkward.

"B" M.L.

A round bilge form had been designed in the Admiralty, and this form had been tested in the Admiralty Experiment Tank, Haslar, and was known to be favourable, both as regards resistance and in sea-keeping ability. An outline general arrangement had also been drawn out in the Admiralty to meet the known requirements for an M.L. It was approved to put this design, the "B" M.L., into rapid production and entrust the building to the Fairmile organization.

The lines drawing and general arrangement drawing were turned over to Fairmile, and the organization arranged the scheme of framing the boat to suit their system of prefabrication.

The original design for a round bilge M.L. had provided for three Hall Scott Defender engines. It was reluctantly decided to fit two engines only and accept the loss of speed involved. This decision was prompted by the limited rate of supply of engines from America. The use of two engines instead of three for each boat resulted in 50 per cent increase of the number of boats produced.

To ensure that production was kept going at full stretch the Admiralty instructed Fairmile to name an adequate number of yacht-building firms, willing to associate themselves with the scheme for the production of the "B" M.L.s. The Admiralty made arrangements to refrain from placing orders for other types of naval boats with these particular firms.

General particulars of the "B" M.L.s were as follows:—

Length: 112 ft.
Beam: 18 ft. 3 in.
Draught: 4 ft. 10 in. forward, 5 ft. 0½ in. aft.
Engines: Two Hall Scott Defenders (each 600 B.H.P. max.).
Fuel stowage below deck: 2,305 gallons.
Maximum speed: 20 knots.
Maximum continuous speed: 17·5 knots.
Endurance at maximum speed: 600 nautical miles.
Endurance at 12 knots: 1,500 nautical miles.
Displacement: 67 tons in early boats; 85 tons in later boats with increased armament.

Fig. 2 shows the design in outline. Fig. 4 shows a constructional section. Fig. 17 is a photograph of a typical "B" M.L.

Accommodation was provided for two officers, two petty officers, and twelve ratings.

As originally put into service, the craft carried a 3-pdr. gun aft, two Lewis guns, and twelve depth charges. Asdic was fitted.

In the early stages of the war there was a great shortage of coastal force craft, and the "B" M.L.s were the one type of craft available in any numbers; at the same time the operational position was critical. To make the most of the craft available, it was arranged that the "B" M.L.s could be tinker, tailor, soldier or sailor at short notice, i.e. were convertible to one or other of the services of minelayer, M.T.B., anti-submarine boat, anti-invasion boat, anti-E-boat or air-sea-rescue, at 48

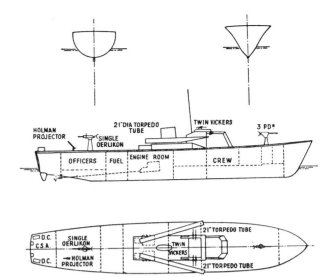

FIG. 2.—OUTLINE OF "B" TYPE M.L.

hours' notice. The quick changes of armament were achieved by arranging a series of steel strips on the deck of the boats in the building stage. These steel strips were fitted with tap holes to suit the base holding-down arrangements of various types of armament, such as depth-charge chutes, torpedo-tube supports, gun supports, mine rails, and so on. The armament was secured to these steel "tapping strips" by means of tap bolts. To effect the change of armament, it was necessary only to take out the tap bolts securing the existing armament, lift out the armament, place the required new type of armament on board, and secure to another set of tapping strips.

Twelve M.L.s were fitted with "A" frames carrying

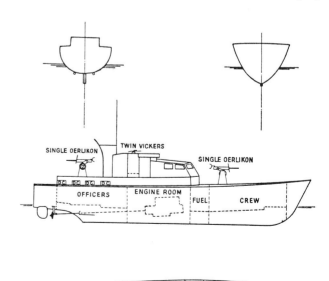

FIG. 3.—OUTLINE OF H.D.M.L. (72 FT.)

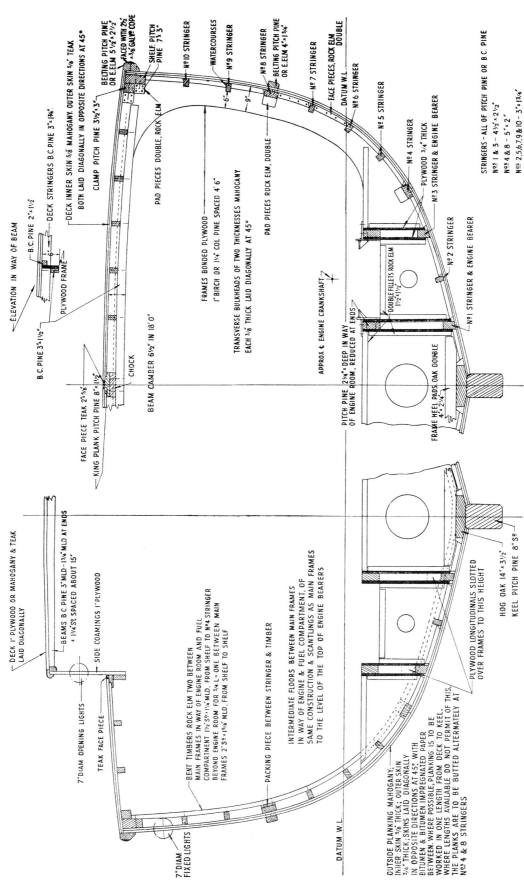

FIG. 4.—TYPICAL CONSTRUCTION SECTIONS, "B" TYPE M.L.

a hammer box, for sweeping acoustic mines in shallow water. In 1943 tapping strips were provided for fitting Oropesa sweep. A number of "B" M.L.s were fitted with special generators and LL cables for sweeping magnetic mines and also carried an acoustic sweep.

Arrangements were made in all "B" M.L.s for carrying temporary deck fuel tanks when necessary, to increase the fuel carried from 2,300 gallons to 5,000 gallons. With the extra deck tanks the boats made long ocean passages. In some cases the emergency fuel tanks were retained after passage, to increase endurance on convoy escort duties.

as follows: 6-pdr. Mk. VI gun forward, Oerlikon Mk.XIA gun amidships, 2-pdr. Mk. VIII gun aft. Radar. A hydrophone was fitted. These M.L.s were used in support of the Arakan landings.

The "B" type M.L. was found to be very seaworthy. A flotilla of eight M.L.s proceeded on their own bottoms to Trinidad, from United Kingdom, via Iceland, Greenland, Newfoundland and the American coast. The boats based on Freetown also maintained long convoy runs off the west coast of Africa. Numerous boats made the passage from the United Kingdom to Gibraltar, and later to Malta, Alexandria, and thence to India.

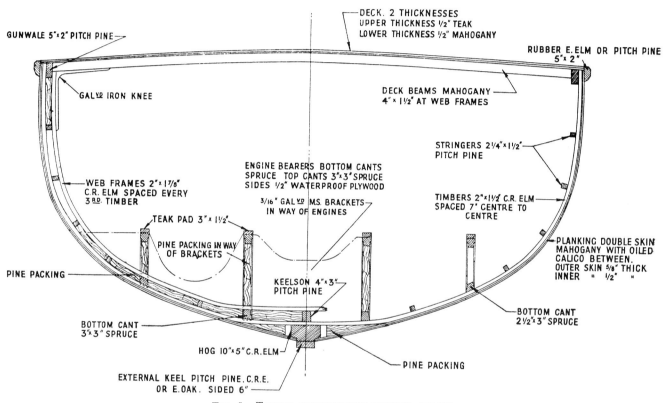

FIG. 5.—TYPICAL CONSTRUCTION SECTIONS, H.D.M.L.

"B" M.L.s intended for foreign service were fitted with copper sheathing.

In preparation for carrying out landing operations, and to assist landing craft some M.L.s were fitted with additional navigational appliances.

At the end of 1944 a number of M.L.s were converted as hospital carriers for the War Office. The conversion consisted primarily in altering the after accommodation to become a hospital ward and adding a deck-house, to become an additional hospital ward, to accommodate a total of twenty stretcher cases.

During 1944, a number of "B" type M.L.s were modified in the United Kingdom for service as M.L. gunboats in the Far East. This type of craft was selected for this duty on account of the reduced amount of maintenance required, compared with the complicated M.T.B.s and M.G.B.s. For this service the depth-charge equipment was removed and the armament was arranged

Boats built in South Africa made the passages to India and the Persian Gulf.

The use of petrol was a source of great danger in these craft, and several boats were lost as a result of fires and explosions of petrol vapour.

The "B" M.L.s were used for all sorts of services in all zones of operations. They formed the bulk of our naval forces in the St. Nazaire raid. Their uses included gunboat, A/S escort, smoke layer to protect convoys, air-sea-rescue, anti-E-boats, M.T.B., and other services too numerous to mention.

Harbour Defence Motor Launches (H.D.M.L.s)

A design of small motor launch, for protection of harbours and estuaries against submarines, was prepared in the Admiralty in late 1939. The staff requirements were for a craft not exceeding 72 ft. in length and capable of being shipped abroad on the deck of a ship.

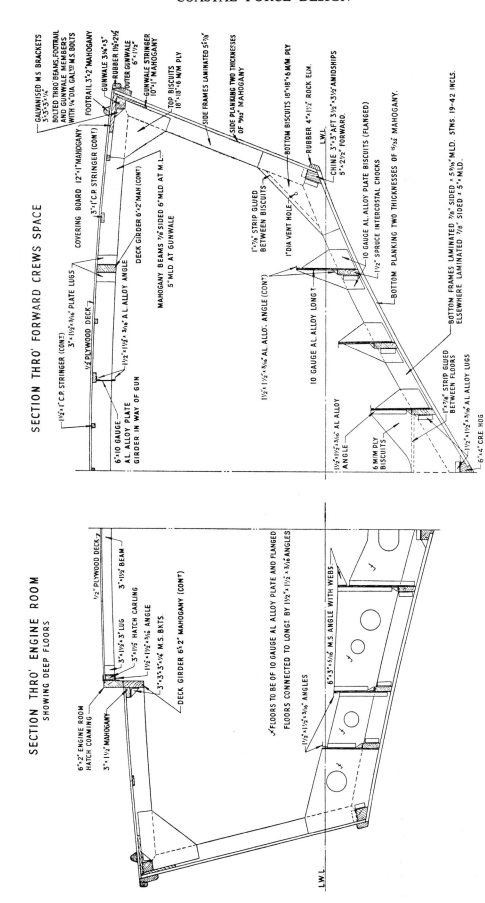

FIG. 6.—CONSTRUCTION SECTIONS OF 70-FT. M.T.B.

134

These craft had the following dimensions:

Length overall: 72 ft.
Beam over rubbers: 15 ft. 10 in.
Draught forward and aft: 4 ft. 3 in.

Fig. 3 shows the design in outline. Fig. 5 shows a typical constructional section. Fig. 18 shows a photograph of a H.D.M.L. Fig. 19 shows a photograph of a H.D.M.L. carrying sail.

The boat was of round bilge form and was provided with two large rudders to ensure quick turning during an anti-submarine attack.

The boats were fitted with two diesel engines, manufactured either by Henty and Gardner (150 H.P. each), Gleniffer (160 H.P. each), or Thornycroft (130 H.P. each). The engines gave the boats speeds between 11 and 12 knots on 54 tons displacement.

The hull was of double diagonal planking with bent transverse timbers outside longitudinal stringers and with reinforcing bent timbers at intervals inside the stringers. This system of framing proved itself resilient and strong. Early boats were planked with mahogany. When mahogany became scarce, it was necessary to use larch for planking, and in some cases this led to leaky boats. The use of larch was discontinued immediately the supply position for mahogany improved.

The craft were armed with one 3-pdr. gun forward, one Oerlikon aft, two Lewis guns on pedestals, and eight depth charges.

Asdic was fitted.

Fuel tanks were provided for 1,250 gallons in the main tanks and 300 gallons additional in tanks in the engine-room. The H.D.M.L.s had an endurance of about 2,000 miles at 10 knots.

Accommodation was provided for two officers, two petty officers, and eight ratings.

The wheelhouse in early boats was fitted with protective plating, but in later boats the bridge was armoured instead of the wheelhouse.

Orders for these craft were placed with yacht builders having well-equipped yards, since, with the exception of fittings such as steering gear, shaft brackets and rudders, the boat builder was required to provide the whole of the hull fittings and material.

The H.D.M.L.s saw service in all operational zones and generally were used for similar services as the "B" M.L.s.

The early vessels were shipped to their destinations abroad. Subsequently arrangements were made for the vessels to proceed on their own keels, as shipping capacity was no longer available.

To make them suitable for service in the Mediterranean and tropical stations, all H.D.M.L.s were sheathed with copper.

A few boats were fitted for service in Iceland, and were provided with additional heating and insulation. The boats proceeded to Iceland on their own keels.

Eight vessels were required for service in the West Indies. To ensure they could make the long passage from the Cape Verde Islands to America, they were given an outfit of sails. Two tabernacle masts were fitted. The foremast carried a standing lug and jib and the mizzen mast a standing lug. A large square sail was provided for running before the wind. The passage across the Atlantic was not made, as these particular H.D.M.L.s joined in the North Africa landing operations after arrival at Gibraltar.

Later boats were fitted so that they could tow one leg of an Oropesa sweep equipment, for minesweeping in sheltered waters.

Numbers of the boats were fitted out as navigational leaders for assisting landing craft, and were equipped with radar.

General

The H.D.M.L.s made a great reputation for themselves. They were sea-kindly little craft and their engines were very reliable. Their actual service was far beyond anything visualized when the staff requirements were outlined.

The M.L.s rendered great service during the evacuation of Crete. They played their part in the landings in Normandy, Sicily and the Arakan. They were used as convoy escorts off the north and west coasts of Africa.

MOTOR TORPEDO BOATS AND MOTOR GUNBOATS

History of Events, 1918–1935

At the end of the 1914–1918 war about a hundred coastal motor-boats were in service. These were skimming boats and the form was single step. They were armed with 18-in. torpedoes carried in troughs.

Main particulars of a 55-ft. C.M.B. were as follows:—

Length: 55 ft.
Displacement: 12 tons.
Armament: Two 18-in. torpedoes in troughs.
Engines: Two 375 B.H.P. petrol.
Speed: 35–40 knots.

Fig. 7 shows a C.M.B. in outline.

The design and exploits of the C.M.B.s are excellently described in a paper, under the heading "Coastal Motor-Boats (C.M.B.)—Their Design and Service during the War," read before this Institution by Sir John Thornycroft and Lieutenant Bremner, R.N., in 1923.

The naval economies of the 1920's put an end to all activity with C.M.B.s.

In the inter-war years the firm of Thornycroft continued to build numbers of C.M.B.s for foreign navies. The boats were substantially similar, in form and construction, to the 1914–1918 war C.M.B., but with improved engines and some increase in engine power.

With the cessation of all building for Admiralty and owing to general lack of interest in coastal forces, there was not much progress in design over the period 1924 to 1935. It is a matter of irony to be aware that in Germany the corresponding period was occupied in the

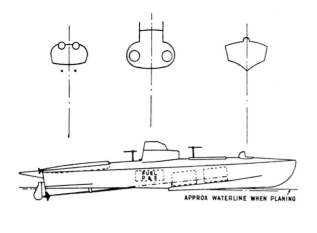

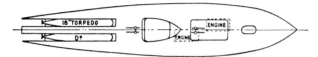

FIG. 7.—OUTLINE OF 55-FT. C.M.B.

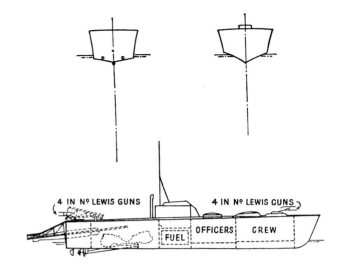

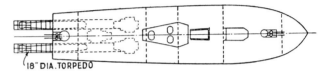

FIG. 8.—OUTLINE OF 60-FT. POWER BOAT CO. M.T.B.

development of high-speed craft leading up to the E-boat and its outstanding Mercedes-Benz-Diesel engine.

One development of the 1924–1935 period which, in retrospect, was found to have considerable bearing on coastal force design, was the hard-chine semi-planing motor-boat, which was introduced into the Royal Navy as a ship's boat round about 1930. Some of the leading boat builders entered on the production of these fast motor-boats, and for a time the boats were very popular in the Navy.

1935–1945

Development of the Modern M.T.B.s and M.G.B.s

60-ft. M.T.B.s (British Power Boat Co. M.T.B.s 1–19)

In 1935 the British Power Boat Company interested the Admiralty in a design for a small motor torpedo boat which was a development of the hard-chine semi-planing boat lately introduced into the Navy. Particulars of the design put forward were as follows:—

Length: about 60 ft. 4 in.
Beam: about 16 ft.
Displacement: about 18 tons in the trial condition, but about 20–22 tons on service.
Engines: Three Napier Lion, petrol, each 600 B.H.P. emergency rating.
Fuel: Normal, 500 gallons, 740 gallons including a deck tank.
Armament: Two 18-in. torpedoes.
Speed on 18 tons displacement: About 35–37 knots on emergency rating and about 29 knots continuous rating. At normal displacement of 20–22 tons the top speed was about 33 knots.

Fig. 8 shows the boat in outline.
The torpedoes were carried in the engine-room on overhead runways and were launched through ports in the transom. Two lattice-work girders, normally carried

hinged down on deck, could be hinged about their after ends on the transom, to form an extension of the torpedo runways in the engine-room. The method of launching the torpedoes was to hinge the lattice girders to their abaft stern position, take the checks off the torpedoes, and suddenly accelerate the boat: due to gravity and inertia effects the torpedo ran aft on the rails and overboard.

The armament consisted of two groups of four ·303 machine guns, one group mounted on a slip ring on a hatch at the extreme fore end of the boat and the other mounted on a hatch at the extreme after end of the boat.

The boat was of wood construction. The bottom planking was worked on the double diagonal system. The side planking was single thickness. The transverse frames were mahogany, sawn, with Canada rock elm capping on the inboard edge; the frame spacing was 1 ft. 6 in. in early boats, but in later boats the spacing forward was reduced to about 12 in. to strengthen the hull against pounding action. The deck was aluminium alloy sheet.

Accommodation was provided for two officers and seven men.

Approval was given to order six boats, and later the order was increased to nineteen boats.

As a test of the seagoing ability of these small M.T.B.s, the first flotilla made the passage to Malta on their own keels, calling at Brest, Corunna and Lisbon on the way to Gibraltar.

The 60-ft. M.T.B.s were good sea-boats on their size, but, in common with all hard-chine boats, it was found that when they were driven into a head sea they pounded heavily and were liable to suffer frame damage. Experience with these boats proved that the gunnery arrangements, with the slip rings at the forward and after ends of the boats, were unsatisfactory. In later boats the guns were mounted on ring supports abreast the bridge. The torpedo launching arrangements were not very satisfactory. The aluminium alloy deck plating gave trouble due to corrosion, and in some boats was later replaced by double diagonal mahogany planking. The single-thickness side planking worked on the seam strip system was not satisfactory, as it was found that the fastenings worked loose.

At the beginning of the war, two flotillas of 60-ft. M.T.B.s were at Malta and one flotilla was at Hong Kong.

The production of the 60-ft. M.T.B.s led to a re-birth of interest in small high-speed torpedo-carrying boats. The good sea-keeping ability of the new designs encouraged belief in the possibility of boats of the type having operational value. At the same time those immediately concerned recognized that these small craft did not fully satisfy operational requirements for high speed, effective torpedo arrangements, and ability to hold their speed in a seaway.

68-ft. Vosper M.T.B. No. 102

In 1935–1936, Vospers, who were among the leading builders of hard-chine fast motor-boats, embarked on the construction of a private venture M.T.B.

Length overall	.. ..	68 ft.
Beam	.. ..	14 ft. 6 in.
Depth	.. ..	7 ft. 3 in.
Load displacement	..	32 tons

Main details of structure were as follows:—

Bottom planking: Three thicknesses of mahogany.
Side planking: Two thicknesses of mahogany.
Framing: Sawn frames of mahogany, 2 ft. 4 in. spacing, with two intermediate bent timbers.
Deck: Double diagonal mahogany.
Engines: Three Isotta Fraschini, each having an emergency rating of 1,150 B.H.P. The boat also carried two V8 engines, geared to the side shafts, for silent approach at low speed.

As initially fitted, the boat carried only 1,000 gallons of petrol.

Accommodation was provided for two officers and eight men.

Initially the boat was fitted with a single torpedo tube on the middle line, arranged on a declivity firing through the stem of the boat. The design provided also for a second torpedo tube mounted on deck on the middle line, firing aft with torpedo head forward. The torpedo tube arrangements were soon seen to be unsatisfactory, and H.M.S. *Vernon* designed two lightweight loose-fit tubes, to be fitted on deck, one each side of the bridge, torpedoes being fired forward, the tubes inclined to the middle line in plan about 10 deg. Cordite firing was used.

Oerlikon guns were carried mounted on ring supports sided and near the middle of length of the boat. These Oerlikon guns were the first of the type seen in Great Britain, and on trial made an impressive showing.

Early works trials with the Vosper boat proved the necessity for more substantial framing, and 100 per cent additional sawn mahogany transverse frames were fitted. The Vosper boat was subjected to rough-weather trials in competition with the 60-ft. British Power Boat M.T.B.

Soon after commissioning, M.T.B. 102 was damaged, due to the side planking tearing away from the gunwale when the boat was driven at speed through sharp seas in the Needles Channel. This accident gave clear indication of the very severe stresses which come on the side, deck and gunwale structure when hard-chine type boats are driven at speed into head seas.

On trial the boat attained a maximum speed of 43·7 knots with a maximum continuous speed of 35·5 knots, displacement 31 tons.

Finally the boat was passed into service as M.T.B. 102. Fig. 21 is a photograph of the boat.

70-ft. P.V. Boat (British Power Boat Company)

Early in 1938, the British Power Boat Company invited Admiralty officers to attend the trials of a new design M.T.B. The boat was about 70 ft. overall length, with a beam of about 20 ft. The form of the boat was conventional hard chine. The maximum beam was carried well forward, giving the boat a bulbous bow, in plan.

The power units were three Rolls Royce Merlin engines which had been converted to marine engines—a new departure for the Rolls Royce Company. Each engine has an output of 1,000 B.H.P. at 3,000 R.P.M. emergency rating.

In the trial load condition the speed was 44·4 knots maximum with continuous rating speed of 40·5 knots on about 30 tons displacement.

It was understood that the intention of the Power Boat Company was to carry four 18-in. torpedoes in swivelling type, loose-fit, torpedo tubes.

The bottom, sides, and deck were of double diagonal planking. The frames were of sawn African mahogany, spaced about 10 in. apart in the forward part of the boat, the spacing being increased in engine-room. At the keel, chines, and gunwale, the sections of frame were connected by plywood brackets, worked double. The inboard edges of all frames were fitted with Canadian rock elm tension strips.

Subsequent to trials of the P.V. boat in Britain, the boat was shipped to America, to take part in a competition for M.T.B.s organized by the United States Navy.

The French Navy placed an order for M.T.B.s of the P.V. type; one boat of the type was ordered for the Royal Netherlands Navy; and similar boats, but 63 ft. in length—were ordered for the Swedish Navy. Most of these boats which were building for foreign navies during 1940 were requisitioned by the Royal Navy.

On service it was found that the hulls of these boats were not sufficiently strong and were liable to damage when driven into head seas at speed. Principal damage was the cracking of the side planking near the middle of length and the tendency of the gunwale to work loose from the frames, deck beams, and side and deck planking.

The prototype hard-chine boats developed by Vosper's and British Power Boat Company have been described in some detail as they were the forerunners of 70-ft. M.T.B.s and M.G.B.s built during the late war.

Other builders also were active; Thornycroft's were building single-step 55-ft. C.M.B.s, on more or less traditional lines but with speeds increased to about 45 knots; White's, of Cowes, undertook the venture-some project of building an M.T.B. on the hydrofoil principle; and Swan Hunter's were building a 100-ft. high-speed launch with welded steel hull and fitted with high-power Paxman Diesel engines. There was no lack of design activity.

By 1938, Admiralty and *Vernon* officers had accumulated experience at sea and on trial of various types of M.T.B.s, 55-ft. single-step, and 60-ft. and 70-ft. hard chine; a decision was reached to go ahead with building 70-ft. hard-chine M.T.B.s.

First Programme of 70-ft. M.T.B.s

1938 Programme

Under this programme, six M.T.B.s were ordered; four of the boats from Vosper's and two boats from Thornycroft's. The Vosper boats were somewhat similar in type to M.T.B. 102, but the hulls were strengthened. The Thornycroft boats were hard chine form to builder's lines.

All boats were powered with three Isotta Fraschini engines, each engine developing 1,150 B.H.P. Each boat was fitted with auxiliary engines, Ford V8, on the wing shafts, silenced, to enable the boats to make silent attacks on the enemy at slow speed.

The torpedo armament was two 21-in. torpedoes in sided, loose-fit, deck tubes.

The gun armament consisted of quadruple Vickers ·303 guns mounted on scarph rings, the rings being sided *en echelon* on towers abaft the bridge.

The wheelhouse was armoured with $\frac{1}{4}$-in. protective plating.

At full-load displacement, 36 tons, the Vosper boats had a top speed of 42 knots emergency rating and 40 knots on continuous rating.

Development of the 70-ft. M.T.B. during the War

During the war, production of the 70-ft. M.T.B.s was continued, with little change of hull form, engine power or engine arrangement. The main progress in the offensive value of M.T.B.s was a vast improvement in the gun armament towards the end of the war. Developments in design of these boats over the war period can be summarized as follows:—

Hull Structure.—Some trouble was experienced with hull structure, especially in the early phases of the war. In some degree the trouble was due to lack of experience

of the young officers in charge of the boats. If a boat is given big engine power and will travel fast, it is human nature—and especially young human nature—to open out the throttle and make it travel fast despite weather conditions. Even with a strong hull it is always possible to smash structure in M.T.B.s by using full engine power and driving the boat nearly head-on into the sharp deep head seas. However, after taking full account of the inexperienced driving, much of the structural damage was attributable to inexperience in design and lack of full appreciation of the destructive power of high-speed driving. There was progressive improvement in hull structure.

Engines.—The engines used in M.T.B.s at the outbreak of war were Italian, Isotta Fraschini, giving about 1,100 B.H.P. per unit. These engines were well liked. When the source of supply of the Italian engines failed in 1940, for a time it was necessary to fit the relatively low-powered Hall-Scott engine, with the result that the top speed of the M.T.B.s was well under 30 knots. The position was relieved when the higher-powered Packard engine became available. In the later phases of the war the Packard engine was a standard fitting in all types of M.T.B.s and M.G.B.s, large and small. The Ford V8 auxiliary engines, which were a feature of the first programme of 70-ft. M.T.B.s, arranged for slow-speed silent approach for attack on the enemy, were not fitted in some later designs, giving place to an arrangement of silencers, on bye-passes, on the main engine exhausts. Reduction gear was fitted in some programmes of M.T.B.s, but omitted in others, the omission of gearing being, on occasion, dictated by lack of gear-cutting capacity.

Displacement.—There was a marked increase in displacement in later M.T.B.s, consequent on the increase of gun armament, fuel stowage, ammunition, and so on, and the fitting of Radar and extra auxiliaries. The

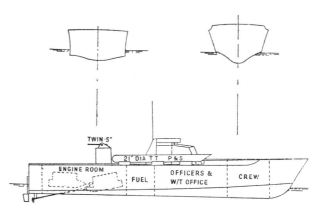

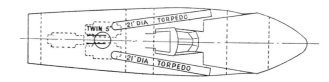

FIG. 9.—OUTLINE OF EARLY 70-FT. M.T.B.

increase of the weight amounted to over 10 tons, and this altogether offset the gain of speed which would have accrued from the increase of engine power (due to fitting of Packard engines) and improvements due to a better propeller design.

Armament.—The availability of really worth-while gun armaments towards the end of the war gave the designers some confidence that any boat produced would be a good operational unit unlikely to let the crew down. Early M.T.B.s were torpedo boats simply, and the ·303 guns fitted were of little value against surface craft such as E-boats. Later boats were fitted with twin ·5-in. power-operated turrets, an improvement. Finally, at the end of the war, the approved gun armament was a 6-pdr. power-operated automatic gun forward and a twin Oerlikon aft. The final design of the 70-ft. M.T.B. was more truly a dual-function torpedo boat and motor gunboat.

Radar.—Radar was fitted in later boats, and added greatly to their effectiveness in actions at night.

Fig. 9 shows Vosper M.T.B. 1939 in outline.

Fig. 22 is a photograph of 1939 Vosper M.T.B.

German Schnell Boats and Raums Boats (E-Boats and R-Boats)

At this stage of this history of design it seems desirable to point the narrative with a brief description of the E-boats and R-boats, which were the enemy boats *vis-á-vis* our coastal craft.

The E-boat is a large craft, of round bilge type, suitable for very high speed. It was designed to sink merchant ships in the narrow waters, by attack with torpedoes; in this respect it was complementary to the U-boat which dealt with merchant ships on the high seas. The gun armament of the E-boat was defensive. The boat delivered its attack and then made off at high speed to escape the attentions of our destroyers. The boat was designed for maximum ability to maintain high speed in

head-sea conditions. Particulars of a modern E-boat are as follows:—

> Length: about 110 ft.
> Displacement: 100–120 tons.
> Engines: Three Mercedes-Benz-Diesels lightweight, each 2,500 B.H.P.
> Speed: 42 knots.
> Torpedoes: Four 530 mm. (21-in. about).
> Guns: Oerlikon forward; one 37 mm. aft.
> Hull: Composite with heat-treated duralumin skeleton.

Fig. 10 shows E-boat in outline, and Fig. 23 is a photograph.

R-Boat

The Raums boat or sweep boat was essentially a light-weight moderate-speed composite minesweeper of the M.L. type. The system of construction was similar to that of the E-boats. This boat was fitted to sweep magnetic, acoustic and moored mines, and was used as a minelayer on occasion. The main particulars of the most modern type are as follows:—

> Length: 140 ft.
> Displacement: 160 tons.
> Engines: Two 1,300-H.P. M.A.N. or M.W.M. diesels.
> Speed: about 20 knots.

Small Motor Gunboats (70-ft.)

In the years before the war there were no boats of the motor gunboat type in the Royal Navy.

In 1940, soon after the German army broke through to the French channel ports, the German E-boats and R-boats commenced raids on our Channel convoys and minelaying in British coastal waters. These enemy craft were almost immune from attack by torpedo, and the provision of very fast small craft armed with automatic guns to shoot up the enemy boats became a matter of grave urgency.

Improvised Gunboats

Failing other sources of supply of gunboats, the M.T.B.s which had been building by the British Power Boat Company for France and Sweden were requisitioned, for conversion to the role of M.G.B. In addition, about a dozen 70-ft. M.A./S.B.s, building for the Royal Navy, were fitted with three Packard engines and converted to motor gunboats.

Armament really suitable for motor gunboats was not available, and guns of various sorts were scratched up to make the best of the circumstances.

The heavy load of guns and ammunition in these improvised M.G.B.s caused overloading of the highly supercharged Rolls Merlin engines, and there were many cases of serious damage to the engines due to detonation.

The lightly-built hulls suffered damage due to operations at high speed in a seaway.

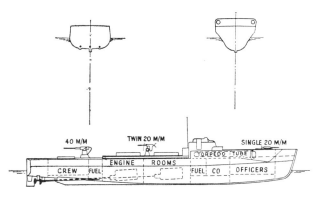

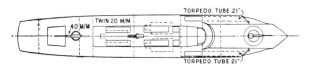

FIG. 10.—OUTLINE OF SCHNELL BOAT ("E BOAT")

71 ft. 6 in. M.G.B.s, M.G.B.s 74–81

All the improvised M.G.B.s which have been described showed structural weakness of the hull and the armament was not satisfactory. Apart from the makeshift guns, the boats were lacking in ahead fire. It was decided to build properly designed M.G.B.s. The design was prepared by the British Power Boat Company in conjunction with the Admiralty. The boats were much stronger structurally than the P.V. boat design. The hull form was almost exactly similar to the P.V. boat, but the hollow back profile of the deck was eliminated and the deck given a hogged sheer. The leading particulars of these boats were as follows:—

Length: 71 ft. 9 in. overall.
Beam: 20 ft. 10 in.
Displacement: 46 tons.
Engines: Three in number, Packards, giving a total B.H.P. of 3,600.

Originally the boats were armed with a 2-pdr. automatic gun, on the middle line forward of the wheelhouse, and a twin Oerlikon gun, power operated, on the middle line aft.

Fig. 11 shows a 71 ft. 6 in. M.G.B. in outline.

Fig. 24 is a photograph of one of these craft.

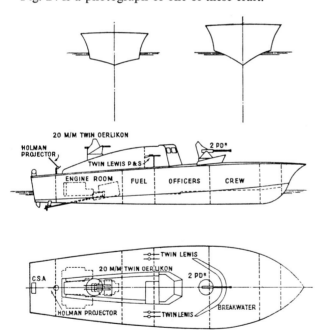

Fig. 11.—Outline of 71 ft. 6 in. m.g.b.

On trials, the earlier boats attained a speed of about 40 knots maximum and 35 knots on continuous rating, on 46 tons displacement.

Late on in the war, and before the invasion of Normandy, it was decided to change the armament of 71 ft. 6 in. M.G.B.s to combined M.T.B. and M.G.B., two 18-in. torpedo tubes being fitted abreast the bridge in addition to the existing gun armament, more or less on the lines of the arrangements in the latest 70-ft. M.T.B.s.

Large Type M.G.B.s

In late 1940 the complete building jigs for the "A" type Fairmile boats were available and not in use. As an interim measure to provide gunboats quickly, pending the design and production of a true motor gunboat, it was decided to build a number of "A" type Fairmile boats, exactly similar as regards construction and accommodation to the original "A" type Fairmile M.L.s, but fitted with three supercharged Hall-Scott engines, each of 900 H.P., to give extra speed. The bridge arrangement was brought into line with M.T.B. practice. These M.G.B.s were called "C" Fairmiles, and twenty-four boats were built.

Fig. 25 is a photograph of a "C" M.G.B.

The armament fitted was a 2-pdr. power-operated gun forward, a 2-pdr. Mark XIV Rolls hand-operated gun aft, and two 0·5-in. Mark V twin power turrets, sided and arranged immediately abaft the bridge. Four depth charges were carried.

The fuel capacity was 1,800 gallons, and the boats had an endurance of about 500 miles at 10 knots.

On a displacement of 75 tons the speed was 26½ knots maximum. The speed on service was about 24–25 knots.

These boats gave good service.

A defect was the unduly large turning circle, due to the large deadwood aft which was a feature of the "A" type Fairmile design.

Steam Gunboats

In 1940 the search was for an effective counter to the E-boat. In the absence of any suitable light-weight high-power diesel machinery in Great Britain, consideration was given to the production of high-speed gunboats using high-power light-weight steam turbine machinery. The limitations of steam machinery, its excessive weight, high fuel consumption and vulnerability were recognized, but it was imperative to produce boats having highest possible sea-keeping ability, in combination with heavy gun armament and high speed, and it was considered feasible to produce a powerful steam gunboat.

Approval was given to build a few boats, and orders were placed with Messrs. Yarrow's, Denny's, Hawthorn Leslie's and White's.

The design of this craft was commenced in October 1940, and the first boat commenced trials in November 1941.

The lines drawing and general arrangement drawing were produced by the Admiralty. The lines were for a round bilge boat somewhat similar in form to the large round bilge wood M.T.B.s. The details of the design of structure were the joint effort of Admiralty technical departments, Yarrow's and Denny's. The design of these craft involved a very high degree of design effort, as the weight of the hull structure was exceptionally low in relation to the overall dimensions of the boat. The hull was of steel.

The main particulars of the design were as follows:—

Length: 146 ft. overall.
Length on water-line: 135 ft.
Load displacement (as designed): 165 tons.

An open bridge was fitted amidships; with a charthouse on its forward side. The charthouse was constructed of wood, but the bridge was built up of 30 lb. non-magnetic protective plating.

The arrangement of machinery was twin-screw, driven by two steam turbines through reduction gear. The power unit was a single boiler, either La Mont or Foster Wheeler, designed to give 8,000 S.H.P. to the propellers.

The total fuel stowage was 50 tons of diesel oil, but on ordinary operations and on trials 30 tons only was carried.

Accommodation was provided initially for three officers and twenty-four men.

An outline and a photograph of an S.G.B. are shown respectively in Fig. 12 and Fig. 26.

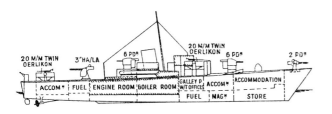

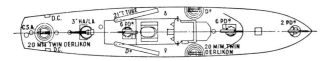

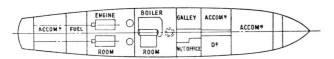

FIG. 12.—OUTLINE OF STEAM GUNBOAT

Armament

The armament carried originally was a 2-pdr. power-operated gun forward, two twin 0·5-in. power-operated turrets abreast the bridge, a 2-pdr. hand-operated gun aft, and arrangements were made for two 21-in. light-weight torpedo tubes.

Trials

The earliest set of trials revealed considerable propeller cavitation and lack of boiler power. By improvements in propeller design and using a boiler which was capable of delivering 8,000 H.P. to the propeller shafts, a speed of 35 knots was attained on a displacement of 170 tons.

Fuel Consumption

The fuel consumption of these boats was very high, about 3½ tons of fuel an hour at full speed; also the boilers used half a ton of fuel per hour even when the boat was not running.

On service it was found that the boiler and its fittings were too vulnerable to machine-gun fire. Actions with E-boats and armed trawlers were often fought at almost point-blank range, and the S.G.B. was easily stopped by a puncture of any one of the numerous steam pipes, boiler drums, water tubes, pumps, etc. After a small amount of operational service, the drastic step was taken of fitting ¾-in. thick protective plating over the whole of the boiler and engine installation. This great weight of armour, together with additions to the armament and complement, resulted in the load displacement of the steam gunboats increasing to 260 tons.

Considerable additions to armament were made during the life of the steam gunboats, and the armament finally approved was as follows:—

One 6-pdr. power-operated gun forward.
One 6-pdr. power-operated gun amidships.
One 3-in. hand-operated gun aft.
Two twin oerlikon hand-operated mountings abreast the bridge.
Two 21-in. torpedo tubes.

The boats were fitted with radar, echo sounding gear, and a pitometer log.

These hulls proved themselves to be very strong on service and suffered very little structural damage due to stress of weather or high-speed driving.

In action, the S.G.B.s were successful against the E-boats, and it is known that the E-boat commanders had a particular dislike for actions with the S.G.B.s and destroyers. One craft only of S.G.B. type was lost in action; it was thought that this particular boat was stopped by a shot in the boiler-room.

"D" Type M.G.B.s and M.T.B.s

The lines of the "D" type Fairmile boat were developed at the Admiralty late in 1939. The form was developed by, in imagination, splicing a destroyer type bow on to a fast motor-boat type of stern, in an attempt to obtain less pounding of the hull when driven at high speed into a head sea. The form also produced a dry boat forward by ploughing over the bow wave. In late 1939 this hard chine form had been tested at Haslar tank in comparison with a round bilge form, also developed at the Admiralty. It was decided to use the hard chine form for the "D" Fairmiles, as it was intended to fit four engines and propellers in these craft, and the rather wide flat transom of the "D" form lent itself well to the arrangement of four propellers. The design of the "D" Fairmile craft was commenced in March 1941, and the first boat ran trials in February 1942.

Dimensions were as follows:—

Length, W.L.: 110 ft.
Beam: 21 ft.

These craft were powered with four Packard engines, on four separate shafts, giving a total of 5,000 B.H.P. Pending the manufacture of gear-boxes, the first boats to be finished were fitted with direct drive, but the shaft arrangement allowed for the introduction of an epicyclic type of reduction gear at a later date. These reduction gears were fitted in later boats built and, retrospectively, in earlier boats.

The design provided for a combination of M.T.B. and M.G.B. but, to get boats on service quickly, the torpedo tubes were omitted in some of the earlier boats, and these particular boats were styled M.G.B.s.

The "D" M.G.B.s carried a 2-pdr. power-operated gun forward, a twin oerlikon power-operated gun aft, and two twin 0·5-in. power-operated turrets abreast the bridge. In addition, twin Vickers G.O. guns were fitted on the wings of the bridge and a Holman projector was fitted on the coach roof over the engine-room.

The fuel tanks had a total capacity of 5,000 gallons. The propellers were designed for a load condition with 3,000 gallons of petrol on board.

The first boats, not fitted with reduction gear, carrying 3,000 gallons of fuel, and on a displacement of 91 tons attained a maximum speed of 30 knots. With reduction gear the speed was about 32½ knots on a load displacement of about 98 tons.

As the war progressed there was a demand for increased gun armament in the "D's," and there came about a succession of re-armaments:—

(a) The twin Oerlikon power-operated mounting aft was moved to a position on the coach roof over the engine, a 6-pdr. Mark VI hand-operated mounting was fitted aft.

(b) The "D" Fairmile boats were fitted as combined M.T.B.s/M.G.B.s. The armament of the combined boats was as follows:

One 2-pdr. power-operated gun forward.
Two 21-in. torpedo tubes amidships.
Twin power-operated oerlikon aft.

(c) "D's" were fitted with the following heavy armament:

6-pdr. power-operated gun forward.
Two 0·5-in. power-operated turrets abreast bridge.
Four 18-in. light-weight torpedo tubes.
Twin oerlikon hand-operated mounting on the coach roof.
6-pdr. power-operated gun aft.

This latest armament increased the displacement of the "D's" to 120 tons, and the speed was reduced to 29 knots when fitted with geared drive.

The "D" Fairmiles carried radar.

The "D" type boats brought to light some of the limitations of the Fairmile method of construction applied to boats over 100 ft. in length driven at high speeds into head seas. On their many passages from Norway the "D's" were often heavily over-driven, to make a quick getaway from the Norwegian coast, and

during the battle of the Cape Bon Peninsula the "D's" were driven at high speed into short head seas, from bases such as Bone, to arrive in tactical positions off the Cape. As a result of heavy driving, it was found that the boats were prone to break their plywood frames in the forward part of the boat; also the keel scarphs were liable to pull and work, and the scarphs of the gunwales and the deck stringers in the way of the engine-room were liable to crepitation. It was found necessary to double the number of plywood frames forward and to fit steel angle bars along the inboard edges of the plywood frames to act as a tension strip to prevent fracture. Steel "fish"-plates about 10 ft. long were fitted over the keel scarphs, which were found subject to movement, to act as a reinforcement. In some cases margin plates were fitted along the deck, adjacent to the engine-casing coaming, to strengthen the deck and compensate for the weakness due to the large deck opening. The strengthened boats were found to be just about adequately strong and kept clear of serious structural troubles.

Several flotillas of "D" type M.T.B.s and M.G.B.s were sent to the Mediterranean on their own keels during the spring and early summer of 1943. To obtain the necessary endurance, deck tanks were fitted to increase the fuel stowage to 8,000 gallons.

The "D" type M.T.B.s saw much service and, being available in large numbers, they were of great value to coastal forces. They were a true mass-production M.T.B. using the Fairmile method of production. The need for quick production, in the circumstances prevailing at the time, ruled out the possibility of using the composite system of construction, which would have been specified in normal circumstances for a high-speed craft over 100 ft. in length. The need for quick production also resulted in the use of heavy stock fittings to the detriment of speed.

Fig. 13 shows an outline and Fig. 27 is a photograph of a "D" M.T.B.

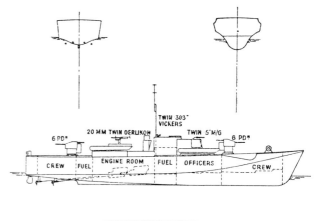

FIG. 13.—OUTLINE OF "D" TYPE M.T.B.

M.G.B. 501

In late 1939 an outline design and set of lines for a large combined M.T.B. and A/S boat was prepared in the Naval Construction Department, and the Director of Naval Construction raised the matter with the Controller to obtain approval to build a vessel of this type. The form of the design was round bilge, and a model to the lines put forward had already been sent to Haslar for test and was known to be very efficient at speeds of 30–35 knots. Approval was obtained to build a boat to this design, and the order was placed with Messrs. Camper and Nicholson. Mr. Charles Nicholson agreed to design the framing system.

The main particulars of the boat were as follows:—

Length: 110 ft. W.L.
Beam: 19 ft. 6 in.
Displacement: 95 tons deep (5,000 gallons fuel).
Engines: Power units were three Packard engines, each giving a horse-power of 1,250 B.H.P.
The propellers were driven through a 3 to 1 reduction gear.
Displacement on trial was 95 tons.

The armament was to be as follows:—

A 3-in. gun aft.
A 2-pdr. gun forward.
A number of depth charges.
Arrangements made for fitting two 21-in. torpedo tubes.
Asdic.

Fig. 14 shows the outline and Fig. 28 is a photograph of M.T.B. 501.

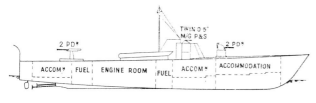

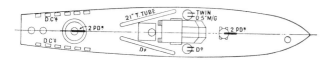

FIG. 14.—OUTLINE OF M.G.B. 501

The structure of the boat was as follows: The main steel frames were web type, fitted 3 ft. 3 in. to 5 ft. apart. Intermediate Canadian rock elm frames were worked, two between each steel frame. Outside the steel frames longitudinal stringers were worked. The planking was double diagonal and was secured to the stringers with screws.

During construction it was decided to complete the boat as an M.G.B., and the following armament was fitted:—

A 2-pdr. power-operated mounting forward.
A 2-pdr. hand-operated mounting aft.
Two twin 0·5-in. power-operated turrets abreast the bridge.
Two 21-in. torpedoes.

Tankage was provided for 5,000 gallons of petrol.
The propellers were designed for a load of 3,000 gallons on trial. On deep displacement of 95 tons the boat attained a speed of 30·3 knots.

Gay Viking, etc. (M.G.B.s 502–509)

These craft, designed originally as M.G.B.s, were similar to M.T.B. 501 and formed an extension of the order for that craft. They were powered with three Paxman 1,000-H.P. light-weight diesel engines instead of Packards.

The first two boats only of this type were completed with their original designed armament. The remaining craft, during construction, were converted for the carrying of cargo, and were employed for a period running the blockade between the United Kingdom and Gothenberg, Sweden, carrying special cargoes. Some of the accommodation was removed and cargo holds fitted in place of the accommodation. Accommodation for the officers and crew was provided in the deckhouse, and as far as possible these boats were disguised to have the outward appearance of small coasters. These craft were given names, *Gay Viking*, etc. Due to shortage of Paxman engines, one boat was fitted with Packard engines.

Fig. 29 shows *Gay Viking*.

General

Operational Objective

The operational ideal of coastal force offensive craft may be summed up briefly in the phrase that "Any enemy vessel which ventured out of port would find attack inevitable." From the point of view of material and design this objective could be achieved only if the boats were:—

(a) Adequate in numbers and always in running order.
(b) Not rendered non-operational because of stress of weather.

i.e. the achievement depended largely on maintenance and on ability to remain operational in a seaway.

Maintenance

M.T.B.s and M.G.B.s are not easy craft to maintain, and their maintenance has involved a large amount of effort and expenditure. In respect of maintenance, the M.T.B. is more nearly akin to the bomber aircraft than to the general run of H.M. ships. M.T.B.s contain almost a maze of complicated and fragile fittings which need constant attention. The engines and their associated fittings are highly sensitive units, which need much attention and whose life between overhauls is short. Elaborate arrangements are required for the supply of spare parts for engines, guns, etc., to be kept at bases and immediately available for replacement of defective fittings in the M.T.B.s.

The other two factors which add to the difficulties of maintenance of M.T.B.s are, firstly, these boats have a short range, therefore operational bases must be close to the zone of action. For operations covering a number of zones, not in themselves very widely separated, it is necessary to have a number of bases, to act as jumping-off points for the boats. The second factor is the requirement for frequent slipping of these craft. It has been the experience on service that damage to under-water fittings necessitating slipping is of very frequent occurrence.

After a slow start, maintenance of M.T.B.s operating in Home waters was taken well in hand. The arrangements were as follows:—

(a) A new department set up in the Admiralty to organise maintenance of Coastal Force craft.

(b) A central depot for the assembly and distribution of spare parts.

(c) An engine works for the periodic overhaul of the M.T.B. engines.

(d) A number of bases around the coast which served as operational bases for the M.T.B.s and organized to carry out running maintenance of M.T.B.s and coastal craft.

(e) For the larger refits, and repairs of action and other damage, the work was turned over to the Director of Dockyards, who arranged for repairs to be carried out in suitable yacht yards under the supervision of the Admiralty Repair Overseers.

During the important phase of the Normandy landings, in which coastal forces played a notable part, the fleet of coastal force craft was kept in a high state of efficiency, being over 90 per cent operational throughout the operation. When the M.T.B.s were advancing along the French coast, following up the retreat of the German army, a lorry-borne maintenance unit was used, based in France and moving from port to port in step with the advance of the M.T.B.s.

The other main zone in which the M.T.B.s operated in strength was in the Mediterranean. Maintenance of M.T.B.s in this area was never easy. One of the German generals has described the land operations in North Africa as "a Quartermaster-General's nightmare." In the sphere of naval operations the maintenance of coastal force craft in the Mediterranean might well have been described as a nightmare of another sort. In the early stages of the operations the attempt to organize bases and build up spares in the Mediterranean area was thrown badly out of gear by General Rommel's advance into Egypt. This advance scattered the spares far and wide. By the time Tunis had been occupied the position had improved and some real attempt was made to organize coastal force maintenance units. The maintenance arrangements included an M.T.B. repair ship and a lorry-borne unit. The position as regards slipping was never very satisfactory, owing to the concentration of shipping in the Mediterranean, the comparative dearth of slips and docks, and absence of tidal range.

Sea-keeping Ability

It has been stated already that the ideal M.T.B. should be operational in nearly all sorts of weather. The little 70-ft. M.T.B.s were good sea-boats within limits, and in a light sea they are very good and operational. The larger round bilge or quasi-chine M.T.B. over 100 ft. in length were better sea-boats than the smaller M.T.B.s and less restricted by the weather.

There is much loose talk, over-statement and general misconception of the speeds of which M.T.B.s are capable under head sea conditions. The small M.T.B.s are designed as semi-skimming boats. If anyone with knowledge of the North Sea, English Channel or the Heligoland Bight, in their less kindly moods, pauses to think, and to imagine small boats of this type skimming over a head sea under such conditions, the extravagance of some of the statements claiming high speed will be very evident.

Stability

The M.L.s and large M.T.B.s built during the war have been severely tested for seaworthiness, both deliberately and incidentally to their service. A typical range of stability curve for an H.D.M.L. may be of interest and is shown in Fig. 15. The curve of stability for a "B" type M.L. is very similar in form.

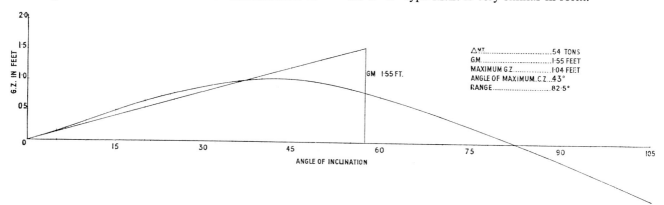

GM 1·55 FT.

△ wt.	54 TONS
G.M.	1·55 FEET
MAXIMUM G.Z.	1·04 FEET
ANGLE OF MAXIMUM C.Z.	43°
RANGE	82·5°

G.Z. IN FEET

ANGLE OF INCLINATION

FIG. 15.—STATICAL STABILITY CURVE OF 72-FT. H.D.M.L.

On the high seas the M.L.s are small in relation to the seas they encounter; they are also light and have little grip of the water. In consequence, they are thrown about and knocked over by the sea in a manner not experienced by larger ships nor even by the relatively small but heavy and deep-draught vessels such as trawlers.

Choice of Form

In this paper it is not intended to go into details of exact resistance of the various types of high-speed craft, but some general remarks on the choice of form may be of interest.

Up to the present the main forms which have reached what may be described as an operational state of development are the single-step, hard chine, high-speed round bilge and quasi-hard chine. The designers' choice of form will depend upon the requirements for a particular service.

1. If a lightly armed boat, required to operate in smooth water at very high speed is in view, a flat-bottom single-step form would show to great advantage at top speed.

2. In a light seaway and with an increased amount of armament load, a modified single-step boat with a broad V-shape (in section) bottom, such as a Thornycroft C.M.B., would show to advantage over the flat-bottom boat and prove a good operational boat.

3. With further increase of displacement and in response to a demand for better endurance at cruising speeds and less fatigue for the crews in a seaway, the tendency has been to choose the hard chine form in preference to the single-step, some sacrifice of operational top speed, under calm weather conditions, being accepted.

4. Usually, for high-speed craft over 100 ft. in length and a hundred tons or more in displacement, the round bilge or quasi-hard chine form have been favoured. The round bilge form has best economy of all types at cruising speeds. For the size, displacement and engine power usually under consideration the sacrifice of top speed involved by using this form in preference to the hard chine, is very small. The gain in ability to maintain high speed under average head-sea conditions, by use of the long lean round bilge form, is likely to be appreciable.

Engines for Coastal Force Boats

It is a likely subject for comment that, apart from the moderate-powered engines fitted in H.D.M.L.s, nearly all the engines fitted in coastal force craft during the war came from either Italy or America. No British engines had been developed in pre-war days suitable for fitting in coastal force boats. This lack of development might have had serious consequences, but for a set of lucky circumstances which made available the American Hall-Scott and Packard engines. The engines fitted in coastal force boats gave very good service, and it is no reflection on the design of these engines to state that the large M.T.B.s, M.G.B.s and M.L.s would have been better circumstanced had high-power light-weight diesel machinery, such as was available in Germany, been installed instead of petrol engines. Tanks containing large quantities of petrol are always dangerous in a boat, involving considerable risk of explosion or fire. When incendiary machine-gun bullets are flying about in action the risks involved amount almost to certainties if the boats are hit in the region of the petrol tanks.

Production

The number of coastal force craft put into production totalled about 1,700 craft. A few of the boats which were in production at ports such as Hong Kong, Singapore, and Rangoon were lost before they were put into service. The numbers produced in the various sub-divisions of coastal forces were roughly as follows:—

"B" M.L.s: 650 craft.
H.D.M.L.s: 450 craft.
Large M.T.B.s, M.G.B.s and S.G.B.s: 300 craft.
70-ft. M.T.B.s and M.G.B.s: 300 craft.

A number of "B" M.L.s were prefabricated and built in Canada, drawings being sent out from England. The majority of the "B" craft were prefabricated in London. About 300 "B" M.L.s were assembled abroad, building being undertaken at Singapore, Hong Kong, Rangoon, India, Alexandria, Dar-es-Salaam, Bermuda, Jamaica, Capetown, Canada, Australia, and New Zealand.

The majority of the H.D.M.L.s were built in yacht yards in United Kingdom, but about 200 boats were built abroad in Singapore, Durban, Mombasa, India, Ceylon, Alexandria, Australia, and U.S.A. For some of the boats built abroad the fittings were supplied from United Kingdom.

The production of 70-ft. M.T.B.s and M.G.B.s was mainly divided between Vosper's and the British Power Boat Company, but some boats were built by Harland & Wolff, White's, Thornycroft, Camper & Nicholson, McGruers of Clynder, Morgan Giles of Teignmouth, Berthon Boat Company, Lymington, McLean of Renfrew, and in America.

All the "D" type M.T.B.s, of which about 250 were built, were prefabricated in London and assembled by yacht yards in the United Kingdom. The builders of the other large M.T.B.s and S.G.B.s have already been named in this history.

The production of the vast fleet of coastal force boats was a very fine achievement on the part of the building yards concerned.

In Britain, mostly yacht yards were concerned, and the peacetime activity of these yards was mainly storage and fitting-out of yachts, with a relatively modest amount of yacht building. It reflects great credit on the management and artisans that such a step-up of production of relatively complicated craft was achieved. There were other difficulties: one famous yacht yard engaged on M.T.B. production was bombed and burnt out, but arose, like Phoenix out of the ashes, and, salving

Fig. 16.—"A" Fairmile M.L.

Fig. 17.—"B" Fairmile M.L.

what was salvable, was soon carrying on again with its building programme. Other yards also suffered bomb damage.

The large-scale production of M.L.s outside Britain may be a matter of surprise, no doubt, to some members.

Conclusion

This paper has detailed something of the development of design. In conclusion, the author wishes to touch on an aspect of the coastal forces which had nothing to do with design or material, but which was a matter of highest importance in coastal force operations. The boats were engaged with the enemy on about 800 occasions; they sank about 400 enemy ships and craft, and about 180 British coastal force boats were lost. The achievement was magnificent, all the more so as some of the early boats put in service were far from being as good as the designers could have wished, but which were all that could be produced with the engines, guns, fittings, and so on, then available. The operational success achieved was due, in the main, to officers and crews of coastal forces craft who sought out the enemy. Had the boats been handled by timid officers, the achievement would have been negligible. Through force of circumstances, the author saw a good deal of coastal force operational personnel and had opportunities to form judgment of the character and courage of some of the young men in this service. He puts on record that included among the officers and crews of coastal forces were some of the best young men of Britain, the Dominions and of our Allies. These young men had the sense of duty and courage associated in the public mind with the "Battle of Britain" pilot. It should also be put on record that, apart from a few young officers of the Royal Navy who formed a leavening of the coastal forces in the early days, and some flotillas manned by our Allies, the officers and crews who bore the brunt of coastal force operations were drawn from the Royal Naval Volunteer Reserve and from Hostilities Only ratings. Many of the ratings were young boys between eighteen and twenty years of age, and in some cases they were in action within a few weeks of their first experience of going to sea in any sort of boat.

DISCUSSION

Sir Charles S. Lillicrap, K.C.B., M.B.E. (Vice-President): The first part of the paper refers briefly to the origin of the Fairmile organization, the conception of which was due to the genius of the late Sir Noel Macklin; it must never be forgotten that without some such organization we could never have got the numbers of boats. Not only did Sir Noel develop the idea of pre-fabrication years before Kaiser, but he was fortunate indeed in the staff which he managed to collect at Cobham. This staff did not, of course, always see eye to eye with Mr. Holt, and no doubt they often regarded him as a tough nut, but it is true, nevertheless, that the later designs were born of co-operation between Mr.

Holt and them, while the whole of the resources of the Admiralty were made available to assist Fairmiles, who in return operated throughout with the utmost enthusiasm. I should like here too to pay tribute to Fairmiles' Lloyd's surveyor, Mr. G. Scantlebury, who was certainly in the highest class, an A.1 man if ever there was one.

Turning now to the M.T.B.s and M.G.B.s, the paper makes it clear again how much we owe to the initiative of the various private firms concerned, the British Power Boat Company, Vospers, and Thornycrofts, for although the author justly criticizes some of their proposals, without their pioneer work we should have been much behind.

If I say that the design of naval ships and craft is a complicated business, none of you are likely to disagree—if I go on and explain that because of the complication it is nearly always impossible for one man to be designer, builder, and sailor, I feel that many of you will still agree. The designer, in the Admiralty, is often the least well known of the above trio, the reasons for his actions are often somewhat obscure and his compromises are often regarded as examples of wilful ignorance.

In Mr. W. J. Holt, however, we have a true Admirable Crichton who was not only responsible in the main for the basic design of many of the craft so ably described in his paper, but who spent many long (and often unofficial) periods at sea in coastal-force craft during the war. In 1943, as Constructor Captain, he made the voyage to Gibraltar in the first flotilla of "D" class Fairmiles to make the passage, and, incidentally, went on to Malta in a B.Y.M.S. I might add that for many years before the war he spent his leisure in sailing and cobbling boats of all kinds, including some vacations before the mast in sail. His crowning achievement of this war was to design and build some shallow draught gun-boats on the Chindwin to assist General Slim's victorious advance through Burma.

When, therefore, Mr. Holt speaks about boats, there is no one to say him nay, and the Institution must, I think, feel honoured to be able to publish in its TRANSACTIONS such a comprehensive account by an author of such unequalled standing.

On page 138 the author remarks that the engines fitted in the early boats were of Italian origin, and later on it will be seen that mainly American types had to be fitted. On page 145 again he calls attention to the fact that throughout the whole of the war very few British engines were used. This leads me to a point which I have made before; in future we must be more self-sufficient; our staff requirements must be related to our industrial capacity, and our industrial thought must in some measure bear relation to possible wartime requirements. In future it will be no good building boats if we cannot propel them.

The author draws attention to the weaknesses of some of the types, and no doubt he feels that all could in some way or other have been improved, yet when we read of some of the voyages made by the craft, whether as flotillas or as blockade runners, the general verdict must be one of amazement that so much could have been done by so little.

I hope that development of these types will not lapse as it was allowed to do after the 1914–18 war, and that Mr. Holt will be able to come here again some day and give us a paper on how we first got a 60-knot boat, satisfactory as regards sea-keeping qualities and propelled by British engines.

Captain F. H. Powys Maurice, C.B.E., R.N. (ret.): I only want to speak on the maintenance problem in regard to these craft. It probably has not struck some of you how the diversity of hull types complicated maintenance, and how, as the war went on, these craft had more and more different types of equipment in them. We really should try and keep the number of types of boat and equipment down to the minimum. I think that possibly one of the most difficult things to resolve was bridge design because as the war went on, and as we got more and more instruments and equipment in the craft, the tendency was to centralize control on the bridge, and it was extremely difficult to find a place for all of it. I think there was probably more controversy over that than anything else. There was also the question of the increased weight of gun equipment, but our greatest difficulty perhaps was that we had no reserve of engine power. The designers always had to design up to the full H.P. to give what the staff required and there was always a tendency to add more personnel or equipment. It is essential to have some reserve engine power.

As to maintenance, the key was spare parts. At the beginning of the war there were no spare parts, and to add to the difficulty the coastal forces were dispersed over many places. Eventually we had central depots and distributed from there to the bases. Towards the end of the war the spare parts position got very much better, but although it was a fairly simple matter to maintain these craft in home waters there were difficulties when the vessels were taking part in operations elsewhere. Then we had to have a depot ship in the background.

The lesson learned from the war was that the maintenance side must be considered in the operational plan and not, as was very often the case, as an afterthought.

Admiral Sir F. T. B. Tower, K.B.E.: When I heard there was to be a paper on coastal-force design nobody could have been more pleased than myself. Because Mr. Holt is essentially a sea-going expert, as exemplified by the occasion when he was on board one of the M.T.B.s which went out in hard weather off Land's End. I was told that during the first 24 hours there were only two people capable of standing up, and one of them was Mr. Holt.

My reason for being here is that I happened to be Vice-Controller or Director of Naval Equipment from 1936–44. On page 186 the author says our coastal forces had little in the way of ancestry and could not, therefore, be based on experience of a type over a period of years. It was not only a question of design. Very few people knew very much about coastal forces and certainly very few had any idea of what they were going to do in the war. Before the war, as our President knows, people thought they might be valuable, but many thought they were mere toys. In any case most people thought that to produce enough of them would cost too much money. As a consequence, we started the war with very few of these craft. The 1938 70-ft. class ("G" boats) was just coming out and we had about twenty 60-footers in commission. That was the position at the beginning of the war, apart from a few being built for foreign governments.

The Fairmile Company started in 1939. Sir Noel Macklin came to the Admiralty and it was arranged that they should build a boat in order to start a sort of nucleus of what was eventually to be a big organization. But the war broke out before the first boat was built.

Engines.—In the early days we were desperately short of engines. We ordered about 30 boats as soon as the war was declared, and it was imagined that we had engines for them. A certain number of Rolls-Merlin engines were to be made available by a pre-war arrangement with the Air Ministry, but, to my horror, I found that we could not have any at all, as all were wanted for aircraft. We had a certain number of Isotta Fraschini with which we were equipping a 1938 flotilla. I tried to get a few more of these from Italy. We got about 30 per cent of the Isottas we ordered before Italy came into the war. No suitable engines for M.T.B.s became available until the Americans produced the Packard.

This was a very serious matter and undoubtedly our earlier M.T.B.s got a bad name because they had to be equipped with engines of far too little H.P., viz. the Hall-Scott, which were intended and were quite suitable for M.L.s, but not for 70-ft. M.T.B.s. The alternative to so equipping the latter was not to equip them at all.

Size of Boat.—As regards the size of boat required for M.T.B. or M.G.B. or both, I agree with the author's conclusion, but I think there is value in the 70-footer nevertheless. At one period of the war the latter became very unpopular—in my view undeservedly. Incidentally their opponents tried to make much of the view that the 70-footers were too small to meet the required excellence as sea-boats. This I think is unfair and open to serious criticism. It is not the case that they are not good sea-boats—they are, but the proper criticism is that although perfectly capable of keeping at sea in bad weather, they are too small and short to be able to fight weapons. This is quite different from saying they are not good sea-boats.

When new hulls and equipment, including engines, became more readily available, a continual struggle proceeded to try to keep in line with requirements. The latter were constantly changing, almost from minute to minute. This was partly due to changing war conditions, and partly to added experience and personal views. The net result meant that no new model by the time it was produced was ever "up-to-date." Consequently changes had to be made during construction, which was very unfair to the design, and not unnaturally had annoying repercussions on performance. This difficulty is probably unavoidable in war and indeed applies to other types of warship; but with coastal forces it was a very serious matter, as a change in weight or position of a

FIG. 18.—H.D.M.L.

FIG. 19.—H.D.M.L. UNDER SAIL

weapon, for example, has, or may have, a very considerable effect on the boat's performance.

Maintenance Bases.—Captain Maurice spoke of the importance of these matters, and the author also refers to them. They are in my view all-important, and without properly equipped bases and proper maintenance facilities the coastal craft is a very doubtful asset. These requirements can of course, and quite possibly should be, in the form of depot ships, but such facilities must be available somehow wherever the coastal craft operate. In the early stages of the late war such requirements hardly existed at all, and for a long time the necessity was not apparent to many people, but towards the end the matter was generally acknowledged. So much so that it was accepted that coastal forces would not operate, and indeed would not be sent to, the Eastern war unless and until proper base and maintenance facilities had actually been provided in the appropriate area. This should never be forgotten—it is vital.

I endorse the author's views of what the coastal craft did in the war. Their achievements were remarkable. Properly treated and their limitations understood they are, I think, a necessary unit of the Navy; but to get real results the lessons of the late war must be digested and activity continued. Mr. Holt's paper provides the necessary information for this to be done, and if used with a similar paper on operations it should be possible to go ahead. One hopes this will be done. There is every reason for it, because apart from their value in war, coastal craft provide first-class training for young officers and men. Such craft are the modern equivalent of "training in sail." A few experimental flotillas, or even a few boats, would provide the necessary nucleus. A base such as H.M.S. *Hornet*, with a firm—such as Vosper to produce the necessary experimental craft—would enable us to go ahead from the end of World War II, and would provide invaluable training in seafaring and leadership.

Sir Stanley V. Goodall, K.C.B., O.B.E. (Vice-President): I have listened with great interest to Admiral Tower's remarks. I hoped he would mention Admiral Sir Reginald Henderson. Perhaps the people of this country will never know how much they owe to the wisdom and energy of that great Controller of the Navy. He foresaw the value of the M.T.B. and was responsible for the introduction of that type into the Navy before the war. Although I did not see eye to eye with him in details, there is no doubt that the actual progress of the war proved that his foresight was correct. I said I did not agree with him in details. One of my thoughts at the time—and I think it was justified by experience—was that the boats then being built were too short. Knowing how requirements grow I felt sure that it would not be long before a demand arose for a bigger boat. That demand was foreseen and provided for by Messrs. Vosper, whose M.T.B. 102 really became the prototype for the later boats.

Reading between the lines of this paper, I hope it is clear that the building of coastal craft was one long struggle to make bricks without an adequate supply of straw. The engine question has already been mentioned. The petrol engine had serious drawbacks. What was badly wanted was a high-powered light-weight diesel engine. Then again the materials available were a handicap. We had to rely largely on wood, and this was a brake on development since, as length increased, a composite system of wood and metal became desirable. But aluminium was out of court because it was all required for the R.A.F. Steel also was out of court; it would have involved a heavier boat but, further, we were employing firms experienced in woodwork but unused to constructions in steel of such essentially light scantlings. The steam gunboats built of steel were constructed by destroyer firms at the expense of destroyers.

This paper should provoke thought on policy. Before the war, Admiralty policy with regard to the production of M.T.B.s was similar to that adopted in the early days of torpedo boats and destroyers. Then private firms were in competition with one another to produce the best design and thereby obtain orders. That was all very well in those days when the successful firms reaped their reward in orders at substantial prices not only from the Admiralty but also from foreign powers. But in the case of M.T.B.s war experience has shown that to produce in peace-time the ideal craft would have involved a firm in expenditure on research and development of the order of £500,000, probably more. Even if a firm had incurred this expense such a sum could hardly have been recovered in the price of such small craft, taking into consideration the few that the Admiralty and foreign powers were likely to order. Therefore, it seems to me that the only way to proceed in the future, if coastal craft are required, is for the Government to undertake its own research and development. Consequently, I heard with pleasure that the first Sea Lord, at the Institute of Marine Engineers' dinner the other night, said that the Admiralty were experimenting with the gas turbine for coastal craft.

We pulled through this last war in spite of our unpreparedness and all the trials and difficulties that have been mentioned, but we may not always be so lucky, and we ought to take this lesson to heart, viz. that research and development are necessary, and indeed essential in peace time even more than during a war, so that if the calamity does befall, production on the right lines can be very quickly achieved.

Mr. R. W. L. Gawn, R.C.N.C. (Member of Council): The paper brings home the large size of the fleet of small high-speed craft of diverse types produced at high priority during the war. This wide development called for a large number of model experiments. The scope may be appreciated from the statement that more than 50 model hulls were tested, some of which were modified two or three times.

One problem was to combine good endurance at cruising speed with maximum full speed. This is complicated, especially for the shorter classes of M.T.B.

In order to attain a speed of 40 knots it is necessary to develop dynamic lift. This can be done by a chine with or without a step. These features promote wave making and eddy resistance which react on the performance at cruising speed. The effect is considerable since the cruising speeds are greater proportionately than the full speed of destroyers. The displacement is three times as great as that of a destroyer in relation to the length so that wave making is increased proportionately. Sea and weather prejudice the full speed and behaviour and involve modifications to the form which gives best performance in calm water. Full speed of the larger types was limited to 35 knots or less by the engine power available. Dynamic lift is then comparatively unimportant and the form is preferably of round bilge type comparable to destroyers, although the transom is necessarily large for best results at full speed. Some compromise must therefore be accepted. The step form leads to higher speeds in calm water, but requires more than double the horse-power at some cruising speeds. When extra fuel to equalize the endurance is allowed for a good part of the full speed advantage disappears.

An important problem for the model experimenter is the correction for skin friction. This is complicated by dynamic lift. For example, a 70-ft. hard chine form will rise about 1 ft. at high speeds and trim 2 or 3 deg. by the stern. The rise and trim are carefully measured at each speed. These data afford means of estimating the reduction in wetted surface throughout the speed range. This gives a consistent if arbitrary basis for reckoning skin friction correction. In order to ensure that the results are truly comparative such models are generally made to the same length of 9 ft. so that the skin friction coefficient will be the same. Some models are larger. Large models must be driven at high speed and to meet this requirement a speed of 40 ft. per sec. is provided for the experiment carriage of the large tank at Haslar.

The pitfalls of cavitation are wide and deep for the designer of propellers for coastal-force craft. The propellers are only just below the water surface. The tip speeds may be as great as 150 to 200 knots. The stagnation pressure is 30 to 50 atmospheres which suggest that large peak suctions may occur on the backs of the blades.

Propeller design is circumscribed by many factors. Large rake of shaft is necessary to accommodate the propellers. Propeller clearance from hull, shaft brackets, rudders, and other propellers is restricted. Underwater engine exhausts emulsify the flow. The engine revolutions are excessive. Production considerations unfortunately largely ruled out reduction gear except in a few designs. Such items intensify cavitation and must be allowed for. In the early days of the war guidance as to the allowance for cavitation was obtained from the few trial results available. These included coastal motorboats tried during and after the 1914–18 war. Some of the results left much to be desired as regards accuracy, but during the war improvements were effected in the method of obtaining trial records, and predictions of the

cavitation factors were progressively refined in consequence. Advantage was taken of the large number of craft built to test propeller modifications on the full scale. Improvements were thus embodied in later classes which always followed close on the heels of the preceding class. The completion of the cavitation tunnel in 1942 proved a great boon. One of the first fruits was an increase of speed of 4 knots in one class by improved design of propeller, one feature of which was two blades in lieu of three. The cavitation tunnel prediction was confirmed by trials a few months later, the increase in speed being $3\frac{3}{4}$ knots. There was some vibration but this was satisfactorily overcome in later classes. The severity of cavitation may be appreciated from the statement that speed trial analysis showed a thrust cavitation factor of 2 or more which was common at one time. In an extreme case a factor of 5 was recorded. A factor of 2 implies that the propeller thrust is only one-half that which could be obtained from a propeller sufficiently immersed to eliminate cavitation. Fortunately the torque is also reduced by cavitation but a loss of efficiency of about 15 per cent was not uncommon. In later designs the factor has been reduced and efficiency improved.

A major bugbear arose with the introduction of supercharged engines. The power curves are conditioned by the maximum permissible boost at high speed. This is only available in short bursts. The power is reduced at maximum continuous boost. If propellers are designed for the full boost to obtain maximum speed, overboosting may result at some lower speed. If the full boost is not used, speed will be sacrificed. The boost must not be exceeded at any speed or hull loading within the operational range as this will reduce the short life of the engines, and may lead to detonation and serious damage. The prediction of boost is complicated by the curve of hull resistance at different displacements as well as engine boost and propeller characteristics. The boost also varies with climatic conditions. Thus the propeller design must strike a nice balance to suit all operational conditions.

Disparities in performance were found initially between boats of the same class. In some, the engines overboosted and in others underboosted although conditions were nominally similar. This reflected on the propellers. Fortunately they could be accurately checked on a machine already installed at Haslar for measuring model propellers. As a result it was found necessary to specify precision propellers. A greatly improved standard was obtained, thanks to the whole-hearted co-operation of propeller manufacturers who worked to fine tolerances without disturbance of their heavy production programme.

The controllable pitch propeller is one answer to the requirement for boost equalization between the different shafts of a boat and for boost grading at all speeds and loading of hull on service. The first model experiments showed serious loss of efficiency compared with fixed blades. Later designs have been improved, but there is scope for further improvement if sacrifice of full speed is to be avoided.

Fig. 20.—S.P. 60-ft. class motor torpedo boat

Fig. 21.—M.T.B. 102

The author is to be congratulated on covering a wide field in such a short space. Coastal forces bristle with problems. The author was associated with them throughout the war and played a very important part in their solution.

Mr. F. H. Sears (Member): During the period of the war covered by the paper I had the honour of serving on the staff of the Director of Naval Construction and was under the immediate jurisdiction of the author. I saw therefore at fairly close quarters the twists and turns of the development described and I would like to congratulate Mr. Holt on compressing all this into one paper. He pays a very well-deserved tribute to the crews of these craft. I would like to say that from the point of view of the naval architect the provision of accommodation for the crews was a very large problem. The greatest difficulty was to improve habitability. No doubt this problem arises in all craft, but the solution is much more difficult in craft of this type where weight and also maintenance are of very great importance. There were various schools of thought as to the desirability of the crews living on board or not, but the facts of war determined that the crews should live mainly on board, and this resulted in a considerable increase in weight.

The principal difficulties centred round heating, cooking, and ventilation, and I think I am correct in saying that in none of these was it possible to reach a satisfactory solution.

Probably the biggest problem was ventilation. I think the worst conditions occurred not so much when the boat was at sea, but when made fast at a deep quay, with three or four other boats abreast. In such a place on a cold night with the crews sleeping below the amount of "sweating" had to be seen to be believed. It certainly was not comparable to a yacht in summer. One solution was the provision of electric fans, but if these ran off the batteries then trouble arose for the engineers, who could not start the engines in the morning. If auxiliary generators were used, their noise and vibration were a nuisance at night, and as the size of these generators tended to grow, a further increase in weight was involved. Moreover, if you ran petrol generators at night there was a chance of taking in some of the exhaust fumes into the accommodation through the fans, especially with a whole block of boats together. The heating and cooking also presented problems. The early boats had pressure paraffin cookers, but whatever advantage there may be with these in peace-time, with decreasing purity of paraffin in war-time these were very difficult to maintain; they were also not good shipmates with high octane petrol. For the slower boats, such as the motor launches, lagged coal cookers and a modern type of enclosed coal-fired heating stoves were adopted, and were found to be reasonably satisfactory for non-tropical service. These were not suitable however for the higher speed craft. For these electric cooking and electric heating were adopted. The same difficulties with auxiliary generator noise (vibration and exhaust gases) as arise with electric-fan ventilation, were involved

and in addition,, in order to have standby capacity for running repairs the number of generators had to be doubled.

Some of these difficulties could be overcome by fitting the boat to receive a shore supply, but such supply would only be available at a well-fitted base and is most unlikely to exist in a captured enemy port. I think I can say therefore that in connection with habitability there exists scope for development in the future.

Mr. I. E. King, C.B.E., R.C.N.C. (Member): The following remarks which are based on my experiences as Fleet Constructor, Mediterranean, during the North African and Italian campaigns, will endorse and amplify the author's remarks concerning the behaviour of coastal-forces craft on active service, and the principal problems which affected their maintenance.

Several new types and classes of ships and craft, including the "D" type M.T.B.s and M.G.B.s, received their early gruelling operational tests in this theatre of war, as did also the maintenance organizations. The large numbers of coastal-forces craft engaged in the Mediterranean operations included "B" type and 70-ft. M.L.s, "D" type M.T.B.s and M.G.B.s and H.D.M.L.s. They were employed fairly continuously on a variety of arduous and dangerous tasks, in waters which are often by tourist agencies represented to be a millpond, yet frequently produce short seas which are menacing to small fast craft when heading into them. On many occasions coastal forces deputized for larger escort vessels.

The "B" type M.L.s and H.D.M.L.s with their comparatively moderate speeds (20 and 16* knots respectively), and their rounded bilge forms, set a very high standard of reliability under all conditions of service. Their hulls were practically trouble free, from a design standpoint.

The "D" type M.T.B.s and M.G.B.s, with prefabricated hulls and hard chines, also performed splendidly. With their very high speed and substantial armament they were a constant thorn in the enemy's side. A few of these boats developed the hull defects mentioned on page 142 when working under excessively hard operational conditions. Any seafarer who has experienced the succession of violent thumps and shudders to which these craft are subjected when driven even at moderate speeds into a head sea, must marvel that such light mass-produced wooden hulls do not disintegrate after short terms of active service.

I wish to pay special tribute to the expeditious way in which the author tackled these, the only hull troubles of any magnitude which were experienced in the coastal-forces craft operating in the Mediterranean. He journeyed to Malta to diagnose, and prescribe immediate remedies. During his visit he passed on much valuable information and advice concerning coastal craft, and he, in turn, obtained a better appreciation of the operational and maintenance problems than would otherwise have been possible. I have a great admiration for all who were concerned with the very courageous decision to

* Actually the speed of these little craft did not exceed 12 knots.
—Author.

Fig. 22.—1939 Vosper M.T.B.

Fig. 23.—German Schnell Boat (E boat)

Fig. 24.—71 ft. 6 in. M.G.B.

adopt this Fairmile prefabricated system for the construction of these "D" type boats.

The author has quoted several of the maintenance difficulties which were experienced in the Mediterranean during this period.

The principal troubles encountered were the shortages and dislocation in the supplies of engine spare parts, and the lack of slipways and dry docks. On the eve of the assault on Sicily only three slips or berths in dry docks could be allocated for the use of the larger types of coastal craft operating to the eastward of Algiers. The small tidal range prevented the use of tidal grids for short emergency jobs. On occasions it was necessary to lift the sterns of boats out of the water by cranes to enable repairs to stern fittings to be effected. Smaller underwater jobs were sometimes carried out by divers. The repair staffs in the bases, mobile units, and at Malta Dockyard put up a wonderful show in spite of these difficulties. Good use was made of these experiences in organizing improved repair and maintenance facilities for subsequent major war operations.

The small N.L. pontoon floating docks which were supplied by the U.S.A. for coastal-forces and landing-craft bases were a great success. They had several important advantages over haul-up slipways in a war of movement. The small docks can be assembled in a week or two by a working party with only one or two mechanics, and can be towed for moderate distances in fair weather conditions. For long journeys when the weather conditions cannot be relied upon for safe towage the docks can be shaken down, and transhipped to the next scene of operation. It is generally easier to find a suitable berth for a small floating dock than a site for a slipway. Although slipway cradles are portable, the preparation of the underwater foundations, and rails, on the edge of a sea with little tidal range, is a lengthy business, a process which has to be repeated when the base is moved forward.

Mr. W. R. G. Whiting, M.B.E., M.A. (Member of Council): May I very briefly make a slight extension of the author's remarks at the foot of page 145 of the paper, in reference to the actual production of these craft. The Fairmile system suited production by small firms with meagre facilities in an admirable manner. Owing to fabrication there was practically no demarcation between trades and as a general result I am certain that a high level of sheer efficiency, i.e. the greatest output from the smallest number of men and appliances, was reached. With such prefabrication you are able to construct these mosquito craft with almost no resources. In many cases there was just a shed on the site and wives and sweethearts came in to help. Moreover, the people employed resided very close to the work-place and work can be carried on quite comfortably for very long hours under these conditions.

Author's Verbal Reply

At this stage I cannot hope to reply to the points which have been raised in the discussion.

On a semi-humorous note, which is not meant to·be taken seriously, I will remark on habitability which has been discussed by Mr. Sears.

I am rather a cynic on the subject of habitability in M.T.B.s. When one has had an over-dose of fresh air during the day, a good deal of cold salt water trickling down one's spine, and generally feeling cold and wet, it is marvellous what a small amount of fresh air is acceptable and adequate when snug down below for the night.

I will give a written reply to the points which have been raised in the discussion.

Written Contribution to the Discussion

Commander (E.) Peter Du Cane, O.B.E. (Member): Mr. W. J. Holt's paper goes a long way towards placing the history, development, and design of the various types of coastal-force craft in their true perspective.

It becomes immediately evident from a study of this paper that those responsible for coastal-force design were struggling against time owing to a rather late start. This situation really lasted all the way through the war years and it is doubtful whether we can really claim that we ever properly caught up with events.

As stated by the author there is no question but that the lack of a suitable power unit constituted the worst handicap, and one which is difficult to overcome short of the outlay of very large sums of money and the allocation of the necessary priorities for the use of manufacturing capacity by engine builders of the necessary experience. Even then several years are bound to be involved in development, so that above all the foresight to initiate the development of such an engine is essential.

However, the firms who undertook the early development mostly had to undertake this at their own expense and on their own initiative in the first instance. It may perhaps be thought that despite certain inevitable limitations it was lucky that they did.

Apart from the handicap of having no really suitable power unit in the early stages to contend with, there was the fact that until the war had been in progress nearly three years there was little operational experience to guide the formulation of requirements. When this started to become available as a result of the offensive on German shipping passing down the coasts of Holland, Belgium, and the North of France, conducted mainly in the first instance from Dover, Felixstowe, and Lowestoft, quite a lot of modifications had to be made at an awkward stage in the production.

I feel that in advertising the series of structural failures it might perhaps with justification be stressed that this was applicable only to the earlier types, and that there were also occasions when the hulls of these little boats stood up to quite phenomenal punishment. To my certain knowledge on two or three occasions these little boats survived the explosion of a magnetic mine and came back to tell the story; while I myself was actually on board a motor torpedo boat which received a direct hit from an 88-mm. shell at about 1 a.m., resulting in destruction of almost the complete transom and opening up the after compartment to the sea. Despite this

70-FT. VOSPER M.T.B.s (SHORT TYPE)—COMPARISON OF MILITARY LOADS

Class of M.T.B.s	1938	1939	1940	1942	1943	1944
Admiralty numbers	20–23	31–40	73–98	347–362	380–395	523–537
Petrol, in lbs.	11,100	14,120	18,818	19,055	18,870	18,870
Lubricating oil, in lbs.	435	610	1,090	796	1,525	1,100
Fresh water, in lbs.	500	930	450	500	450	450
Crew and effects, in lbs.	2,160	2,400	1,800	1,800	2,160	2,880
Miscellaneous items of equipment which constitute additions, in lbs.	360	713	703	809	1,384	1,572
Armament, ammunition and armour protection, in lbs.	12,860	14,805	15,147	16,294	18,362	19,000
W/T and radar or A/S, in lbs.	540	927	836	1,064	1,800	3,632
Total weight, in lbs.	27,955	34,505	38,844	40,318	44,551	47,504
Per cent increase in military or useful load compared with 1938 M.T.B.s	—	23·2%	38·5%	44·0%	59·2%	69·5%
Total displacement on trials, in tons	35·79	39·70	46·90	44·73	44·39	48·80
Per cent of total displacement made up by military load	34·9%	38·8%	36·9%	40·3%	44·7%	43·4%

damage the boat remained operational and continued on her job for the remainder of the night, returning to harbour safely the next morning. Many such instances could be recorded if space allowed of this.

In referring to the sea trials of M.T.B. 102, the author mentions that this boat was submitted to rough weather trials in competition with the 60-ft. British Power boat, but my recollection of nearly ten years is that our competitor in this particular instance was a destroyer! The result in a south westerly gale, officially recorded as force 7, outside the Isle of Wight was admittedly somewhat in favour of the destroyer, but I have a vivid recollection of the author's face expressing the utmost satisfaction and pleasure, which was increased as the severity of the conditions increased.

His satisfaction could only have been slightly increased by the occurrence of actual structural failure, which strangely enough did not occur on this occasion.

The above table has been prepared to show the increase in military or useful load, including fuel, carried by the various classes of Vosper M.T.B. as produced throughout the war period. It will be seen that in comparison with the 1938 M.T.B.s mentioned in the author's paper, the 1944 class carried 70 per cent more useful load, while the maximum speed was practically the same.

It is true that the brake horse-power available had increased by about 17 per cent, but nevertheless it represents quite an achievement on the same length of hull. Many factors contributed to this result, the main being that of saving weight in the hull structure without detriment to its strength qualities, the same is applicable also to the engine installation and fittings.

It is not possible to quarrel with the author's statement under the heading of "sea-keeping ability", and it is agreed that much loose talk, over-statement, and general misconception of the all-round capabilities of these M.T.B.s were at one time freely published in the press. It is, however, difficult to believe that those responsible for these over-statements can have had any real seagoing experience in its widest sense.

In my opinion, whether the boat under discussion is 70 ft. or 115 ft. in length, they are both small craft in the generally accepted sense of the word, and almost equally subject to the limitations imposed by the open sea in its angrier moods. Despite this, the results achieved in action were magnificent, and I heartily endorse the author's statements on the subject of the young men who operated these craft with such outstanding determination and success.

Mr. J. W. Thornycroft (Member): The author says in the introduction that it is difficult to do justice in a single paper to this subject, but I think with the unique position he has held that he is to be congratulated for adding this record to the proceedings of the Institution, and that when the executives of the private companies who contributed to this war effort are not so harassed as they are to-day, time will be found to supplement the information that has been given.

I think it is important, from the point of view of the private small craft building industry, to make it clear that coastal-forces craft were only a section of the operational forces. There are many other sections, such as:—

(a) Combined operations.
(b) R.A.F. marine section.
(c) Royal Army Service Corps and War Department marine craft.
(d) General duties craft. Those carried by H.M. ships, harbour craft, target training boats, etc., which all required boatbuilding capacity to meet their extensive demands.

Between 1934 and 1938, owing to great showmanship and intensive publicity on the part of a firm, newcomers to the small boatbuilding industry, officials, and responsible naval officers were mesmerized into being persuaded that a "V" bottom or hard chine type of hull was something new (in fact a new invention), which made obsolescent all former designs of round bilge hulls. It was even suggested that destroyers, cruisers, and the *Queen Mary* should adopt a "V" bottom hard chine form

Fig. 25.—"C" Fairmile M.G.B.

Fig. 26.—Steam gunboat

Fig. 27.—"D" Fairmile M.T.B.

and be driven on the surface of the water instead of through it.

The author's paper shows what a limited application this form, of what he so rightly describes as semi-planing craft, has for craft up to 110 ft. in length. This fact is nothing new, and was well appreciated by naval architects, but unfortunately there were a great number of people who half thought that the old school of naval architects were being conservative and were not prepared to advance with the times. "V" bottomed hard chines were no novelty; in fact examples were racing at Monaco in the south of France in 1910.

Single-step skimming or planing craft are mentioned in the paper. It is my view that displacement being equal, and provided the step boat is trimmed as designed, that the sea-keeping qualities at equal speed are very similar to the hard chine type. The step form can be so arranged as to make a very stiff bottom where the heaviest pounding takes place. This is not so easy in the hard chine type.

I do not advocate step form for naval craft, because the designer has no control in service to ensure that the centre of gravity is maintained in the correct position, thereby trimming the boat correctly. As an example, during the early part of the war my firm, who were building a number of 55-ft. single-step boats which had been taken over, were ordered by the Admiralty to fit depth charge equipment which would have overloaded the boat and brought the centre of gravity several feet aft of the design position. When we refused to do this we were accused of being obstructionist. The aeroplane designer is in a better position to deal with a service department if it adopts such dictatorial methods, as the danger to the lives of the crew is more apparent.

It will be clear from the author's paper that none of the coastal-forces craft ended up with the fighting equipment that it was originally designed to carry. With the scientific advances that are always made in war-time, this condition will always be a serious consideration, and designers of hulls must legislate for changes. If the technical limitations of a single-step boat are so circumscribed as to make it an undesirable type, the remarks apply doubly to any hydrofoil craft, and I deprecate Admiralty financial resources being spent on further development and experimental work on these lines.

It would in my view be of great interest to the industry if a paper were written dealing with all the fighting equipment which was fitted to the craft which are the subject of this paper.

The torpedo launching gear fitted to the 1914–18 C.M.B.s has already been described. The author refers to the method employed in the 60-ft. British Power Boat Company M.T.B.s. Possibly the history of the development of the M.T.B. light-weight tubes may be of interest. In 1938 my firm built for the Philippine Government a 65-ft. single-step 1,950-B.H.P. 23-tons M.T.B. fitted with twin 18-in. tubes, weighing 840 lb. each. These were positioned one each side at an angle of 10 deg. to the fore and aft line, which became standard practice eventually in M.T.B.s. In these tubes the torpedo was carried by lugs on guide rails, this being the normal practice at the time. These light-weight tubes, I think, spurred the technical staff of H.M.S. *Vernon* to develop a great improvement in what was known as a close-fit tube, the torpedo resting on its own belly in the tube. The author's description of the tubes is, I think, misleading as he calls them loose-fit tubes. They were close-fit tubes, as my company was made to appreciate by the inspectors during the manufacture of some 175 during the war.

In the introduction it is stated that during the period 1918–38, *stray* proposals for M.L.s were received. I certainly know one firm that put up many proposals from improved picket boats to M.L. minesweepers and M.T.B.s. Up to 1935 there was no money for developments provided by the Treasury. After this date until 1938 one firm mainly were favoured with new development orders; the others had to try out developments on foreign nations or as private ventures. The Royal Corps of Constructors were given every opportunity of following developments, and did so with interest, and I think they will agree acquired considerable useful data free of charge.

Engines.—The history of the development of these specialized craft is interlocked with the engines of high power and light weight that were available. When war was declared in 1939 there were six power units which could be described as light-weight high power.

(*a*) My Company's R.Y. 12, 650-B.P.H. engine which had been developed from the 1918 C.M.B. engine, the power having been increased from 400 H.P. to 650 H.P. The Admiralty had ordered a total of ten engines since 1923, six in two 75-ft. 54-ton 18-knot motor minesweepers in 1937–38, and four in wireless-controlled target boats in 1939.

(*b*) Napier-Lion power boat, marine conversion.

(*c*) Rolls-Royce power boat, marine conversion.

(*d*) Isotta Fraschini, developed at the expense of the Italian Government and introduced in this country as a private venture by Vospers.

(*e*) Paxman C.I. diesel. The Admiralty I believe contributed towards the cost of this development.

(*a*) During the war my company produced 390 R.Y. 12 engines. The difficulties of obtaining materials in competition with M.A.P. who rightly had first priority, were very great for an Admiralty sponsored firm. It was not until the R.A.F. adopted this engine in their air-sea rescue craft in 1942 that any real Government assistance was obtained to acquire materials.

(*b*) Continued in production all the war. Napier were fortunate in being an M.A.P. sponsored firm.

(*c*) Rolls-Royce were not available for marine purposes as all the Merlins were required for the R.A.F.

(*d*) As soon as Italy came into the war supplies naturally ceased. Peter Du Cane's efforts in 1938–39 to persuade the Admiralty to give an order of sufficient size to justify tooling up the engine in this country for production, should be recorded. I doubt, even if this had been done, whether crankshafts, connecting-rod

FIG. 28.—M.G.B. 501

FIG. 29.—"GAY VIKING"

forgings, and alloy steel would have been obtained readily, against M.A.P. priority for aircraft until 1942–43.

(e) This unit was still in the development stage but was used operationally at the latter part of the war.

The author rightly says it was fortunate that U.S.A. engines were available.

The Hall Scott defender 620 B.P.H. had the same cylinder size as the R.Y. 12 engine, and was developed to meet substantial orders placed by the U.S.A. Coast Guard Service in the bootlegging era. The availability of the Packard was no doubt accelerated by Scott Paine going to U.S.A. with his 70-ft P.V. boat in 1939 and his association with the Elco Co. This we have to thank him for, although he is not now contributing to the Chancellor of the Exchequer as a resident British citizen in the United Kingdom.

Before passing on mention must be made of the Sterling Admiral and Hall Scott super-charged engines which were used in limited numbers.

I have dealt with engines at some length in the hope that this history may prevent the Navy being caught in similar circumstances in the event of another war. Military power units of this type have practically no commercial demand, and private enterprise cannot be expected to finance development.

Hull Construction.—The author has not gone into any great constructional detail in describing the different types. He has drawn attention to some defects that showed up during war service. Those firms who were building new boats and also carrying out repairs did gain great experience of the different methods of construction, and my firm hope to contribute a paper on this subject on a future occasion. In time of war a compromise has to be made between methods suitable for volume production, and possibly better methods having regard to maximum strength for the minimum weight. It is suggested that only by regular prototype orders year by year can the disabilities mentioned above of the forced compromise be minimized.

Many "B" type M.L.s are being fitted with diesel engines which will give a boat speed of 10 to 15 knots and will be used commercially or as yachts. It would therefore be fair to compare these hulls with the 72-ft. M.L. for durability. Both types in my view are excellent designs, but I would hazard a guess that the 72-ft. M.L.s will outlive the "B" type Fairmiles by many years owing to the method of construction. The scantlings and method of construction of the 72-ft. M.L.s followed very closely the two experimental 75-ft. motor minesweepers built in 1938. Steamed rock-elm web frames inside the stringers was a feature of C.M.T.B. construction. They were not designed for prefabrication in the same way that the "B" type Fairmiles were. The following details of design may be of interest having regard to some of the defects referred to in the paper. The dovetailing of deck beams in the gunwale, although costly, is in my view well worth while. It is extremely difficult to ensure reliable fastening between the planking and sawn frames. This is one of the snags of this form of construction as compared with close-spaced steamed timber on hulls.

Mention is made of fastening a steamed rock-elm timber on the inboard face of sawn frames as a tension member. It is suggested that more value can be obtained from the rock-elm timbers if they are fastened to the side of the frame outboard and inboard, the outboard timber being through-fastened to the planking, and the inboard timber acting as a tension member. Fastenings into end grain are always unsatisfactory. The method of stiffening up the forward plywood frames of D.M.L.s, as described in the paper, did not in my view make the best use of the weight of the material used, as the planking was not given additional rigidity and support by the frames.

A great deal can be said on the merits of a large number of continuous longitudinal stringers with close-spaced steamed timbers, intercostal panel stiffening being arranged in the bottom between the stringers. M.T.B.s 23 and 24 were an example of this construction, surviving the whole war and many changes of engines. Unfortunately M.T.B. 28, which embodied a number of improvements over these two boats, met with disaster through fire, doing more damage to the Hornet Base than was ever done by enemy action.

Notching the sawn frames for the stringers, as described in the paper, unfortunatly greatly reduces the strength of the frames. In fact it is very difficult to get it both ways, continuous strength fore and aft and athwartships. I am in full agreement with the author that for boats over 80 ft. and 25 knots, composite wood-steel construction is desirable.

May I finish with a word about Mr. Holt. Two trial trips I will not forget when the author of this paper was on board. The first was in a 45-ft. diesel-engined picket boat. We left Green Hythe at 6 a.m. for Portsmouth. The author, who was staying some 20 miles away, bicycled in so as to arrive in time. This was something that I had not expected from the Royal Corps. The second trip was in motor minesweeper No. 1, where, after a roughish trip between Dover and Portsmouth, we arrived with a carbon monoxide casualty; not so good. That incident cost the insurer's company a third of the value of the boat, and involved some loss to my company. But maybe the incident saved other casualties of this nature during the war. The author mentions in his paper fire risk of petrol engines, but not those arising from carbon monoxide poisoning. He may be able to tell us if my surmise is correct.

I know that Mr. Holt believes in going to sea to obtain first-hand knowledge, and is also fully competent to handle any of these craft himself, although for pleasure I understand he prefers to dispense with motors and rely on wind. He must have had a very difficult time during the war answering critics and trying to meet almost impossible requirements at short notice, and I think we are all very indebted to him for his paper.

Rear-Admiral (E.) W. G. Cowland: I should like to make further mention of, and pay tribute to, the Fairmile organization which played such an outstanding part in the conception, growth, and expansion of coastal forces.

Starting as an organization with no marine connections, they not only introduced and proved more or less original methods of construction, but they also, very early on, converted many yacht yards to their views.

The combination of "new" methods of construction, using materials of which many yards had little experience, together with the system of prefabrication, must have caused initially very serious misgiving in the minds of many.

These departures from previous practice and, in particular, the speed at which the building programme was set moving, is a lasting tribute not only to the Fairmile organization but also to the associated yacht yards.

On the engineering side credit is also due. The problems involved in the installation of petrol engines of from 600–1,500 H.P., and up to four in number per boat, together with the necessary screening, petrol tanks and systems, hydraulic pumps and systems, and auxiliary engines, were of no mean order and far beyond the experience of most of the yards concerned. Of minor troubles there were many, but none that was really persistent.

Of the most troublesome was that of designing a correct propeller. This was constantly being aggravated by continual increase in load of the craft, necessitated by operational requirements, involving a change in pitch and in diameter.

The propulsive H.P. curve against propeller R.P.M. of the hard chine craft is not very concaved downwards from a straight line, while the engine H.P. curve against R.P.M. is similar but slightly less concave. Hence with an increase in displacement of the craft (or too "heavy" a propeller) the propulsion curve will cut the engine curve at a reduced R.P.M. and the speed of the craft will suffer seriously because the engines will not be able to obtain their full R.P.M., and cannot therefore give their B.H.P.

Mr. J. H. B. Chapman, R.C.N.C. (Member): I served with the British Admiralty delegation in the U.S.A. during the war and some remarks about the coastal-force craft built in that country and transferred to Great Britain under Lend-Lease may be of interest. In all ten 77-ft. Elco M.T.B.s, fifty-six 70-ft. Vosper M.T.B.s, and seventy-four 72-ft. motor launches were assigned to this country. Six of the 70-ft. Vosper M.T.B.s built under a British requisition were transferred to the Russian Navy.

In general, the craft were built by yacht and boat yards with little, if any, previous experience of this type of work. Among the better-known firms were the Anapolis Yacht Yard and Herresoffs. The Elco M.T.B.s were, of course, to American design, and supplied under one of the first requisitions. The remainder were built to Admiralty and Vosper drawings and some of the equipment was provided from this country. Naturally, owing to the rapid expansion of the shipbuilding industry in the U.S.A., difficulties occurred with the supply of suitable materials, particularly seasoned timber, and

also due to the lack of experienced labour. However, we received the fullest co-operation and help from the Bureau of Ships, Navy Department, Washington, and the U.S. Navy supervisors of shipbuilding responsible for overseeing the work. The shipyards did all they could to meet our requirements, which differed in many respects from those of the U.S. Navy.

The Vosper M.T.B.s were engined with Packard 4M—2,500 type W. 14 engines rating 1,550 H.P. at 2,500 R.P.M. At first we did not get the speeds anticipated but a fortunate visit from Mr. Gawn of the Admiralty Experiment Works, Haslar, and the co-operation of the Federal Mogul Company (Marine Division) enabled us to track down the cause of the trouble, which was principally due to errors in pitch of the propellers and incorrect edge finish. Some improvement was also obtained by tracking the rudders. Commander Du Cane visited the U.S.A. several times during the building of the M.T.B.s. These visits, added to the experience of the officers appointed to command the M.T.B.s on completion, were most valuable to all concerned with the construction and fitting out of these craft.

Mr. F. C. C. Rogers, R.C.N.C. (Associate-Member): A very noticeable feature of these craft has been the great amount of damage which these vessels could stand up to and yet survive. One motor gunboat was cut through from deck to below the chine, but the main bulkheads remained intact and the vessel found her way back to port. Other cases of almost equally severe damage could be recounted. One of the most important decisions regarding the hulls was the insistence on a double skin which contributed greatly to their strength. The author is to be thanked for putting on record a considerable amount of information which will be of value in the days of peace which lie ahead.

Constructor Commander E. C. S. Hepden, R.C.N.C.: This paper has been read with great interest and has brought to mind the difficult but interesting period (1943–45) when, as a junior dockyard officer at Malta, the Manager of the Construction Department made me responsible to him for the hull repairs of such coastal force craft as the dockyard labour force would permit.

Captain, Coastal Forces, Mediterranean, had no constructor officer on his staff, and soon I was working in very close co-operation with this organization, staff headquarters being in Malta. Several visits to coastal force bases in Italy were made, chiefly to advise on damage repairs and to organize the hull spares and stores required for them. During these periods I had the opportunity of seeing advanced and intermediate bases together with the difficulties under which they worked.

The maintenance and repair difficulties were enormous; shortages of almost everything, together with transport and communications difficulties, were common in the early days. At first, major repairs could only be carried out at Malta Dockyard, largely owing to shortage of overseeing staff. There were few well-equipped yards where good repairs were possible, and, except for one at Bari and some in French North Africa, the coastal force organization had to be content with small schooner building yards around the coast. These yards were not well equipped and were accustomed to a class of work much heavier than that for our craft. There was a great tendency in these yards to avoid the difficulties of working deck stiffening continuously, and, where deck obstructions occurred, the stiffening would be cut away or stopped short. Compensation was truly not a word in the vocabulary of the Italian yard foreman. Broken frames were often doubled up with a 6-in. to 9-in. length of $\frac{1}{4}$-in. $\times$ 2 in. or similar strip steel with one or two bolts at the most either side; it was not surprising that these worked loose.

Stores were exceedingly difficult to obtain in Italy, and many of those required for hull work came from Malta. In the very early stages, when the coastal force craft first came into Malta, demands for hull stores were made on the United Kingdom and when these did not materialize, which occurred all too frequently due to enemy action, fresh demands were forwarded. Eventually, it often happened that our initial, duplicate, and sometimes triplicate, demands arrived one after the other. This was indeed fortunate, for Malta was then in a position, so far as hulls were concerned, to supply much of the Mediterranean requirements until the spare parts distribution centre organization was in full working order.

The weakness of the forward frames and the deck in way of the engine-room of the "D" boats broke suddenly on us and coincided with Constructor Captain Holt's arrival in the Mediterranean area. After his examination of some of the craft, carried out in conditions which were far from ideal, he advised us how to stiffen the "D" boats and so keep them operating. Fairmile's excellent kit of parts for this work had, I believe, at this time not been conceived, and Malta started by manufacturing her own stiffening. They were difficult days; no $\frac{3}{8}$ in. bolts of the required length for securing stiffening were available, they all had to be made and thousands were required. The small bolt-making machine had been "blitzed," so we had to use one too big for this work. There was no tool steel of a size suitable to make the dies, an existing die block had to have a piece milled out and a die piece for the $\frac{3}{8}$ in. bolt head fitted. Careful work was required as the machine was too powerful and fins were liable to be formed on the bolt head. Apprentices were sent to all ships docking to collect old zincs so as to keep our small galvanizing bath going; the small stock of zinc held by the yard was required for zinc protectors and could not be spared for galvanizing. It was not long before we ran out of bolt stave; a cycle trip round the dumps in the vicinity of the harbour revealed a pile of what appeared to be steel bar for reinforced concrete work. Sufficient for our needs was quickly commandeered.

After struggling for many months under difficult conditions, the Fairmile kits of parts for alterations and additions slowly filtered through and thereafter the work proceeded more smoothly. It was found that the Fairmile deck stiffening was insufficient and it had to be extended to cover the midship two-thirds of the deck.

The demand for always bigger and better guns was probably as strong in the Mediterranean as elsewhere. It was always difficult to persuade coastal force officers that one could not place a certain gun mounting on the deck, secure it with a few bolts to keep it steady in a seaway, and then fire the gun without doing damage to the boat. Officially there were strict regulations as to the armament allowed for these craft; when new mountings were approved, it took many months for them to arrive in Malta. In the meantime, operations necessitated bigger mountings and something had to be done with such mountings as were available. Army bofors were fitted forward in "B" type M.L.s to replace some of the 1895 (or thereabout) vintage pieces. Italian Breda's were fitted forward in Vosper M.T.B.s; hand-operated oerlikons replaced power-operated twin machine guns so that, in the event of the boat's being caught with engines stopped and no power on the guns, some immediate defence was possible.

The demand for minesweeping in the Mediterranean called for the conversion of "B" type M.L.s. The vessels then available were not up to the all-purpose standard of the later types, the special fittings were not available, and again wrecks in the harbour were searched for suitable reels to assist in the conversion of M.L.s to minesweepers.

Slipping and docking of small M.T.B.s presented a very difficult problem. They cannot be docked on their keels, a cradle being required. All docking facilities were very limited and the time required to build a cradle in a dock, together with the resulting loss of space, was, in many cases, not consistent with the overall docking requirements in the Mediterranean. This again tended to force the coastal force craft to the small, ill-equipped ports, where there were small slips with operators not very mindful of the relatively delicate nature of an M.T.B. Small numbers of cradles were sent to the Mediterranean specially for slipping or lifting, but as the war front moved forward, so the boats had to move, and because of the unwieldy nature of these cradles, they were very slow to follow. For slipping or lifting, boats had to come back many miles to an established base. At Malta, the yard manager was sympathetic to these small craft and gave them the fore end of No. 1 Dock, and, in addition, flat-topped lighters were used to house boat and cradle lifted out of the water by crane. This arrangement kept the quays of the large cranes free and the larger units of the Navy were able to refit alongside unhampered by a large quay obstruction.

Many were the difficulties faced by those associated with coastal force craft, but throughout all remained cheerful. I too would like to add my tribute to those officers and men who operated these boats; their keenness knew no bounds. They were intensely interested in all alterations or additions to their boats and would only accept that arrangement which gave the greater fighting efficiency.

Author's Written Reply to the Discussion

Consideration of coastal forces may be fragmented into a whole cluster of problems (operational uses, sea-keeping ability, maintenance, design characteristics, engines, possible lines of development in the future, and so on). The cluster has been partly investigated, and now at any rate there is the whole background of war experience behind us, but when looking ahead it is true to say that the cluster of problems lies in a mist; it is a region of some facts, some surmise and much controversy. In such circumstances the very informative discussion on this paper on coastal forces design is of great value, and the record of the discussion in the TRANSACTIONS will be helpful to the designers and operational officers of coastal force craft in the future. We have been privileged to have had an expression of the views of the senior officers who were in general control, in control of design, and in control of maintenance during the critical period; their views in general and on policy for future development in particular are important.

Sir Charles Lillicrap states that the author went to sea in some of the craft designed. The author holds strong opinions on the importance of a designer of small craft having first hand knowledge of the craft he has designed, at any rate in the development stage of a new type. There is a well-known book of advice to seamen written around the text of "Know your own ship." Making a slight play upon words, the designer of small sea-going craft would be well advised to "Know the behaviour of your own ship."

Engines

Admiral Tower has given an idea of the nightmare position as regards engine supply in the early days of the war, and Mr. Thornycroft has indicated the small volume of buying of high power marine engines to be anticipated in peace time. These contributions help to point the clear line on policy on future engine development which is contained in the contribution of Sir Stanley Goodall. A small volume of peace time buying could not finance an engine development policy involving sums of the order half a million or a million pounds.

Admiral Cowland and Mr. Gawn have drawn attention to a design problem imposed by the use of highly supercharged engines in hard chine or step hull M.T.B.s. Expressed from the point of view of the designer the trouble is as follows:—

1. A highly supercharged engine shows the feature of a very steep torque-R.P.M. characteristic curve, for the maximum permissible boost of the engine (see Curve A B of the accompanying figure).
2. The combination of M.T.B. hull and its associated propeller has also a certain torque-R.P.M. characteristic curve, i.e. for each R.P.M. at which we succeed in turning the M.T.B. propeller a certain torque must be supplied. (C.D.E. in figure is the hull-propeller torque R.P.M. characteristic.) This torque-R.P.M. characteristic shows humps and hollows which are also features of the

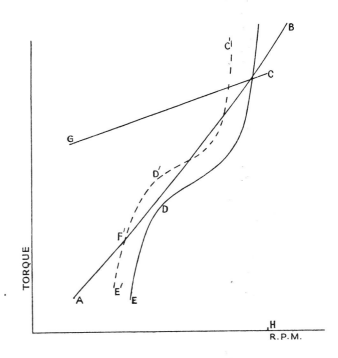

resistance humps of the hull form of the M.T.B. when plotted to a base of speed (or R.P.M.).

3. On examining the figure it will be clear that if we design a propeller to be suitable for maximum engine R.P.M.(H) and maximum power, i.e. for condition C of the maximum permissible boost curve, any increase of displacement or any condition of driving the M.T.B. into a head sea will raise the torque-R.P.M. characteristic of the hull to a new position indicated by the dotted line C′, D′, F′, E′, with the result that the maximum speed without over boosting is given by the position F′.
4. From the point of view of the designer, an engine most suitable for use in an M.T.B. would have a torque R.P.M. characteristic curve more of the nature C G. A characteristic low slope curve of this nature could take account of increases of displacement or increases of resistance due to fouling, head seas and so on, without much reduction of top speed. The problem is to find a propulsive unit with these amiable torque characteristics yet retaining the virtues of high horse-power and very low weight.

Structure

Sir Charles Lillicrap, Commander Du Cane, and Mr. Thornycroft have made references to structure.

The development of structure and "teething" troubles with structure in M.T.B.s was in many respects a repetition of the history of development of structure in early aeroplanes and early machines and structures of many kinds. For such pioneer structures the book of calculations, mathematical and arithmetical approaches to the problem of design have limited application, and the designer is to some extent driven to design using his existing judgment. Inevitably in sailing these uncharted seas rocks are struck here and there. It was thought by the author that it was likely to be of more interest to the navigator of the future (the naval architect with a structure to design) that he should be aware of the rocks in these partly charted seas. Accordingly an account was given of the main structural weaknesses revealed during the development of coastal forces. As Sir Charles Lillicrap infers, in the main the structures served very well.

Commander Du Cane and Mr. Rogers instance cases where coastal force craft withstood heavy damage; to these examples of virtue may be added a case where an M.L. was torpedoed aft and remained afloat five hours, and an incident in the Mediterranean during the Sicily landing where an M.L. was rammed by a destroyer and cut through in the engine-room from keel to deck at middle line. This M.L. was towed to a North African port and when the author inspected her on the slip a band of optimists were discussing repairs.

Sea-keeping Qualities

Admiral Tower and Commander Du Cane have compared the sea-keeping qualities of the 70-ft. and 115-ft. types of M.T.B.

The author's view is that the 70-ft. M.T.B. and the several types of 115-ft. M.T.B. are well able to merely ride the sea in very bad weather. They are light on the water (some have a buoyancy reserve of the order 400 per cent), they have large range of stability, good G M, and the hard chine types are very free from rolling, but riding the sea is not necessarily the same thing as being operational in a seaway. The criterion of value of an M.T.B. as an effective operational craft *in a seaway* hinges upon its ability, or otherwise, to proceed to windward at high speed to gain position to intercept and attack a ship, itself of fairly high speed, which initially holds the weather gauge. It is in respect of this criterion of value that the small M.T.B.s are at a disadvantage. As an example, the author has a very pleasant memory of a passage across the Bay of Biscay in 1937 in one of the early 60-ft. M.T.B.s. There was a following wind, force 4–5 Beaufort, and a moderate following sea. The little craft behaved very well. A degree of nursing the craft and easing down on speed was found to be necessary when running down the faces of the big waves, to prevent the boat gaining too much momentum and plunging her nose into the wave back in front of her, but on the average good speed was made on the passage. Later on, continuing the passage to the Mediterranean, these small M.T.B.s were called upon to make headway through the Straits of Gibraltar against a Levanter; they were driven to making tacks to windward and made Gibraltar with difficulty. A more or less flat-bottomed craft is not of ideal shape for driving to windward at high speed in a seaway. It is on this question of size that the author must join issue with Commander Du Cane. It is agreed that 70-ft. and 115-ft. types of M.T.B.s are small in relation to the waves encountered on occasion, but the author does not concur in the idea that an increase of length from 70 ft. to 115 ft., other

things remaining unchanged except *pro rata* increase of engine power for extra displacement, exercises no influence on behaviour to windward. (To follow along the line of Commander Du Cane's argument, it might be said with just as much reason that an increase of waterline length from 30 ft. to 40 ft. in a sailing yacht would have no influence on the ability of the boat in beating to windward in a seaway, with which conclusion no sailorman would agree.) Another disadvantageous feature of the 70-ft. M.T.B. as compared with the larger M.T.B.s (for working to windward) is that the 70-ft. boats are a closer approach to a flat bottom than the 115-ft. boats, which are sharper V section in transverse view or are of round bilge type. The small M.T.B.s have many virtues and in a light seaway are good on all points of sailing, but under moderate head sea conditions they have their limitations; the big boats also are limited by head sea conditions, but to a lesser extent.

Maintenance

During the war, Admiral Tower, Captain Maurice, and Mr. King, each in his own sphere, were in control of maintenance, and their contributions to the discussion on this particular aspect of coastal forces operations are informative and important.

Captain Maurice makes a good point where he stresses the effect of a multiplicity of types of craft and types of engines in increasing maintenance. The author seems to remember one occasion, when Captain Maurice and he were discussing ways and means together, and when affairs on maintenance were more than usually difficult, Captain Maurice remarked: "The trouble with you, Holt, and with all designers is that you are always trying to design something better."

The N.L. pontoons mentioned by Mr. King are a good solution of the docking problem in non-tidal waters and with sufficient depth available.

Experiments on Hull Form and Propellers

Mr. Gawn has given us an outline of the problems with which the designers of coastal force craft burdened the shoulders of himself and his staff. It is difficult to express full appreciation of the great debt owed to the Admiralty Experiment Works over the development of the coastal force designs. At the outset the field of investigation—the relation of form to resistance for high speed craft of M.T.B. type—was largely virgin country; there had been no methodical series of resistance experiments on a whole family of models, and no great numbers of any sort of models of planing boat types had been tested.

In these circumstances it will be appreciated that the large amount of information on M.T.B. hull forms and information on the drive characteristics of propellers which are being driven perilously near the point of prohibitive cavitation, which has become available as a result of the war-time efforts of Mr. Gawn and his staff, has been invaluable to coastal force designers. In particular the author wishes to pay tribute to the value of the recently installed cavitation tunnel. When first he saw this tunnel under construction he reflected it was a very well thought out design, but could not help wondering whether it would be of immediate help to a designer. The sequel was that the author was nearly the first customer of the cavitation tunnel, with the problem of a highly cavitating propeller in a steam gun boat. The Admiralty Experiment Works set to work on the problem and achieved a speed gain of about three knots.

Habitability

Mr. Sears speaks with good authority on the subject of habitability in M.T.B.s as he was in charge of the coastal force design section under the Director of Naval Construction.

The accommodation arrangements in any small craft in British waters during the winter months are rarely very satisfactory; the thin skin of the boat does not give adequate insulation from the outside cold, and in conjunction with inadequate ventilation and a large number of men occupying a small space there is inevitably a large degree of "sweating" on the underside of deck and down the sides, which leads to damp bedding. The author has had winter experience of living on a yacht and also winter experience of life in an M.T.B. stationed in far northern waters. The conditions were not ideal, but not much hardship was involved. The cure for sweating is to be found in insulation of the boat's side, adequate ventilation and a coal stove; these features are possibilities in an M.L. but not allowable in an M.T.B., on account of weight considerations.

In the author's opinion the weakest feature of M.T.B. accommodation and amenities lies in the galley. Even a first class cook with good sea legs would have found it difficult in light weather to prepare a meal in the galley of a small M.T.B., and in moderate weather, with the contents jumping out of the pan and the pan jumping off the stove, cooking was out of the question. The Hostilities Only cooks of the M.T.B.s deserved sympathy; they were untrained conscripts to the galley; they rarely acquired sea legs to the degree required of a cook in a small boat, and their understandable ambition was to escape the job of cook as soon as possible.

Loading

The table of loading contained in the remarks of Commander Du Cane furnishes a good indication of the growth of striking ability as the war progressed. From the point of view of speed performance, heavy loading was bad but, on the other hand, a lightly loaded boat which shows a knot or two advantage in calm water speed but which runs about the seas at high speed without ability to see in the dark and without the striking ability to hit the enemy and really hurt does not seem to be operationally worth while.

Bearing on the remarks of Mr. Thornycroft on weights added, it has been the author's experience as a designer that it is the inevitable fate of the would-be ideal design to lose its fine edge and balance due to added weights. On the other hand, it is the function of design to be servant of the operational requirement *as far as possible and as far as good reason will allow.*

Production

Mr. Whiting and Mr. Chapman have given interesting sidelights on the production aspects of coastal forces which do not require comment from the author.

General

The discussion contains many other points of interest but which do not appear to call for critical comment.

On a lighter note and bearing on the rough weather trials of M.T.B. 102, the author's recollection, and he has so low an opinion of his treacherous memory that he has checked the memory by the official report of the trial, is that M.T.B. 102 and a 60-ft. British Power Boat Company M.T.B. were the boats on trial and the destroyer was sent out by a thoughtful C.-in-C. Portsmouth to provide a rescue party in case of accident. I do not recognize the pen portrait of the Naval Constructor on this rough weather trial; as with so many efforts at portraiture it has not altogether reflected the soul of the subject.

Sir Charles Lillicrap has provoked a vision of a 60-ft. M.T.B. on its rough weather trials. The author feels fairly happy in the contemplation of a 60-knot design of the future which does some rough weather trials, but, having a healthy respect for the destructive power of a blow from the sea at high speed, would not be happy in the contemplation of a small craft proceeding at 60 knots to windward in a moderate seaway. At very high speeds, probably it would be better to lift the small craft completely clear of the troublesome water surface. If an attempt were made to run to windward at 60 knots in a moderate seaway, the author doubts whether there would be enough of himself left afterwards to tell the story to the Institution.

Acknowledgments

The author heartily concurs in the appreciation of the Fairmile organization. The Fairmile scheme of prefabrication was brilliant in conception and was also most ably organized. Mr. Scantlebury has a warm corner in his heart for a wooden ship and he did his very best in the face of growing shortages of timber to cling on to a good standard of quality in all Fairmile built craft.

Commander Du Cane showed great initiative in the development of M.T.B. 102, which had a big bearing on the success of the 70-ft. type of M.T.B. It was certainly very fortunate for the Admiralty that the leading builders of M.T.B. type craft were prepared to risk big sums of money in building experimental M.T.B.s for trial.

The author acknowledges with gratitude the help he has received from Mr. Charles Nicholson. In spite of Mr. Nicholson's great experience of design he has always been diffident in expressing his opinions in public, but in the author's private talks with him he has always freely given his informed, sane, and kindly advice.

The great help received from Mr. Thornycroft and other private designers in the matter of invitations to attend trials is fully appreciated. The sea experience of various types of planing and semi-planing boats has been most valuable.

Mr. Sears was loaned to Admiralty "for duration" and has now returned to his old post in the Patent Office. I should like to pay tribute to his very able handling of coastal force design problems during the war. He worked hard and cheerfully, his grasp of detail was excellent, and his co-operation with Fairmile and the design organizations of private builders always made for smooth flow of the production line. Mr. Sears was a modest but important and efficient link in the chain of design and production of coastal forces craft.

The author wishes to pay tribute to the able control of coastal force design and production effort exercised by Sir Stanley Goodall and Admiral Tower during the critical early period of development. With the play of a large number of ideas, little in the way of material resources and conditions of extreme emergency, any major wrong decision might have led to serious conse-quences. The best commentary on the quality of the control exercised is to be found in the fleet of craft produced and in their operational achievement.

Admiral Tower must have lost count of the numbers of discussions on coastal force design and production problems over which he presided and kept the peace. It was a tribute to his good understanding of "horse" nature and his general good temper that the many horses of various dispositions in the team were kept in harmony and pushing hard against their collars.

The author's thanks are due to his chief, Sir Charles Lillicrap, for the encouragement given to prepare this paper and for his kind remarks in his contribution to the discussion.

In conclusion the author expresses his thanks for the kindly reception of the paper on Coastal Force Design and for the many and most valuable contributions to the discussion.

FIG. 30.—PREFABRICATED ASSEMBLY

Notes on the Development of Landing Craft
by R Baker, OBE, RCNC, MINA

Originally published in *Transactions*, Volume 89, Number 3,
July 1947, pages 218-258

NOTES ON THE DEVELOPMENT OF LANDING CRAFT

By R. Baker, O.B.E., R.C.N.C., Member*

(*Read at the Spring Meeting of the Eighty-eighth Session of the Institution of Naval Architects, March 27, 1947, Sir Stanley V. Goodall, K.C.B., O.B.E., Vice-President, in the Chair.*)

Although all landing craft are not boats, all boats are landing craft, and the use of a boat for landing is its fundamental function. Combined operations have featured in almost every war from earliest antiquity until the present day, but only the developments of the last few years have necessitated using special craft for special landings in the face of the enemy. Earliest invasion craft have usually been ferry craft commandeered for the occasion.

Briefly, therefore, the whole of the development of special landing craft as we know them has taken place since 1938. There were certain projects considered during the 1914–18 war and between its close and 1938, viz.: the X-lighter, the Y-lighter, and the motor landing craft (M.L.C.). In this war there has been no development of the first two, but the M.L.C., first proposed in 1924, is of importance because some of the subsequent craft were developed from it.

These craft fall into three main categories:

(1) Primarily personnel carriers.
(2) Primarily vehicle carriers.
(3) Support craft.

Each group is subdivided into types A and B; A craft to operate from ship to shore, B types from shore to shore.

In the following the three types are dealt with separately and roughly in chronological order within the groups.

Group 1.—Personnel Carriers A

Motor Landing Craft (M.L.C.1)

In the 1914–18 and all earlier wars for amphibious operations, the soldiers were carried in the ships and put ashore in the ships' boats, except that in the first Great War the Y-lighter (a simplified boat) was used a little. In 1924, an inter-service committee was set up to review the provision required for opposed landings. This was the Landing Craft Committee. Somewhat naturally, attention was first turned to landing personnel, and the result was the design and construction of M.L.C.1 (Fig. 1) to carry 100 troops. This craft was built by J. S. White of Cowes and completed early in 1926. The light weight was 16 tons and she was intended to be used from a troop-ship which would carry her to near

* Chief Constructor, Naval Construction Department, Admiralty.

the beaches. Gill type jet propulsion was used; the speed was poor (4¾ knots).

The requirements were then stepped up and it was desired that the craft should carry either 100 troops or a 12-ton tank. The resulting design was developed mainly as a vehicle carrier (q.v.).

Assault Landing Craft (L.C.A.)

At various times between 1926 and 1938, the Army members of the Landing Craft Committee put forward plans for improved boats for landing troops, but these came to nothing until in 1938 the old committee was disbanded and a new organization set up. This new organization, the Inter-Service Training and Development Centre, soon recommended that first importance be given to the development of a ship-borne boat to carry one infantry platoon and land it in not more than 18 in. of water. The boat was to weigh less than 10 tons so that ordinary lifeboat davits could be used to lift her.

This was investigated first by Mr. Fleming of Fleming propulsion, who for a long time had been trying to get the Admiralty interested in landing boats propelled by his system.

Definite proposals were put forward in November 1938. The boat was expected to carry 40 men on a displacement of 8 tons and dimensions 27 ft. × 9 ft. 6 in. × 2 ft. 9 in. Model tests proved her unseaworthy. Fleming then put forward an improved design and at this time J. S. White and Thornycroft were each asked for designs. The Thornycroft boat was preferred and orders for prototypes of the Fleming (M.L.C.50) and Thornycroft boat (M.L.C.51) were placed in the middle of 1939. Comparative trials were carried out in August. The Fleming boat was of Birmabright and unprotected, the Thornycroft of wood (double diagonal) and protected by ¼ in. protective plating. Neither boat was entirely satisfactory, and after the trials it was decided to modify them for use as prototype support craft.

Meanwhile, the Admiralty had considered the reports of the trial and a new design for assault landing craft was produced by D.N.C. in conjunction with Thornycrofts. This was based generally on the original Thornycroft boat, but included the lessons of the trials. An order for a prototype to this design was placed at the end of September 1939.

Fig. 2 is a general arrangement of the Fleming boat.

Fig. 31 is a photograph of A.L.C.2, the first Admiralty boat. The type was from this time on known as A.L.C., until early in 1942 when the names of all types were

MOTOR LANDING CRAFT
M.L.C. (1)

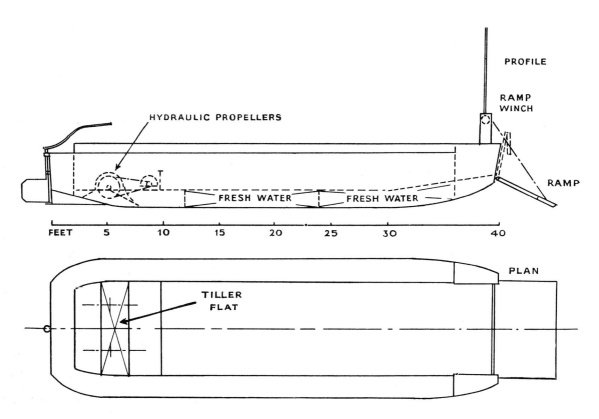

Fig. 1

reclassified. Assault craft were from then onwards landing craft assault (L.C.A.).

A.L.C.2 had a total weight of about 9 tons and was 38 ft. 9 in. × 10 ft. × 4 ft. 7¾ in. depth. She was protected with ¼ in. Hadfields Resista, and was propelled by two Ford V.8 engines which gave her a maximum speed of about 11½ knots. Buoyant material, Onozote, was fitted in sufficient quantity to enable the full load to be supported with the boat swamped. Although the first order for a prototype was only placed at the end of September, further orders were placed with Thornycroft during October. The first boat was completed in April 1940. Experience with her led to demand for various modifications, for example, the control position was moved from aft to forward, protection was improved, a Bren gun position was included, etc. At first, chain slings were used, but these were, very much later, replaced by bars. Fundamentally, however, the boat was not altered, although the continued addition of requirements added to the weight, and when operational experience was gained it was found that the troops when completely equipped continued to weigh more and more. Thus at the end of the war the all-up weight of the boat was about 13½ tons, and the original staff requirement regarding the use of existing davits was, perforce, given up.

In order to improve delivery prospects, Thornycroft sub-let some of the orders to small yacht- and boat-building firms. This procedure was followed until in 1941 when over 200 boats had been ordered and requirements as regards numbers were very much increased, some alternative capacity had to be found. The Admiralty then placed contracts direct, and widened the field by encouraging mass production in the works of some of the firms already engaged by Thornycroft, and by bringing in public works contractors, joinery firms and furniture makers, many of whom had never had a boatbuilding job before. The first few boats produced from this source leaked a little, but after the teething troubles were over the firms had a remarkable record. The design was kept under review so as to facilitate production and the later boats had plywood sides, supplied in one piece. Altogether 1,929 were built and during 1944 production averaged 60 boats per month.

Fig. 3 is a general arrangement of the L.C.A. in its final form and Fig. 32 a photograph.

L.C.P.(M) or Coble

In 1941, after the L.C.A. had been used operationally in Northern European waters, there was a period when it seemed that many of our operations would consist of raids on rocky coasts in exposed positions. The suggestion was made that the L.C.A. was not the most suitable type of boat because of her flat bottom; a coble type was suggested. A Northumberland Coble was taken and slightly modified as a prototype and subsequently a boat on these lines was designed in the Admiralty. The first orders were placed in August 1941; by the time the boats began to come into service conditions had changed again, and the type, which of all the

special craft was the nearest to an ordinary boat, was not much used; a total of 60 were completed.

Fig. 4 is a general arrangement of this boat and Fig. 33 a photograph.

American Types

Before Lease-Lend, there was a British Supply Mission in Washington, and the Admiralty naturally tried to meet some of their outstanding demands through this channel. It was not practicable at this time to get craft to British design, but it was found that Higgins of New Orleans had a standard product which might be useful. This was the celebrated Eureka, a hard chine motor boat about 37 ft. long fitted with a Kermath engine of 225 B.H.P. and capable of a speed of 18 knots in the light condition. These boats could carry about 30 men, and, although the speed was very much reduced as the displacement went up, and they had no protection, it was thought that boats of the type would be of great use as raiding craft. An initial order was placed for 50, and the first of these was delivered in October 1940. Exactly similar boats were then being sold by Higgins to the United States Navy for the same purpose.

Slight modifications were made in the craft to enable them to meet British requirements more fully (e.g. the slinging arrangements) and from the very beginning the boats were a very great success. Although the sides were planked in plywood the bottom was of normal timbered construction and they were extremely robust. According to Higgins, they could be driven at any beach, however steep or flat, so as to land personnel dryshod. This was not literally true, but the boats were in fact very often driven over sandbanks.

Fig. 5 is a general arrangement of the British type L.C.P.(L), as it was subsequently called, and Fig. 34 a photograph.

Several follow-on orders were placed and, when the Lease-Lend Act was passed, very large demands were laid. When the Americans entered the war they were very much influenced by what had already been done here as regards the provision of assault craft, and they modified the original Higgins boat by the incorporation of a light personnel ramp in the bow (this idea being borrowed from the L.C.A.). Then the L.C.P.(L) became the L.C.P.(R). Later on an even larger ramp was fitted so that the boat could carry a jeep or handcart. This version, which had become standard by the end of the war, was the L.C.V.(P), the original Kermath engine being replaced by the Gray diesel.

All the American boats had the advantage over the L.C.A. that they were lighter and had much more power. Although a little protection was fitted from time to time no attempt was made to armour fully any American craft. Events proved that, in spite of the success of the L.C.A., American type boats were generally more satisfactory for operation under the conditions they had to meet, and at the end of the war, when large-scale British operations were planned in the Western Pacific, the demand was beginning to arise for British production to be changed over; this never actually arose.

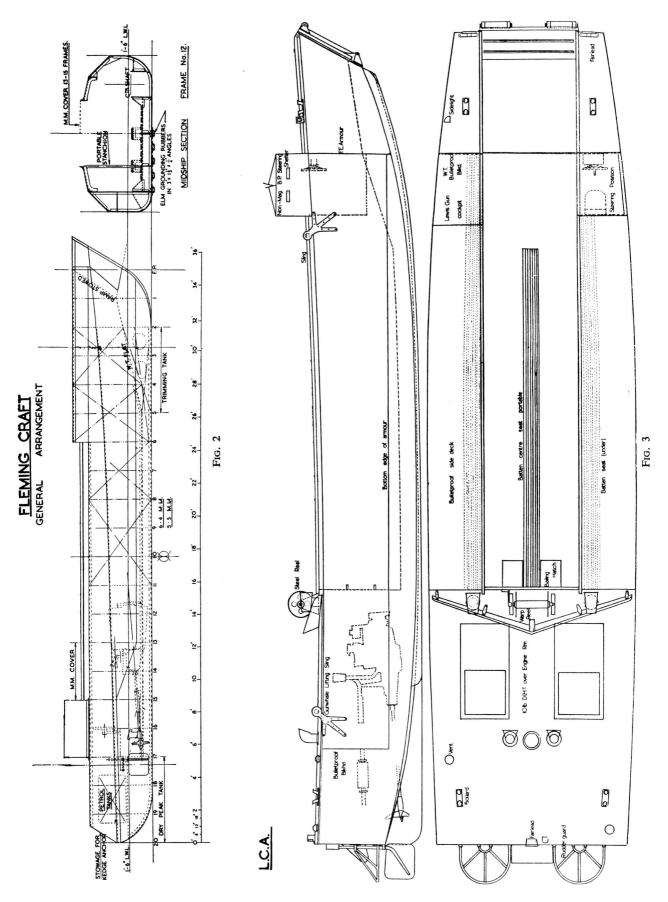

FLEMING CRAFT
GENERAL ARRANGEMENT

FIG. 2

L.C.A.

FIG. 3

L.C.P.(M.)
Landing Craft Personnel, (Medium).

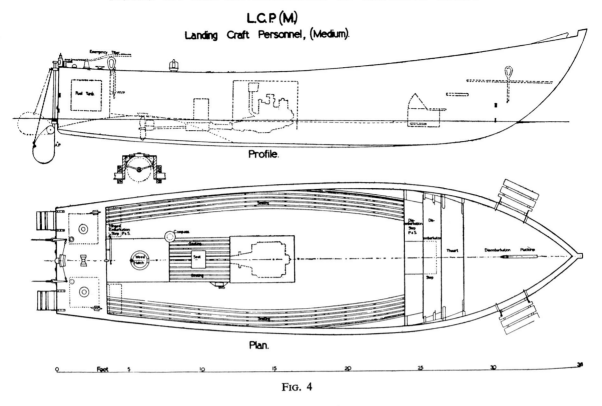

Profile.

Plan.

FIG. 4

L.C.P.(L.)
LANDING CRAFT PERSONNEL, (LARGE.)
U.K. Type.

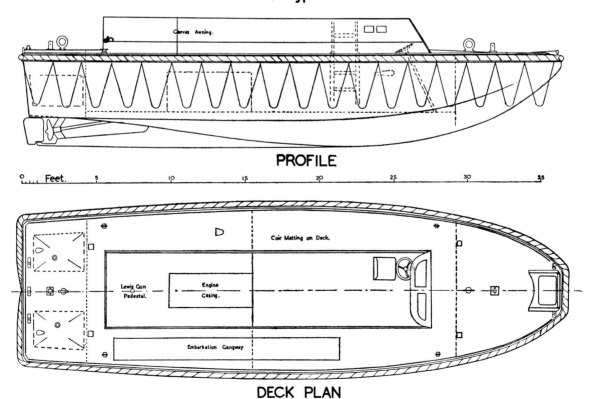

PROFILE

DECK PLAN

FIG. 5

L.C.P.(S)

Early in 1942, before L.C.A. production had been organized, and before the vast capabilities of American industry were fully realized, it was decided to augment the assault craft programmes by the provision of "Second Flight Boats," later known as L.C.P.(S). These boats had to be such that they could be lifted by L.C.A. davits and stowed on deck and also that they could be lifted by the general run of merchant ship davits, either of the gravity or luffing types This limited the length to about 28 ft. 6 in. They were of simple construction, hard chine, plywood planked throughout, and were propelled by a single 60–90 H.P. motor-car engine. With a crew of two, 30 fully equipped troops could be carried.

The details of the design were worked out by Messrs. Aldous Successors, Brightlingsea, and most of the boats were built by non-shipyard labour in building contractors' shops. The first orders were placed May 1942, and the first deliveries were made in August 1942. Some of these boats were specially fitted up for ambulance service, but, apart from these, the boats were never used in the manner originally planned, because of the large numbers of L.C.A. and the American types which were ultimately forthcoming. They were, however, widely used as general service harbour craft.

Fig. 6 is a general arrangement of one of these boats and Fig. 35 a photograph.

Group I B.—Larger Types of Personnel Carriers

Landing Craft Infantry (Large)—L.C.I.(L)

The early success of the Germans in the war gave the impetus to the developments already described, not only because the craft could be used for an ultimate re-invasion, but because if ship-borne, in suitable vessels, they could be used for raids on enemy-held territory far from a home base. In 1942, when the whole of Western Europe was occupied, it was thought that comparatively large-scale raids from a home base would be fruitful. Various demands were, therefore, put forward for Giant Raiding Craft as they were called.

At this time the whole of the shipbuilding industry was fully employed, and, in addition, a large proportion of the structural engineering capacity and joinery trades were already engaged in what was really shipbuilding. When first proposed the raiding craft was not proceeded with, because its construction could not be undertaken. In April 1942, however, a firm requirement was produced for a boat to carry 200 fully equipped men, as against the 35 of the L.C.A., to have a speed of 17 knots and beaching draughts not much greater than L.C.A.

Messrs. Thornycroft made some early investigations into wooden craft, but it was finally agreed that steel hulls would be necessary if the load was to be carried on the stipulated draughts. This would have meant conflict with destroyer building.

The outcome was that American help was sought and, before the end of 1942, they produced the first of the new type, L.C.I.(L). This vessel practically met the British staff requirements and the design was developed from drawings first prepared in this country.

Principal particulars:—

Length	158 ft. 6 in.
Beam	23 ft. 8 in.
Loaded displacement ..	384 tons
Power	1,440 B.H.P.
Speed	14 knots
Beaching draughts ..	F. 4 ft. 9 in. / A. 6 ft. 6 in.
Number of Troops carried	182 (or 210 in Nos. 354 *et seq.*)
Crew	3 officers and 21 men

Fig. 7 is a general arrangement and Fig. 36 a photograph.

Landing Craft Infantry (Small)—L.C.I.(S)

Concurrently, the staff requirements were reduced so that it would be possible to build some craft of this type here. The help of Fairmiles was sought and they produced the design known as L.C.I.(S). Orders were placed in May 1942 and the first boat was delivered in February 1943.

Principal particulars:—

Length	105 ft. 1 in.
Beam	21 ft. 5 in.
Loaded Displacement ..	110 tons
Power	1,140 B.H.P. (unsupercharged)
Speed	14·5 knots
Beaching draughts ..	F. 3 ft. 3 in. / A. 3 ft. 10 in.
Number of Troops carried	6 officers and 96 men
Crew	2 officers and 15 men

Fig. 8 is a general arrangement and Fig. 37 a photograph.

The design includes several features of interest; all the items were prefabricated on the usual Fairmile system. The scantlings were in some instances reduced below what was then being fitted in coastal force craft, and the whole of the deck and sides were planked in plywood, laid double diagonal. In spite of the light scantlings, the craft had to carry very heavy personnel loads and also a considerable weight of protection in the form of $\frac{1}{4}$-in. D.1 H.T. steel fitted as scales.

In a few details the scantlings were cut too much for the heavy work expected of the craft, but on the whole they were satisfactory.

Neither the L.C.I.(L) nor L.C.I.(S) were ever used quite in the manner originally intended, but, the former in particular, were used for nearly everything else, and the performance and production of the craft was a great credit to our Allies.

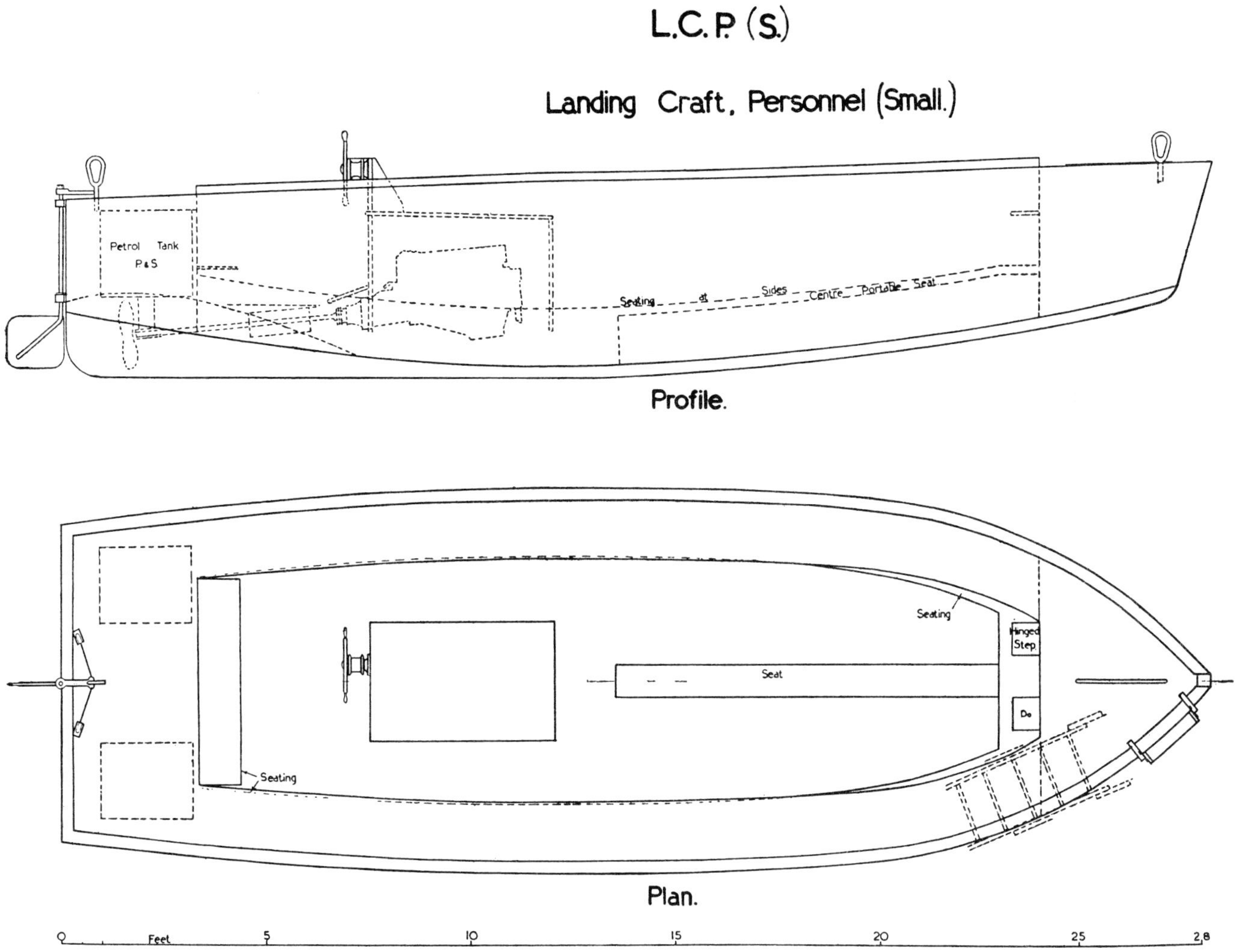

L.C.P. (S.)

Landing Craft, Personnel (Small.)

Petrol Tank
P & S

Seating ___ at ___ Sides ___ Centre ___ Portable ___ Seat

Profile.

Seating

Hinged Step

Seat

Do

Seating

Plan.

Feet 5 10 15 20 25 28

Fig. 6

L.C.I. (L).

Landing Craft Infantry · Large.

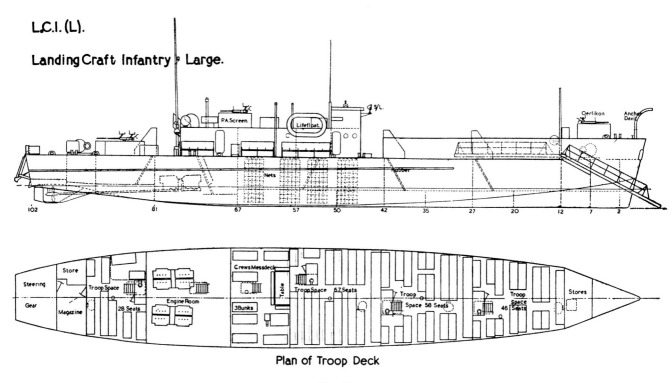

Plan of Troop Deck

Fig. 7

Landing Craft Infantry (Small).
L.C.I. (S).

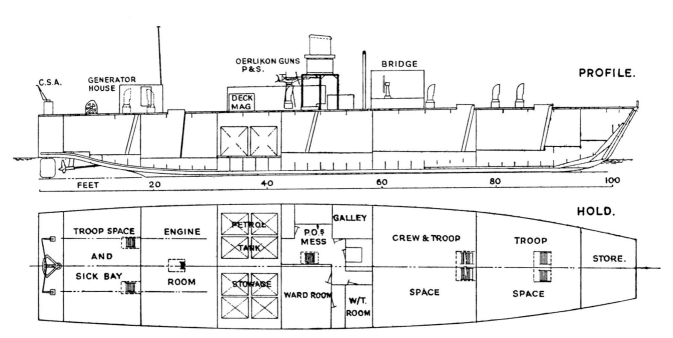

Fig. 8

LANDING CRAFT MECHANISED.
M.L.C.(10).

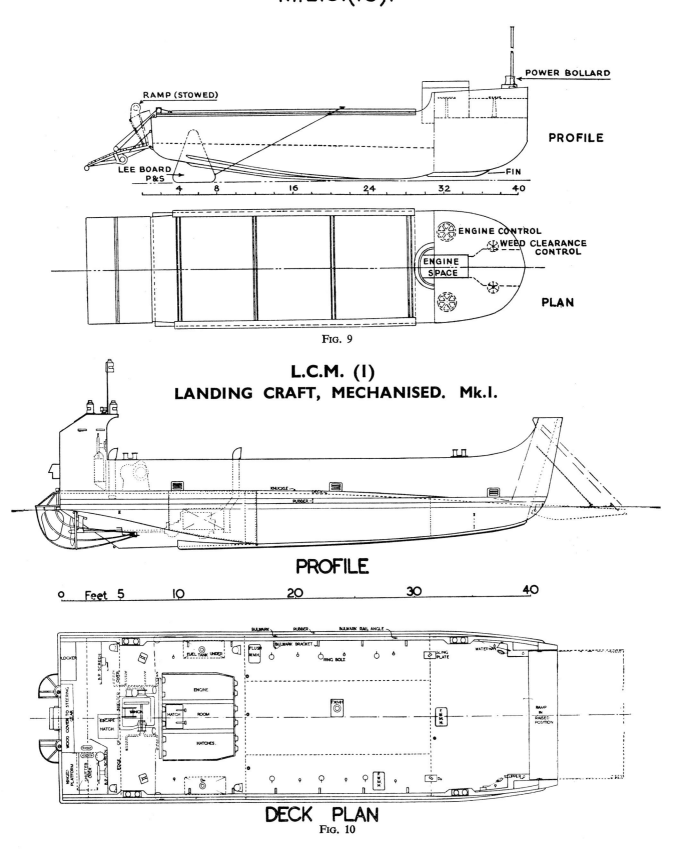

POWER BOLLARD

RAMP (STOWED)

PROFILE

LEE BOARD
P & S

FIN

4   8   16   24   32   40

ENGINE CONTROL

WEED CLEARANCE
CONTROL

ENGINE
SPACE

PLAN

FIG. 9

L.C.M. (I)
LANDING CRAFT, MECHANISED. Mk.I.

KNUCKLE

RUBBER

PROFILE

0   Feet 5   10   20   30   40

BULWARK   RUBBER   BULWARK RAIL ANGLE

LOCKER

FUEL TANK UNDER   FLUSH   BULWARK BRACKET   RING BOLT   SLING   WATERWAY
   MMH   PLATE

L.P. SCREEN

ENGINE

ESCAPE   WINCH   HATCH   ROOM

WOOD COVER TO STEERING
GEAR

ESCAPE
HATCH

RAMP
IN
RAISED
POSITION

HINGED
PLATFORM

HATCHES.

SCUPPER

DECK PLAN
FIG. 10

Group 2 A.—Vehicle Carriers to Operate from Ship to Shore

Landing Craft Mechanized Mk. I—L.C.M.(I)

This series of craft begins with Motor Landing Craft No. 1 of 1926 (referred to previously). After her trials, a requirement was put forward for a boat capable of carrying a 12-ton tank on a light weight of not more than 20 tons. A prototype of such a vessel was approved in the 1927 estimates and this craft, 42 ft. × 12 ft. × 20 tons, known as M.L.C.10, was completed (in slow time) in September 1929, by Messrs. Rowhedge Iron Works. She was jet propelled. Although not a great success M.L.C.10 did not fail in her trials and remained the standard prototype vehicle landing craft until 1938. During this period of 10 years a few craft were ordered, generally on the lines of M.L.C.10 and all jet propelled. Their speed was poor, being of the order of 5 knots.

Fig. 9 is a general arrangement and Fig. 38 a photograph of M.L.C.10.

Towards the end of 1938, revised requirements were put forward; the weight of tanks increased from 12 tons to 14 and a speed of 7 knots was required. Thornycroft prepared a design in May 1939 and a prototype craft was ordered later in the year. This craft was completed and carried out successful trials in February 1940.

Principal particulars:—

Length	44 ft. 8 in.
Beam	14 ft. 0 in.
Loaded Displacement	36 tons
Hoisting weight	21 tons
Power	120 B.H.P.
Speed	7·5 knots
Beaching draughts	F. 2 ft. 6 in. A. 3 ft. 6 in.
Tank load	16 tons
Crew	6 men, 1 officer to 3 craft

Fig. 10 is a general arrangement and Fig. 39 a photograph.

The main difference between this craft and its forerunners was that screw propulsion was used. This gave for the same power 7½ knots instead of 4½. Upper works were of protective plating as in the earlier models.

Before the prototype trials further orders were placed, and at the time of Dunkirk this little boat was the only craft we had capable of carrying a tank and beaching. The German invasion of the Low Countries gave an impetus to our programmes and most of the principal warship builders turned out a few of these craft in the spring and summer of 1940. This was the beginning of our Invasion Fleet proper, but the work was extremely inconvenient for ordinary shipyard facilities which were urgently required for other tasks. Later, these boats were built in large numbers by the Great Western Railway Company at Swindon and by the Southern Railway at Eastleigh. These companies developed a technique quite different from that of the shipbuilders, and from 1942 onwards they were followed by various structural firms.

These boats were subsequently known as L.C.M.(1).

L.C.M.(3)

The next development was the L.C.M.(3).

In the spring of 1941, the United States Marine Corps was preparing for a combined operation which involved putting tanks ashore. The only boat available was an American version of the L.C.M.(1), which was not able to carry sufficient load. The Marine Corps paid a visit to the Higgins Yard at New Orleans where they saw 4 shallow draught tugs building for the Peruvian Government. They mentioned their problem and the result was that Higgins modified the tugs and made them into M.L.C.s. He also, in under a month, delivered eight more. They were all-welded, double-hulled craft capable of carrying a 16-ton tank. After delivery no one took much interest in them until a British Mission visited U.S. at the end of the year, when it was immediately realized that, with very slight modification, they could be used for 30-ton tanks. Accordingly orders were placed under Lease-Lend for 150 modified craft. The U.S. Authorities were sceptical, however, and it was not until comparative trials of the Higgins boat against a Bureau of Ships type similar to L.C.M.(1) that they were convinced. From that date on the L.C.M.(3), as she was called, became standard, and thousands of them were built in America for Allied use.

Principal particulars:—

Length	50 ft. 0 in.
Beam	14 ft. 0 in.
Loaded displacement	52 tons
Hoisting weight	22 tons
Power	330 B.H.P.
Speed	8½ knots
Beaching draughts	F. 3 ft. 6 in. A. 4 ft. 6 in.
Tank load	One 30-ton tank.
Crew	3 men, 1 officer to 3 craft

Fig. 11 is a general arrangement and Fig. 40 a photograph.

The fundamental difference between the L.C.M.(1) and the L.C.M.(3) lies in the fact that the former is really a powered pontoon with bulwarks, with the load carried on the pontoon deck, whilst in the latter the load is carried on the inner bottom and the c.g. of the load is very low. If the hold is flooded there is still residual stability, whilst in L.C.M.(1) if the deck is flooded there is danger of capsizing. The L.C.M.(3) carried a pay load of over twice that of the L.C.M.(1) on about the same light weight. L.C.M.(3) was impossible as a riveted project.

In spite of the advantages of the L.C.M.(3) type over the older type, L.C.M.(1) production was continued, because the craft had the advantage of being hoisted with the load on board.

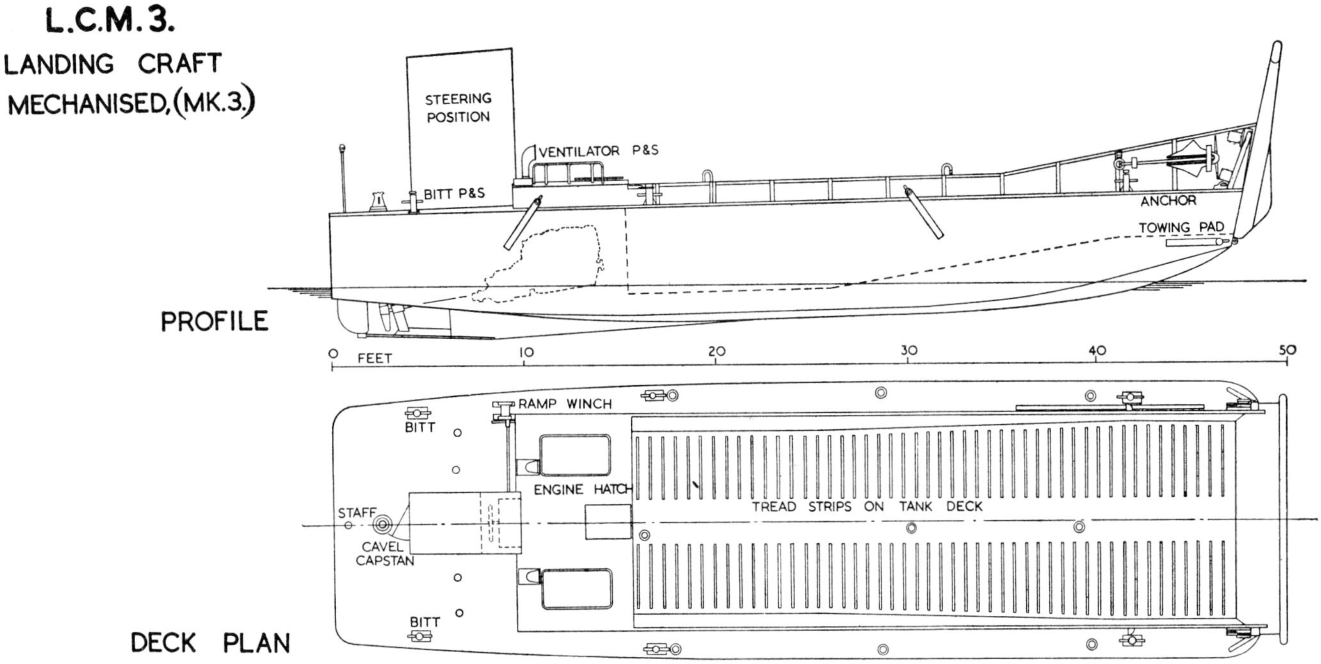

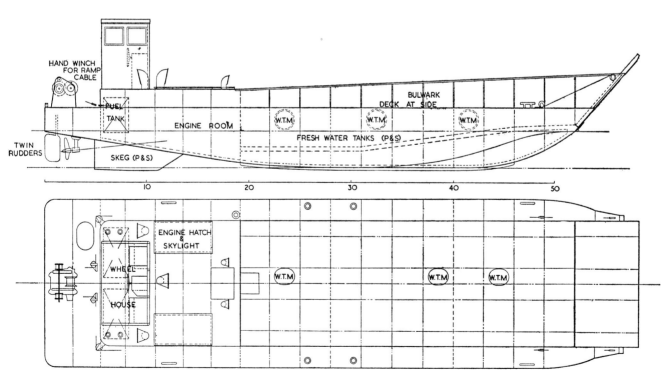

L.C.M.3.
LANDING CRAFT MECHANISED, (MK.3.)

STEERING POSITION

VENTILATOR P&S

BITT P&S

ANCHOR

TOWING PAD

PROFILE

FEET 0   10   20   30   40   50

RAMP WINCH

BITT

ENGINE HATCH

TREAD STRIPS ON TANK DECK

STAFF

CAVEL CAPSTAN

BITT

DECK PLAN

Fig. 11

L.C.M.(7)
LANDING CRAFT MECHANISED (MARK 7)

HAND WINCH FOR RAMP CABLE

FUEL TANK

ENGINE ROOM

W.T.M   W.T.M   W.T.M

BULWARK DECK AT SIDE

FRESH WATER TANKS (P&S)

TWIN RUDDERS

SKEG (P&S)

10   20   30   40   50

ENGINE HATCH & SKYLIGHT

WHEEL HOUSE

W.T.M   W.T.M   W.T.M

Fig. 12

179

L.C.T. (1)
LANDING CRAFT, TANK (MARK 1)

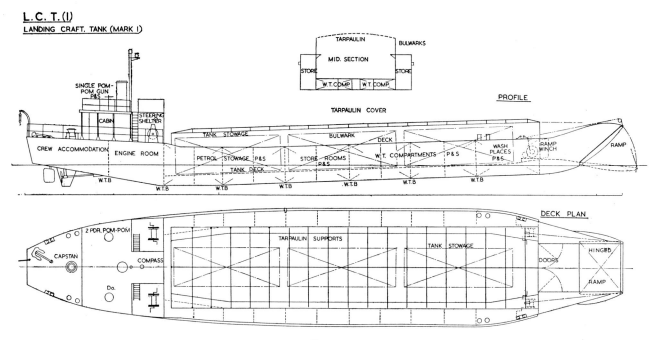

Fig. 13

L.C.T. (2).
LANDING CRAFT TANK, (MK. 2.)

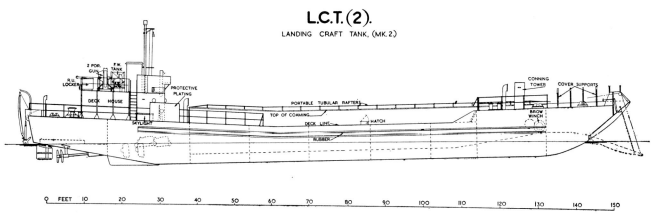

Fig. 14

L.C.T. (3)
LANDING CRAFT TANK, (MK. 3.)

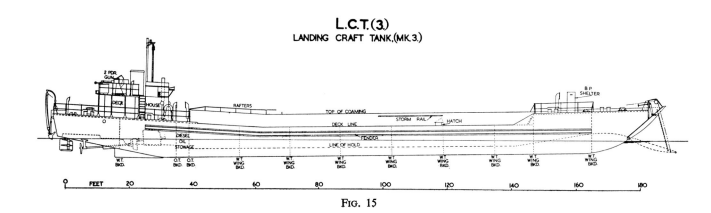

Fig. 15

L.C.M.(7)

In the spring of 1944, a new design was asked for, specifically for operations planned for the Far East. In this, a craft which could be hoisted and which could carry either a 40-ton tank or a bulldozer was required. Thus developed the L.C.M.(7), details of which were worked out by Thornycroft and which was a big sister of L.C.M.(3). The design was all-welded (although some craft were built composite) and the prototype was completed by Messrs. Thornycroft in October 1944. Bulk orders were placed with any firm willing to undertake the welding, including S.M.T., Millen Bros., John Thompson W.T. Boilers, Tilbury Contracting Co., etc. The programme was in full swing when the war ended. There were a few teething troubles, but on the whole the craft successfully met very heavy requirements.

Fig. 12 is a general arrangement and Fig. 41 a photograph.

Principal particulars:—

Length	.. .. ..	60 ft. 3 in.
Beam	.. ..	16 ft. 0 in.
Loaded displacement	..	63 tons
Hoisting weight	..	28 tons
Power	.. ..	290 B.H.P.
Speed	.. ..	9·8 knots
Beaching draughts	..	F. 3 ft. 8 in. / A. 3 ft. 8 in.
Tank load ..	..	One 35-ton tank
Crew	.. ..	3 men, 1 officer to 3 craft

Group 2 B.—Shore to Shore Vehicle Carriers

L.C.T.(1)

In 1937 the old Admiralty Landing Craft Committee gave some thought to the provision of shore to shore tank carriers and a design for what was called a new X-lighter was worked out. The project was subsequently dropped, largely because there were few tanks, and it seemed unlikely that we should want to engage in offensive amphibian warfare.

Nothing more was done until after Dunkirk when, if we were to win the war, a landing on the Continent seemed necessary, even if it were a long way off. Towards the end of June 1940, the Prime Minister asked for *Tank Landing Craft*, and this request started an entirely new series of craft (and ships) for combined operations.

It was decided that the new craft should be capable of carrying three of the heaviest tanks then envisaged (40 tons), should be required to land them in 2 ft. 6 in. of water on a 1-in-35 beach, should have a speed of 10 knots and should be suitable for operations as far afield as the west coast of France. At the time when a design was worked out to fulfil the requirements, the only craft available for landing tanks were L.C.M.(1), referred to previously, whose maximum load was 16 tons (later 18 tons was accepted as an emergency load). The new requirements, therefore, had revolutionary possibilities.

An emergency meeting of some of the principal shipbuilders was called early in July, when the project was explained to them and their advice sought. As a result of this meeting, the details of the design were worked out by John Browns and Fairfields. Resistance experiments were carried out at the Admiralty Experiment Works, Haslar; and although the L.C.T. would undoubtedly have looked clumsy to a yachtsman, her propulsive characteristics were as favourable as could be arranged in view of the function and limitations of the type. Similar experiments were carried out on all the later types.

The first craft was delivered by Messrs. Hawthorn Leslie in November. This remarkably quick delivery of an entirely novel type of barge was only made possible by the co-operation and enthusiasm of all concerned. Among the novel features—which are now familiar—may be mentioned the type of ramp with hinge just above the water line and the double floating dock type of hull. Moreover, the vehicles were entirely concealed from view and protected from the weather by means of the side tanks and canvas covers over the hold. The craft were powered by two 500 H.P. Hall Scott petrol engines, originally intended for coastal force craft.

Owing to the shallow draught the vessels were very tricky to steer, a pronounced sheer being difficult to check. As the prototype craft sped down the Tyne at 10 knots, running from side to side, all kinds of fears arose, and no one who was present on that trip is ever likely to forget it.

After the design had been approved, and while the first 20 craft were being built, it was decided that in the first instance craft would have to operate from the Eastern Mediterranean, so they were arranged in 4 sections bolted together. After trials the sections were shaken and shipped out as deck cargo. On more than one occasion the carrying ships were sunk and the sections floated off. Perhaps there are still some of these sections in the Sargasso Sea.

Fig. 13 is a general arrangement and Fig. 42 a photograph.

Principal particulars:—

Length	.. ..	152 ft. 0 in.
Beam	.. ..	29 ft. 0 in.
Loaded displacement	..	372 tons
Power	.. ..	700 B.H.P.
Speed	.. ..	10 knots
Beaching draughts	..	F. 3 ft. 0 in. / A. 5 ft. 9 in.
Tank load ..	..	3 Churchills or 6 Valentines
Crew	.. ..	2 officers and 10 men

This craft was later known as the L.C.T.(1). She was the first real heavy vehicle landing craft the world had seen. Twenty of the boats were ordered in the first instance; they were followed by repeat orders for 10 craft. Until this craft had been designed and building started, the staffs concerned were to some extent planning in the dark, and no one really knew whether the basic idea was practicable or not. However, once started, there was no limit, and long before the first craft was complete a flood of ideas began. It became clear that all types of military tank, not only the heaviest ones, would need to be carried, together with army and civilian vehicles of all other types. A slight increase in beam would make possible a very much increased load. Higher speed was also thought possible.

L.C.T.(2) was therefore developed on almost the same lines as L.C.T.(1), but with 2 ft. more beam and provision for three engines instead of two. The supply of Hall Scott engines began to run out, so the early L.C.T.(2) were fitted with three Napier Lions, originally intended for aircraft. At the same time, two new developments were put in hand; one of these was to arrange for the production of suitable diesel engines, the other came with the realization that enormous numbers of the craft would ultimately be required and that the continued use of existing shipyard facilities was uneconomical.

The Paxman 500 B.H.P. engine was developed and its production expanded, whilst on the other hand the structural engineering industry was co-opted to prefabricate the hulls, and then to arrange for their final erection and completion in disused shipyards specially opened for the purpose. This method, which proved to be extremely successful, was economical not only in shipyard labour and plant, but also in management.

The first of the new type of vessel was ordered in December 1940.

Fig. 14 is a general arrangement and Fig. 43 a photograph.

Principal particulars:—

Length	.. ..	159 ft. 11 in.
Beam	.. ..	31 ft. 0 in.
Loaded displacement	..	590 tons
Light displacement	..	296 tons
Power: Petrol driven	..	1,050 S.H.P.
Diesel	..	1,380 B.H.P.
Speed: Petrol	..	10·5 knots
Diesel	..	11 knots
Beaching draughts ⎱ (with Churchills) ⎰	..	⎧ F. 3 ft. 8 in. ⎨ A. 7 ft. 0 in. ⎩
Tank load ..	..	3 Churchills or 7 Valentines
Crew	.. ..	2 officers and 10 men

L.C.T.(3)

The demand for more craft, and for a greater carrying capacity in each, continued, and this led in May 1941 to the introduction of the third type—L.C.T.(3). In these vessels a 2-engine arrangement was reverted to, but the carrying capacity was increased by increasing the length by the insertion of a parallel 32 ft. section so that the craft were built in five sections as against the original four. A prototype for this lengthened L.C.T. was obtained by the addition of such a section to one of the L.C.T.(1) building at Messrs. John Brown's. This vessel was satisfactory in all respects and if anything a little faster than in her original form.

Apart from this prototype, all the early L.C.T.(2) were produced by structural engineers, who did, however, continue to receive drawings prepared by Fairfields and John Brown's. All these craft were fitted with the Paxman engines, which had now become standard.

Fig. 15 is a general arrangement and Fig. 44 a photograph.

Principle particulars are:—

Length	.. ..	.. 192 ft. 0 in.
Beam	.. ..	.. 31 ft. 0 in.
Loaded displacement	..	640 tons
Power	.. ..	.. 920 B.H.P.
Speed	.. ..	.. 10 knots
Beaching draughts ⎱ (with Churchills) ⎰	..	⎧ F. 3 ft. 10 in. ⎨ A. 7 ft. 0 in. ⎩
Tank load ..	..	.. 5 Churchills or 11 Valentines or 11 Shermans
Crew	.. ..	.. 2 officers and 10 men

A total of 235 L.C.T.(3) were completed. This total includes 71 to slightly modified plans, which were built by the main shipbuilders during the winter of 1943–44. In this version Sterling Admiral petrol engines were fitted in lieu of the Paxman. Many shipbuilders, particularly Cammell Lairds, at this time broke all records for speed in producing the craft.

The next step came in the autumn of 1941, when the need for even larger numbers of even bigger craft was again expressed. It was also decided that still shallower draught would be essential. At this time the original idea behind the L.C.T. had been expanded and ships for landing tanks had been proved practicable. For the future, then, there were two alternative possibilities:—

(a) To build shallow draught tank landing craft capable of making cross-channel trips.

(b) To build tank landing ships and/or M.T. ships and use landing craft only for use between ship and shore.

L.C.T.(4)

On the whole (a) seemed more promising and to meet such a requirement the L.C.T.(4) was designed. The first orders were placed in October 1941. This class was developed to suit the facilities of the structural engineer and of their yards as then laid out. No recognized shipbuilder was ever employed on any of these craft or on the drawings.

To help production, the gun armament and protective devices which had been included in the earlier craft were given up and the craft as originally completed was able to carry 300 tons of tanks on draughts of 3 ft. 8 in. forward and 4 ft. 2 in. aft. To save weight flimsy construction was accepted and some discontinuity in the structure at the break of the poop could hardly be avoided. Owing to the great beam the speed was poor as compared to the earlier craft.

The first of this type was completed in September 1942 and production continued until the end of the war. The requirement for armament was reintroduced, the endurance was increased, the craft were strengthened, and it is the final version of the unstiffened Mk. 4 illustrated by Figs. 16 (general arrangement) and 45 (photograph).

Principal particulars:—

Length	187 ft. 3 in.
Beam	38 ft. 9 in.
Loaded displacement ..	586 tons
Power	920 B.H.P.
Speed	10 knots
Beaching draughts ..	{ F. 3 ft. 6 in. / A. 4 ft. 7 in.
Tank load	6 Churchills *or* 9 Valentines *or* 9 Shermans
Crew	2 officers and 10 men

Much later, when the issue of the war in Europe was no longer in doubt, it became necessary to envisage using this class in Far Eastern waters. To suit them for this they were "tropicalized" and further stiffened. The stiffening was effected by raising the side deck to the height of the old bulwark and fitting heavier plating here and to the bottom. The various additions considerably increased the draught, but the ships were still very light. A large number of them had successfully made the voyage to India when the war ended. Fig. 17 is a general arrangement of this modified group. All the L.C.T.(4) retained the floating dock type of sections first arranged in L.C.T.(1), but in these craft the actual tank or pontoon deck was above the normal waterline and not below it.

L.C.T.(5)

Reverting to (*b*) above, no serious plan was ever made for building the vast numbers of tank landing ships that were ultimately required, but it became clear that this problem could only be settled if American help was forthcoming. In August 1941, Mr. Barnaby of Thornycroft had suggested a small L.C.T. more or less double ended which would be able to load from an L.S.T. and discharge ashore. The craft was hardly suitable for a channel crossing. Subsequently it was decided to ask American help for building craft of the type of Mr. Barnaby's "go-between," i.e. something smaller than British L.C.T.

This craft, which was known as the L.C.T.(5) was designed by the Bureau of Ships on the general lines of Mr. Barnaby's suggestion, but not double ended, and was soon put into production in America, concurrently with a large L.S.T. programme. One of the features of this design lies in the fact that the craft and ship were considered together so that the smaller could be carried as deck cargo on the larger. This involved the use of 150-ton cranes for stowage and off-loading, but at a later stage off-loading was effected by broadside launching. These L.C.T.(5) were all built, mainly by non-shipbuilding firms, in the United States, and were all primarily in three sections so that delivery could also be made sending the sections as deck cargo in ordinary transports. Large numbers of craft were delivered in

this way, the three sections being hoisted off the ship into the water, joining up being done afloat.

Craft of this type also made long delivery voyages in the Pacific whilst on tow.

Fig. 18 is a general arrangement drawing and Fig. 46 a photograph.

Principal particulars:—

Length	112 ft. 4 in.
Beam	32 ft. 9 in.
Loaded displacement ..	311 tons
Power	675 B.H.P.
Speed	8 knots
Beaching draughts ..	{ F. 2 ft. 11 in. / A. 4 ft. 7 in.
Tank load	4 Churchills *or* 7 Valentines
Crew	2 officers and 11 men

L.C.T.(6)

The Americans used L.C.T.(5) for training purposes, long before either they, or we, were able to use them operationally, and as a result produced the L.C.T.(6), which was generally similar to the L.C.T.(5), but incorporated the double-ended arrangement, which it was again thought would facilitate working between ship and shore.

L.C.T.(7)

Passing mention must be made of yet another purely American development, the L.C.T.(7), later known as L.S.M. This was a larger craft, 203 ft. 6 in. × 34 ft. 6 in. × 1,095 tons deep displacement, with a ship-shape bow, the main features being similar to earlier types—but improved as regards speed and sea-keeping qualities.

L.C.T.(8)

The last stage in this group started in the autumn of 1943, by which time all the craft required for European operations were complete or in sight of completion, and plans began to be concerned with operations in the Far East. The early types of landing craft, intended for comparatively near at hand operations, were not suitable for sustained effort in the new theatre, so that although many of them were improved by various additions, and in fact before the end of the war many of them had arrived on their station, demands were put forward for an improved type.

This new craft, the L.C.T.(8), was to a certain degree inspired by the L.S.M.—which could not be copied because of lack of availability of engines, and which did not altogether meet the wishes of the British staffs. In it an attempt was made to combine the best features of the earlier types, and in addition to increase speed, endurance, and sea-keeping qualities.

The best features of the L.C.T.(3) were its relative robustness and the depth of the girder; the best feature of the L.C.T.(4) its shallow draught, light construction, and its suitability for production by the facilities available. To improve speed, the power was doubled and

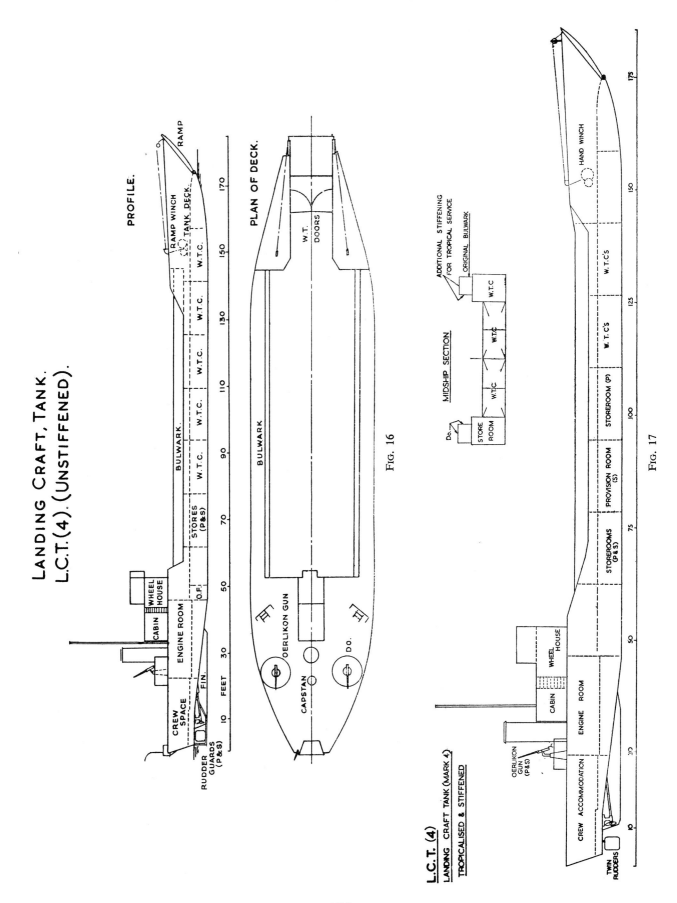

LANDING CRAFT, TANK.
L.C.T.(4). (UNSTIFFENED).

PROFILE.

PLAN OF DECK.

FIG. 16

L.C.T. (4)
LANDING CRAFT TANK (MARK 4)
TROPICALISED & STIFFENED

MIDSHIP SECTION

FIG. 17

L.C.T. (5).
LANDING CRAFT TANK, (MK5.)

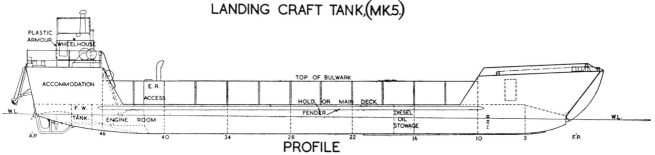

PROFILE

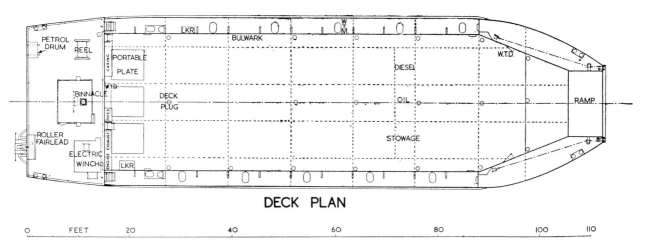

DESK PLAN

FIG. 18

L.C.T. 8
LANDING CRAFT, TANK (MARK 8)

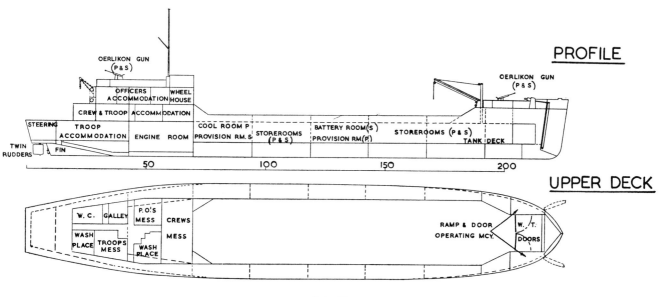

PROFILE

UPPER DECK

FIG. 19

the new craft were propelled by four Paxman 460 S.H.P. engines geared together two per shaft; sea keeping was improved by increase in depth and by the fitting of a ship-shape bow as in the L.S.T. and L.S.M.

Accommodation was provided on board for the crews of the tanks when embarked, and altogether the project was most formidable when compared with the work formerly undertaken by the landing craft yards. It would not have been practicable for the structural engineers to have undertaken the whole development of the design, so once again we fell back on our friends at Thornycrofts, who worked out a lot of the details and produced a complete set of shipbuilder's plans. These plans were then handed to the contractors who made from them the complete sets of detailed working drawings. To facilitate development of the accommodation drawings, the whole of the after end of the ship was mocked up at Pinewood Studios, and the drawings used by the builders were "as fitted" drawings taken off this mock-up. The whole of the accommodation was ventilated and insulated in accordance with the latest general service arrangements.

In these craft power was provided for operating the bow ramp and bow doors, the necessary machinery being specially designed for the job, as was the after winch required for kedging off the beach. The pumping and flooding system was a good deal more elaborate than formerly, and a large proportion of these items and the fittings generally were ordered direct by the Admiralty for supply to the builders. In brief the L.C.T.(8) was nothing like the simple L.C.T. of 1940.

The first orders were placed in May 1944, and the first craft, an all-welded vessel built by Sir William Arrol in their Alloa yard, was completed in June 1945. The other firms associated with the production were just commencing deliveries when the war ended.

Fig. 19 is a general arrangement of the craft and Fig. 47 a photograph.

Principal particulars:—

Length	225 ft. 0 in.
Beam	39 ft. 0 in.
Loaded displacement ..	895 tons
Power	1,840 B.H.P. limited to max. of 1,600
Speed	12·6 knots
Beaching draughts (with Shermans)	F. 3 ft. 9 in. A. 5 ft. 0 in.
Tank load	8 Shermans
Crew	Naval (3 officers and 19 men). Military (6 officers and 36 men)

Group 3 A.—Support Craft to Operate from Ship to Shore

L.C.S.(M)

The requirement for the first support craft was put forward in 1938, concurrently with the requirement for assault landing craft. The underlying idea was that both the support and assault craft should have the same hulls which could be carried at the same davits, but that whilst the assault craft would carry men the support boat would be armed and would "cover" the others on their run in. Fleming's and Thornycroft's original L.C.A.s were therefore modified to form the prototype support landing craft (S.L.C.). They were armed with two ½-in. Vickers' machine-guns on tubular mounts, a smoke mortar and two light machine-guns. As a result of trials with these prototypes a proportion of the L.C.A. on order were fitted out for use in the support role on the lines indicated. In these craft the armament was carried in the compartment known as the troop well in the L.C.A., and the main hulls of the two types were identical. The craft were subsequently known as L.C.S.(M)(1). Fig. 20 is a general arrangement and Fig. 48 a photograph.

In the autumn of 1941 it was decided to improve the performance of the craft without changing their general characteristics. A new series of boats was then begun in which, although the basic hull remained the same, the well was decked over and a power-operated ½-in. twin turret type mounting fitted in place of the two pedestal mounts. The smoke mortar remained. This type was subsequently known as L.C.S.(M)(2). Fig. 21 is a general arrangement.

In the event, too much attention had been given to maintaining L.C.A. features and the L.C.S.(M)(2) was not as satisfactory as had been hoped, so in the spring of 1942 the boat was completely redesigned, with the same armament and power unit (that of the L.C.A.). The result was all that could be expected in a boat of this size, known as the L.C.S.(M)(3). Production of this type continued until the end of the war. Fig. 22 is a general arrangement, and Fig. 49 a photograph.

Principal particulars:—

Length	41 ft. 8 in.
Beam	10 ft. 0 in.
Loaded displacement ..	13·3 tons
Power	130 B.H.P.
Speed	10 knots
Armament	1 4-in. B.L. Smoke Mortar 2 0·5-in. Vickers (Twin Power Mtg.) 2 Lewis guns.
Crew	1 officer and 10 men

L.C.S.(L)1

The first shipborne support craft was derived from the L.C.A.—the next step, which was first suggested in December 1940, came in the same way from the L.C.M. This new craft was at first known as the Heavy Support Craft (H.S.C.) and the intention was to provide a boat capable of dealing with a tank, whilst being of a size that could be carried in the ordinary trooper, i.e. the weight limitations were the same as for the L.C.M.—20 tons.

After a great deal of preliminary discussion, Thornycrofts were asked to produce a design, which they did in May 1942.

Principal particulars were:—

Length ..	.. ..	46 ft. 11 in.
Beam ..	.. ..	12 ft. 7 in.
Displacement ..	..	24·5 tons
Power ..	.. ..	330 B.H.P.
Speed ..	.. ..	10·75 knots
Crew ..	.. ..	1 officer and 12 men
Armament ..	..	1 2 pdr.
		1 Besa in Daimler turret
		1 4-in. smoke mortar
		2 0·5-in. Vickers (Twin Power Mtg.)
Protection ..	..	15 lbs. to sides, bulkheads, and turret fidley
		10 lbs. to deck and top of turret fidley
		Steering { sides—20 lbs.
		Position { top—12 lbs.

The idea of using the craft against tanks is illustrated by the tank type of weapons provided. The first craft was not ready until April 1943, the delay being mainly due to difficulty over the supply of the turrets. Trials proved what had been feared, the project was too ambitious; in brief, it was not possible to design a 20-ton boat that could stand up to a 40-ton tank.

Fig. 23 is a general arrangement of the boat and Fig. 50 a photograph.

This experience proved that the idea of shipborne support craft had only limited application and there was no further British development of these types directly. There were later American models and at the end of the war some L.C.A. were fitted with spigot mortars, mainly for use against beach defences.

Group 3 B.—Support Craft to Operate from Shore to Shore

L.C.F.

In June 1941, and as a result of our experiences in the evacuation of Crete, the view gained ground that even if landings were possible owing to the weakness of the enemy's shore defences, it would be impossible to maintain them because of the dangers of air counter attack. In the possible absence of air superiority, something would have to be done to defend the beaches. The landing craft must be able to defend themselves. This led at first to an increase in the anti-aircraft armament of major landing craft—viz.: fitting oerlikons, fast aerial mines, and balloons, and then to a demand for special anti-aircraft craft or flak ships.

There was considerable controversy as to what form of anti-aircraft armament should be fitted, and as a result two L.C.T.(2), then under construction at the works of the Tees Side Bridge and Engineering Company, were taken over and put in hand at Palmers, Hebburn; the first, known as B.P.C.1, later L.C.F.(1), was fitted with two 4-in. twin mountings and three single oerlikons, the second, L.C.F.(2), with a battery of eight 2-pdrs. and four oerlikons.

L.C.F.(1) was really a remarkable little craft, or monitor, her armament being equivalent to that of many ships three or four times her size. In the early stages it seemed doubtful whether such heavy guns could be mounted in such a flimsy structure, but all went according to plan. L.C.F.(2) was less spectacular, but she proved to be the prototype of a number of subsequent L.C.F. specially provided for close range anti-aircraft defence. Some of these craft were also found to be of great value against personnel.

Fig. 24 is a general arrangement of L.C.F.(1), Fig. 51 a photograph and Fig. 25 a general arrangement of L.C.F.(2).

Principal particulars:—

L.C.F.(1)

Length ..	.. ..	159 ft. 11 in.
Beam ..	.. ..	31 ft. 1 in.
Displacement ..	..	539 tons
Power ..	.. ..	920 B.H.P.
Speed ..	.. ..	11 knots
Armament ..	..	2 4-in. Twin Q.F.
		3 20-mm oerlikons
Crew ..	.. ..	4 officers and 70 men

L.C.F.(2)

Length ..	.. ..	159 ft. 11 in.
Beam ..	.. ..	31 ft. 1 in.
Displacement ..	..	470 tons (Light)
Power ..	.. ..	920 S.H.P.
Speed ..	.. ..	11 knots
Armament ..	..	8 2-pdr. pom-pom
		4 20-mm oerlikons
Crew ..	.. ..	4 officers and 63 men

L.C.S.(L)2

In the spring of 1942, when the idea of shipborne raids was giving way to the idea of L.C.I.(S), the problem of dealing with tanks from the sea was acute. It was by this time agreed that small boats would be ineffective, so ten of the L.C.I.(S) were converted into support craft. Their armament was still of the tank type and their protection very meagre; the particulars of the craft are, however, of considerable interest as showing what could be done on wooden hulls.

Fig. 26 is a general arrangement and Fig. 52 a photograph.

Principal particulars:—

Length ..	.. ..	105 ft. 1 in.
Beam ..	.. ..	21 ft. 5 in.
Displacement ..	..	116 tons
Power ..	.. ..	1,140 S.H.P.
Speed ..	.. ..	14 knots
Armament ..	..	1 Q.F. 6-pdr. (tank turret)
		1 4-in. B.L. smoke mortar
		2 oerlikons
		2 0·5-in. Vickers (twin power Mtg.)
Protection ..	..	10 lbs. D.I.H.T.
Crew ..	.. ..	2 officers and 23 men

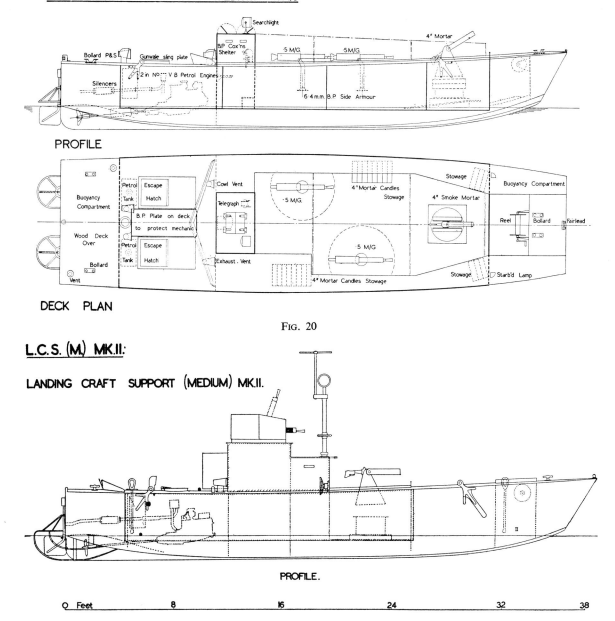

L.C.S. (M) I
LANDING CRAFT SUPPORT MEDIUM MK.I

PROFILE

DECK PLAN

FIG. 20

L.C.S. (M) MK.II:

LANDING CRAFT SUPPORT (MEDIUM) MK.II.

PROFILE.

DECK PLAN.

FIG. 21

188

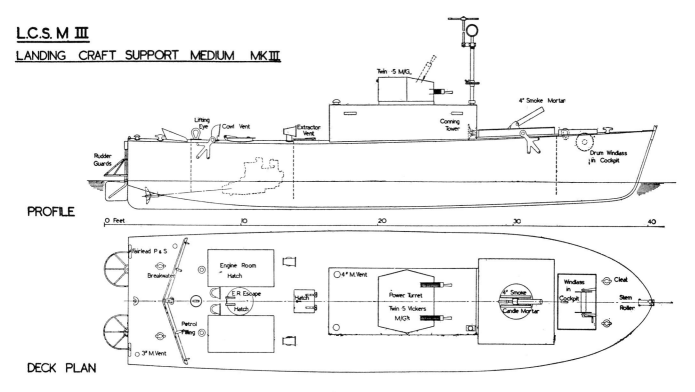

L.C.S. M III
LANDING CRAFT SUPPORT MEDIUM MK III

PROFILE

Rudder Guards — *Lifting Eye* — *Cowl Vent* — *Extractor Vent* — *Twin ·5 M/G.* — *Conning Tower* — *4" Smoke Mortar* — *Drum Windlass in Cockpit*

O Feet   10   20   30   40

DECK PLAN

Fairlead P & S — *Breakwater* — *E.R. Escape Hatch* — *Engine Room Hatch* — *Petrol Filling* — *3" M.Vent* — *Hatch* — *4" M.Vent* — *Power Turret Twin 5 Vickers M/Gs.* — *4" Smoke Candle Mortar* — *Windlass in Cockpit* — *Cleat* — *Stem Roller*

FIG. 22

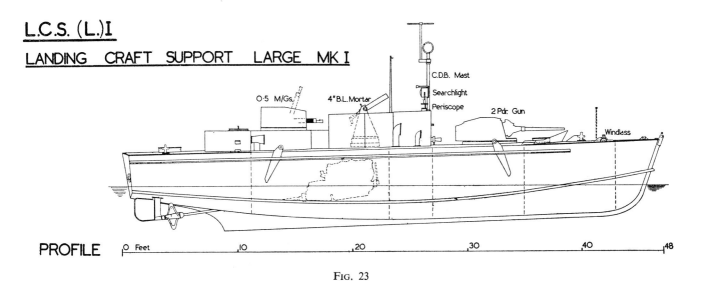

L.C.S. (L.) I
LANDING CRAFT SUPPORT LARGE MK I

0.5 M/Gs. — *4" B.L. Mortar* — *C.D.B. Mast* — *Searchlight* — *Periscope* — *2 Pdr. Gun* — *Windlass*

PROFILE

O Feet   10   20   30   40   48

FIG. 23

L.C.G.(L)

In the late autumn of 1942, when the Sicilian operations were being planned, there were great fears as to the damage likely to be done to the invasion forces, not so much by mobile defences, but by fixed coast defences. Monitors were unlikely to be available, destroyers and other small warships were too precious; so it was decided, following the experience in L.C.F.(1) to fit out some L.C.T.(3) with 4·7-in. guns ex-destroyers. The resulting craft, which proved most successful, was known as the L.C.G.(L).

Fig. 27 is a general arrangement of one of the earliest conversions and Fig. 53 a photograph.

Principal particulars of L.C.G.(L)(3):—

Length ..	..	.. 192 ft. 0 in.
Beam ..	..	.. 30 ft. 0 in.
Displacement ..		.. 491 tons
Power ..	..	.. 920 B.H.P.
Speed ..	..	.. 10 knots
Armament	..	.. 2 4·7-in. Q.F. or B.L.
		2 or 4 single oerlikons
Protection	..	.. 25 lbs. D.W.
Crew ..	..	.. 3 officers and 44 men

Subsequently the very much flimsier L.C.T.(4) was converted to gun craft on generally similar lines; later again, for the Far East campaign, a more elaborate conversion was made. In its final form the L.C.G.(L)4 had a ship-form bow, 2 in. or 1 in. N.C. armour over vitals and considerably improved accommodation.

Fig. 28 is a general arrangement of L.C.G.(L)4 of the earlier type and Fig. 54 a photograph.

Principal particulars:—

Length ..	..	.. 185 ft. 6 in.
Beam ..	..	.. 38 ft. 8 in.
Displacement ..		.. 570 tons
Power ..	..	.. 1,000 B.H.P.
Speed ..	..	.. 10 knots
Armament	..	.. 2 4·7-in. B.L.
		3 20-mm. oerlikons
Protection	..	.. 25 lbs. generally
Crew ..	..	.. 3 officers and 45 men

Although all these types of converted support craft carried very large amounts of dangerous ammunition above the waterline, and were therefore vulnerable to explosions, the very close subdivision associated with the L.C.T. type of structure made them almost proof against solid shot, small arms fire, etc. Their principal disadvantage against shore targets arose from the low trajectory of the shell which made it difficult to use them against hidden targets.

L.C.T.(R)

This development, which took place almost concurrently with the L.C.G.(L), was the first major naval venture into the rocket field. In the first conversion a L.C.T.(2) was fitted out with 792 rocket projectors fixed in bearing and elevation. A single complete reload for all the projectors was stowed in magazines below the upper deck.

The method of operating the craft was fascinating to one who had experience of the vagaries of the L.C.T., for the range and bearing being fixed, in order to operate the craft she had to be navigated to an exact firing position. The release of the rockets drenched an area 750 yards × 160 yards with one rocket to each 100 square yards (10 × 10); if H.E., the charge was 29 lbs. and 7 lbs. burster, the total weight of explosive being 17 tons. The ships were a great success, particularly from the morale point of view.

Subsequently L.C.T.(3) were also converted in this way.

Fig. 29 is a general arrangement of L.C.T.(3) as finally fitted, and Fig. 55 a photograph.

Principal particulars:—

Length ..	..	.. 192 ft. 0 in.
Beam ..	..	.. 31 ft. 0 in.
Displacement ..		.. 560 tons
Power ..	..	.. 1,000 B.H.P.
Speed ..	..	.. 10 knots
Armament	..	.. 1,080 projectors Mk. I or
		936 projectors Mk. II,
		2 single oerlikons
Protection	..	.. 15 lbs. and 20 lbs. D.I.H.T.
Crew ..	..	.. 2 officers and 15 men

L.C.G.(M)

The invasion of Sicily was only a prelude to the invasion of N.W. Europe, so at the same time as the L.C.G.(L) was being provided, a great deal of thought was being given to the problem of support fire in a full scale invasion. It was recognized now that air cover was a *sine qua non*, but the army authorities in particular could not accept the view that air cover by itself would be sufficient. The guns of the fleet would fill part of the gap, but in the end the army claimed that army type weapons must be available from the moment the first wave of troops touched down.

This demand led to two developments; one, regarded as a short term policy, in which artillery, either self-propelled, or mounted in tanks, or on ordinary field mountings, could be fired from landing craft; the other in which attempts were to be made to mount army type guns in naval craft.

It is often difficult for the designer to feel that in a design he can completely meet purely naval staff requirements, but when the army staff wishes are added a very intricate problem is inevitable.

The first military requirement in the L.C.G.(M) was that she should be able to meet a tank or pill box on equal terms; the second that she should be able to give artillery cover to troops ashore up to ordinary artillery ranges. The first naval requirement was that the craft should be capable of making ocean passages.

The resulting design was one of considerable novelty. Arrangements were made so that the craft could, by flooding tanks, ground itself on a beach; this had the

LANDING CRAFT, FLAK.
L.C.F.(1).

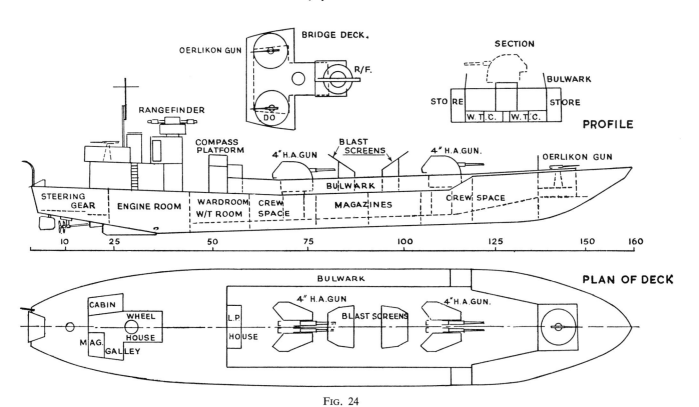

FIG. 24

LANDING CRAFT, FLAK.
L.C.F.(2).

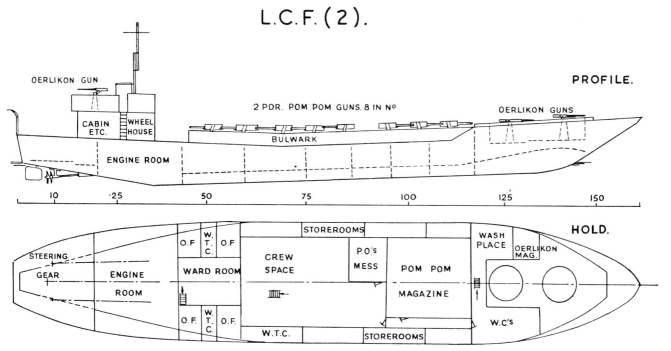

FIG. 25

191

LANDING CRAFT SUPPORT (LARGE).
L.C.S.(L).

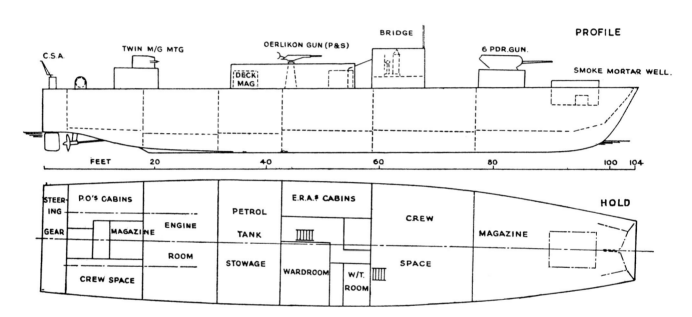

FIG. 26

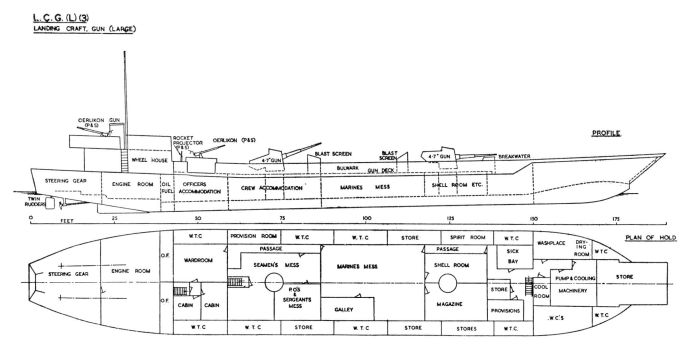

FIG. 27

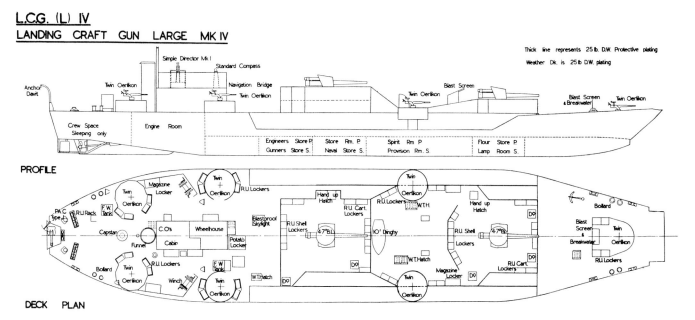

FIG. 28

advantage of improving the protection by the deflective powers of the water and of enabling fire to be directed to a map reference. In order to provide against variable tidal conditions, flooding was done through a pipe line and the same pipe line was used for pumping. The capacity of the pump was 460 tons per hour at the very small heads required. The pump and the gun turrets were all specially designed and produced for use in connection with this project. The craft were of hard chine form but, unlike the L.C.T.s, of conventional form above the water. They were armoured.

Messrs. John Brown were of very great assistance in the development of the design and provided the essential drawings, but the whole of the production of the vessels was placed in the hands of the structural engineering firms, among whom the Tees Side Bridge and Engineering Company took the lead.

The first orders were placed in May 1943 and the first craft was delivered in June 1944 by Tees Side.

Fig. 30 is a general arrangement of L.C.G.(M)1.

Principal particulars:—

Length	..	..	154 ft. 6 in.
Beam	..	..	22 ft. 4 in.
Displacement	..	..	380 tons
Power	..	..	1,000 B.H.P.
Speed	..	..	11·75 knots
Armament	..	..	2 17-pdr. or 2 25-pdr. (naval mtgs.). 2 single oerlikons
Protection	..	..	80 lbs., 40 lbs., and 15 lbs.
Crew	..	..	3 officers and 28–32 men

By the time that the first of these craft were completed the invasion of Europe was over; the requirement for support craft in the Far East was different and in the later L.C.G.(M) the grounding requirement was given up, the protection reduced, and additional anti-personnel armament fitted.

Fig. 56 is a photograph of the earliest type.

L.C.S.(R)

The L.C.G.(M) was a better sea-going proposition than the L.C.T. and much more manoeuvrable because her form was less extreme, so the success of the L.C.T.(R) led to a suggestion being made that L.C.G.(M) armed with rockets would be a worth-while alternative. There was no capacity available, however, except that of the L.C.T. firms already engaged on the L.C.G.(M), and in the event L.C.S.(R) never really got to the production stage, although the prototype was completed just as the war ended.

Conclusion

This story would not be complete were it not made clear that so far as numbers are concerned, American production was fantastically great. In this phase of warfare British ideas were on the whole taken up by our Allies with tremendous enthusiasm, and they almost always had the advantage over us that they could start where we left off. Not only was the programme an outstanding example of allied co-operation, but also an outstanding example of the benefits of co-operation in this country. The ideas in many cases came from the naval or military staffs, or from the Prime Minister; they were first developed inside the Admiralty, the detailed design work was done by shipbuilders, and finally the naval shipbuilding and structural engineering industries produced the goods.

This paper does not attempt to describe the steps taken by the various firms. Perhaps some day one of them will tell the story of how they operated new yards on old foundations.

Nomenclature in Order in which Quoted in Paper

M.L.C.	Motor Landing Craft—later known as L.C.M. (Landing Craft Mechanized).
I.S.T.D.C.	Inter-Service Training and Development Centre.
A.L.C.	Assault Landing Craft—later L.C.A. (Landing Craft Assault).
L.C.P.(M)	Landing Craft, Personnel—Medium.
L.C.P.(L)	Landing Craft, Personnel—Large.
L.C.P.(R)	Landing Craft, Personnel—Ramped.
L.C.V.(P)	Landing Craft, Vehicle—Personnel.
L.C.P.(S)	Landing Craft, Personnel—Small.
L.C.I.(L)	Landing Craft, Infantry—Large.
L.C.I.(S)	Landing Craft, Infantry—Small.
L.C.M.(1)	Landing Craft, Mechanized—Mark I.
L.C.M.(3)	Landing Craft, Mechanized—Mark III.
L.C.M.(7)	Landing Craft, Mechanized—Mark VII.
L.C.T.(1)	Landing Craft, Tank—Mark I.
L.C.T.(2)	Landing Craft, Tank—Mark II.
L.C.T.(3)	Landing Craft, Tank—Mark III.
L.C.T.(4)	Landing Craft, Tank—Mark IV.
L.C.T.(5)	Landing Craft, Tank—Mark V.
L.S.T.	Landing Ship, Tank.
L.C.T.(6)	Landing Craft, Tank—Mark VI.
L.C.T.(7)	Landing Craft, Tank—Mark VII.
L.S.M.	Landing Ship—Medium.
L.C.T.(8)	Landing Craft, Tank—Mark VIII.
L.C.S.(M) (1)	Landing Craft—Support (Medium)—Mark I.
L.C.S.(M) (2)	Landing Craft—Support (Medium)—Mark II.
L.C.S.(M) (3)	Landing Craft—Support (Medium)—Mark III.
L.C.S.(L) (1)	Landing Craft—Support (Large)—Mark I.
B.P.C.(1)	Beach Protection Craft, Mark I (Later L.C.F. (1)).
L.C.F.(1)	Landing Craft, Flak—Mark I.
L.C.F.(2)	Landing Craft, Flak—Mark II.
L.C.S.(L) (2)	Landing Craft, Support (Large)—Mark II.
L.C.G.(L)	Landing Craft, Gun (Large).
L.C.G.(L) (3)	Landing Craft, Gun (Large)—Mark III.
L.C.G.(L) (4)	Landing Craft, Gun (Large)—Mark IV.
L.C.T.(R)	Landing Craft, Tank (Rocket).
L.C.G.(M) (1)	Landing Craft, Gun (Medium)—Mark I.
L.C.S.(R)	Landing Craft, Support (Rocket).

DISCUSSION

Captain R. C. Todhunter, R.N.: I was connected with the material side of combined operations from the start in 1940, and saw it grow from the days when it was the cinderella of the party to the period just before the invasion when most (but not all) of those in authority realised that without landing ships and craft no invasion could take place.

The unique nature of the design of landing ships and craft meant that under normal circumstances nothing would have been done without building a prototype, but there was no time to build a prototype of any one of the many unique types produced, and every class had to go into production straight from the drawing board. This gave us many anxious moments, not only from the design aspect, but also from the operational point of view. For example, when the Mark IV L.C.T. was first projected there were many experienced naval officers who thought that their extremely shallow draught would make them completely unmanageable. Similarly with the Mark II L.C.T. (R) there was some fear whether the heat generated would blow up the whole vessel when rockets were fired. But time was so short that these risks had to be taken.

The second major difficulty was that whereas in the standard type of naval ship the sailor is inclined to take what is given him (although he may grumble), in combined operations vessels all those serving in them, from whichever Service, felt that they could radically improve the design, the armament, the amenities, the accommodation, and everything else to do with the craft. It was quite right that they should spend their time thinking about those things; but the result of it was that, in the early days at any rate, we were inundated with proposals for alterations, many of them exceedingly valuable, but many of them utterly impracticable. Any proposals for alteration, particularly when the mass-production stage was reached, were fought tooth and nail by those whose business it was to construct the craft, because the smallest alteration meant a complete dislocation of the production programme. On the other hand, it was D.C.O.M.'s unenviable task to decide whether any particular alteration should, or should not, be made. In many cases the alterations were proved by experience to be completely unnecessary. If they were turned down one had the responsibility that men's lives might be thrown away, whereas by agreeing to them one might put back the whole programme, with even more serious results.

On the whole, however, I think the balance was reasonably well held between the D.N.C., the shipbuilders, and those concerned on the operational side; we got along extremely well with the D.N.C. Department and C.O.H.Q. through whom all the proposals came. From the naval point of view we owe a tremendous debt to Mr. Baker for all the work he did. Many of the projects put forward seemed at first to be impossible. He never said that any suggestion made could not be effected, but always went out of his way to see how it could be done.

Mr. A. J. Merrington, C.B.E., B.Sc., R.C.N.C. (Member): This paper is packed with information, and I think the author deserves great credit for the amount he has compressed into so few pages. I was on the staff of the Chief of Combined Operations, Viscount Mountbatten, in 1942–43, and worked in close association with Mr. Baker, Captain Todhunter, and various officers of combined operations and, of course, the several Admiralty departments, and I saw the excellent work and the resource with which the author tackled all these problems; he always came up, smiling, with answers to the most difficult questions.

After leaving combined operations staff I joined the staff of the Commander-in-Chief Mediterranean Fleet for the invasion of Sicily and Italy, and subsequently the Allied Naval Commander-in-Chief's staff for the Normandy invasion. So that I had unique opportunities of seeing many of these craft under operational conditions, opportunities which few naval constructors have. I should like first to refer to a few of the principal landing craft and comment on what appear to me to be interesting operational features.

I suppose that the success of the L.C.A. (landing craft assault), is shown by the substantial numbers that were built, amounting to 1,900, and I think that one of the special features was the armour protection. There is no doubt that all soldiers who went ashore on defended beaches were very pleased to be behind that $\frac{1}{4}$-in. of armour plate.

The Americans had similar types of craft. The L.C.P.'s (landing craft personnel) were un-armoured, and they had better performance in speed, and so on; but in an opposed landing operation both the American and the British soldier preferred the L.C.A.

Of the larger types of personnel carriers the L.C.I.(L) is outstanding, and the Institution will be interested to hear one or two comments on that craft. It was American-built and as the author has said, the staff requirements and guidance designs were prepared in this country; but one difficult feature which we asked the Americans to provide for in the design when they produced these craft was that they should steam across the Atlantic. The shipping position was such that it was absolutely impossible to freight these craft over. The requirement that they should be able to steam across the Atlantic sounds small in words, but it was a big requirement in design. To the great credit of the Americans the craft did steam across the Atlantic and they gave splendid performances. The first flotilla came over, via Bermuda, maintaining a speed of something like 11 knots the whole way to Gibraltar, in bad weather conditions. That is a striking performance, subsequently equalled in many operational theatres.

As regards vehicle carriers operating from ship to shore, I can confirm that the L.C.M.(3) was undoubtedly preferred. I suppose we could have had second thoughts; and then probably the L.C.M. would not have been built at all towards the end of the war.

Coming to shore-to-shore vehicle carriers, we have the L.C.T.s. The L.C.T.(3) was the one preferred from the point of view of making lengthy open-sea passages from the United Kingdom to Mediterranean, etc. It was a robust craft, much more sturdy than the L.C.T.(4), whose scantlings had to be cut to give the necessary shallow draught. I still feel that the L.C.T.(4) was a good type of craft, particularly with its advantage of shallow draught. Perhaps the author would add a certain amount of information concerning the structural failures of the L.C.T.(4). They were well known to break their backs, especially when drying out on an uneven beach and in prolonged heavy weather.

As distinguished members of the Institution have said, we sometimes learn most from our failures. However, the L.C.T.(4) was a fine craft. Many of them steamed to the Mediterranean, crossing the Bay of Biscay, and they went to North Africa, Italy, and Sicily and did unceasing and marvellous work there. The floating dock type hull gave them stability, reserve of buoyancy, and ability to take care of action damage, light and loaded; and, as has been stated, one L.C.T.(4) captain towed his own bow home by his after half!

The L.C.G. type were probably the most successful of the gun craft. They did invaluable service in Sicily and Italy, in spite of the fact that they represented a rather hurried conversion from L.C.T.

There is one noticeable omission from the paper; no mention is made of all the sturdy, and perhaps surprising, feats of the landing barges. Perhaps some day someone will write about them. They did splendid work in the Normandy landings, putting ashore in the harbours a large tonnage of stores from the various ships lying off the assault beaches. I have seen these small harbours, such as Courseuelles, which normally dried out with the falling tide, packed with these barges discharging all sorts of war materials. Then, of course, we had barges carrying oil fuel and water for landing craft, and kitchen barges and repair barges. They were developed in a series of conversions, and they really earned great praise in the Normandy landings.

I should like to say a few words about German landing craft. They are not mentioned for comparison purposes in the paper, and I propose to make a few comments. If the author could enlarge a little on the subject it would be of considerable interest.

I saw a number of German L.C.T.s in North Africa, Sicily, and Italy and in the Low Countries, and in my view they were substantially inferior to any of the British designs. They were a little faster, but rather narrow-gutted and unseaworthy, and I prefer the British type, although we used some captured German L.C.T.s in the Mediterranean.

With regard to the German invasion fleet for the English Channel, on seeing a number of converted barges in the Low Countries when we moved in there in 1944, one realised that the Germans had planned the assault on this country in craft and in a manner which was very amateur compared with our assault technique with the highly specialised set of landing craft we had at the end of the war. So far as I could see, the Germans had intended to use for their major lift, the river barges which had been in service in the continental canals and rivers in peace time, large open vessels with no sub-division,

no double bottoms, no double walls, and a primitive bow ramp. I think they would have been very vulnerable to any sort of attack, and if they carried the heavy loads they could have carried, hundreds of men or 1,000 tons or more of stores each, undoubtedly there would have been heavy loss of German life and material.

In his Conclusion the author has referred to the naval and military staffs, and to the Prime Minister, contributing their ideas to the development of the many novel landing craft which were produced. I should like also to mention, with admiration, the Chief of Combined Operations Viscount Mountbatten, who did probably more than any one man to make this tremendous force of landing craft possible.

Mr. J. M. Murray, M.B.E., B.Sc. (Member of Council): I shall comment briefly on two aspects of the landing craft dealt with in the paper.

The first matter is that of production, and here I am only concerned with L.C.T.s 2, 3, 4, and 8, which were produced by prefabrication methods. In principle, the arrangements adopted did not differ from those which had already been established for merchant ships, but there was the important difference that prefabricated parts of merchant ships went to shipyards to be erected, whereas in the case of the L.C.T.s the prefabricated parts were sent, not to shipyards, but to erection sites. This was an important step to take, and as in many other aspects of the development of landing craft, there was little precedent for it. In fact, the arrangement worked extremely well, and the successful work done in these erection yards which grew up in many parts of the country is well known. L.C.T. 8, a reasonable size of craft, was erected under the same conditions. Here I think that the work done by Mr. A. T. S. Sheffer, of Lloyd's Register, in the initial stages of the programme deserves mention.

The second matter I wish to mention is that of the disposal of landing craft. The author's troubles in connection with them finished when the war ended, but other problems arose. Many of these ships have been sold to shipowners for conversion to merchant ships. It is generally agreed that it is difficult to convert a merchant ship to a warship, but in my opinion the reverse operation is equally difficult. Several of the vessels have been converted for certain limited services, but from the commercial point of view it seems that this expedient can only be justified by abnormal scarcity of certain classes of tonnage.

Finally, I would like to say that this programme was carried out with enthusiasm and energy on the part of all concerned. But enthusiasm and hard work are not quite enough; a spark of imagination is required, and here it appears to me that this necessary factor for complete success was supplied by Mr. Baker.

Major E. F. J. Plowden, R.E. (Associate): Previously I joined issue with Mr. Baker on the subject of troop accommodation in landing craft; but I found that on the L.C.I.s it was very good indeed.

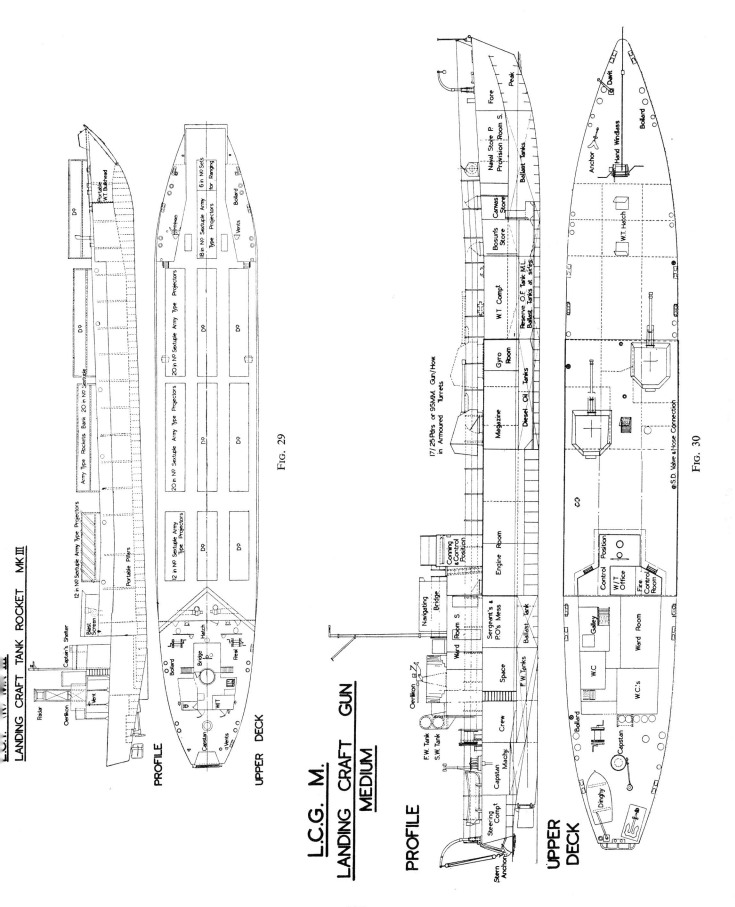

LANDING CRAFT TANK ROCKET MK III

PROFILE

UPPER DECK

FIG. 29

L.C.G. M.

LANDING CRAFT GUN

MEDIUM

PROFILE

UPPER DECK

FIG. 30

Fig. 31.—A.L.C. (2)

Fig. 32.—L.C.A. (in its final form)

Fig. 33.—L.C.P. (M). 36-ft. operational coble

I should like to ask the author if he can give us any information in regard to the Coble type of landing craft, its performance, the type and size of engines employed, and the steering. Was it as good as the original?

I should like to mention that the Army had a landing craft of their very own. I do not think that any of them were built in this country; they were designed in the Middle East, and were pre-fabricated in India and erected on the Suez Canal. They were of more ship-shape form than the normal type of landing craft, and were really similar to an ordinary American river barge; they were powered by two 4-cylinder engines, and were 145 ft. long, 30 ft. beam, and drew about 4 ft. draught. Their real use was for taking cargo ashore from ships at anchor, rather than taking part in assault landings. Later we had a "B" type craft, of box-shaped mid-section, having 6-cylinder engines.

These vessels had one big advantage over the landing craft, in that for taking cargo ashore they had a large unrestricted deck. The landing craft, on the other hand, had a kind of floating dock construction, and in any kind of seaway it was very difficult to load a vehicle on the deck without losing a wheel or an axle, or something of that sort.

Mr. K. C. Barnaby, O.B.E., B.Sc. (Member of Council): The author has referred on page 183 to a suggestion I put forward in 1941 for a small double-ended L.C.T. At that time we were both feeling a little pessimistic—not, of course about our own ideas but about each other's. The author's qualms were about the longitudinal stability of my suggested design. My trepidations concerned Mr. Baker's bow doors and ramps. Having been brought up to fear all leaks from such trivial matters as side scuttles and so forth, the author's barn doors right in the eyes of the ship were somewhat alarming as I visualized them punching into head seas. I believe I reminded Mr. Baker of the mere half doors that led to the sinking of the *Vestris*.

I must confess that I was so nervous about these bow doors that I wanted one at the aft end also—to let out the water which came in at the bow. The author's qualms had to do with the free surface that might result. There were side buoyancy tanks, however, so that the water was confined to a central driveway. Under these circumstances the loss of transverse G.M. was small, and if 25% of the longitudinal buoyancy remained this would have been very ample, in view of the enormous ratio of longitudinal to transverse G.M.

Anyway, my fears were also groundless, as Mr. Baker was able to design bow doors that kept out the Channel, the Mediterranean, the Atlantic, and the Pacific. I think he deserves very great credit for this and these bow doors and ramps must have contributed greatly to the defeat of our common enemy.

It is an interesting speculation as to how much history would have been changed had earlier designers been able to fit those bow doors. The Spanish Armada might have been quite a different proposition. Much earlier, Noah might not have been such a timid navigator. Instead of laying out all his anchors on the slopes of Mount Ararat, he might have ventured much further afield. Secure in his mind about the weatherly properties of his doors and ramps he might have gone a very long way from Palestine—and saved us all an infinity of trouble!

Vice-Admiral A. D. Read, C.B. (Associate): In the paper an L.C.P.(S) is described. This was a wooden craft, and it is explained in the paper that "Some of these boats were specially fitted up for ambulance service, but, apart from these, the boats were never used in the manner originally planned, because of the large numbers of L.C.A. and the American types which were ultimately forthcoming." It may be of interest if I mention operations in which these boats were used. In the East Indies, in the early part of 1945, landing craft that were on the station were fully employed by the Army in operations off the Burma Coast. It was decided to mount an operation to capture the Island of Cheduba, off the Burma Coast, without calling upon any of the military resources. 12 L.C.P.s were available at Bombay, and these were embarked upon the flight deck (4 to each of three cruisers). The landing party consisted of 500 Royal Marines, and the necessary air cover was provided by the fleet air arm and an escort carrier. This operation was successfully carried out, although it was not until after the landing had been effected that it was found the enemy had retreated two days before. Simultaneously with this operation, the Army were taking the Island of Ramree, a couple of miles north of Cheduba; here a patrol of Ghurkas had crossed one of the rivers and in doing so their own boats had been sunk by the Japanese, and they had to dig in, and were in rather a tight corner until, hearing of their plight, we despatched two of these L.C.P.s with their Marine crews, who embarked them at night and carried them back across the river with only a few casualties. As will be seen, even the L.C.P. was put to some useful purpose.

Mr. I. E. King, C.B.E., R.C.N.C. (Member): The remarks which I made this afternoon on Mr. W. J. Holt's paper concerning the difficulties encountered in maintaining coastal force craft in distant active war theatres, due primarily to shortages of engine spare parts and lack of docking and slipway facilities, apply also to major landing craft.

My experience confirms most of the comments made by Mr. Merrington on the several types of landing craft. This speaker asked the author to give more information concerning the strength of the L.C.T.4s. The author has stated that these craft were designed for cross-channel trips. It seems pretty clear to me that it would be impracticable to produce a landing craft with the principal characteristics of a L.C.T.4 with anything like the normal factor of safety of strength for general operation at sea. Presumably it was essential to accept a marked reduction in this safety margin to enable the severe staff requirements to be met.

The first major structural troubles in these craft developed when they were nearing the end of their long winter voyage to North Africa to take part in the Sicilian landings. They were sent to the Mediterranean at very short notice and there was not time to reinforce them before departure from home ports.

Two of them parted amidships. One of these was repaired at Gibraltar. The remainder received a severe shaking and presented the limited repair organisations with a very big task.

However, despite these difficulties they turned up in strength on "D" day of the Sicilian assault and gave a very good account of themselves.

The L.C.T.3s were much more seaworthy and reliable. Their maximum beaching draughts when fully loaded were much more than for L.C.T.4s. A number of these craft made the return journey from the United Kingdom to the Mediterranean and took part in both the Sicilian and Normandy landings.

It is of interest to place on record how production bottlenecks and other difficulties influenced important features in the design of major landing craft. I will give two examples.

The L.C.I.(L)s were fitted with variable pitch propellers. I was very surprised to discover this when the first of these craft arrived in Algiers from America. One of the most vulnerable parts of a landing craft is the propeller. A variable pitch propeller is a complicated fitting for the job. I understand the reason for its adoption in this instance was caused by the bottleneck in the production of gearing.

The major landing craft constructed in the United Kingdom were generally of riveted construction, to suit the facilities which were available. The craft constructed in the United States were all welded. My experience showed that the all-welded craft is the more reliable of the two, and reduced hull maintenance problems appreciably.

The hulls of several non-operational L.C.T.s were converted in Italian shipyards for special services. An L.C.T.(4) was equipped as a floating diesel driven electric generating station with an output of about 2,000 kilowatts. This craft supplied power to essential services in Leghorn.

A L.C.T.(5) was fitted out as a floating sheer legs with a lift of 50 tons, for use with the naval salvage section.

I congratulate the author on his splendid contribution to the production of these craft, and thank him for placing on record some of the history of their development.

Lieut.-Commander J. W. Thornycroft, R.N. (Retired) (Member): The author has touched on possible future developments of these craft and one of the speakers in the discussion has referred to the landing craft which the military had produced.

In the latter part of the war, some time after the Americans had made great strides with their DUKWS wheeled amphibious vehicles and also various types of tracked vehicles, developments on similar lines were started in this country. An amphibious craft was developed by my firm, fitted with pneumatic tyres, which was known as "Terrapin." Full description will be found in the Spring Proceedings of the Institution of Automobile Engineers.

Some hundreds of these amphibious vehicles were produced and used in the Antwerp operations.

A further type was under development, known as "Terrapin II" which was 7 ft. longer and 3 in. greater beam; production orders were placed but cancelled after V.J.-Day. There was also a tracked type known as the "Neptune" in production at the end of the war but I think it was never used operationally.

It has recently featured in the press in connection with the floods in the Eastern Counties a few weeks ago.

The particular point which I should like to make is that I think the Minister of Defence will have to make a decision as to whether the Navy or the Army is going to develop amphibious craft of the future, having either tracks or pneumatic tyres. I thing that it is a mistake to have two departments working on the same problems. I have a little knowledge of the problems connected with tracked vehicles and I think the Navy will be well advised to leave the developments of these types of craft in the future to the Army, who have gained great experience in connection with tracks from the use of tanks, and also of very heavy artillery tractors using the largest size pneumatic tyres.

Author's Verbal Reply to the Discussion

In the main I have only to thank the speakers for all they have said. I had fully expected that a few bricks would have been thrown, but apparently the speakers did not wish to do that; their contributions, particularly that of Mr. Merrington, will add to the interest of the paper when published in the TRANSACTIONS.

Of course, the adaptability of landing craft to all kinds of purposes other than those for which they were originally intended would enable one to cover a very wide field; one could easily write a book on what they did, apart from what they were supposed to do. In writing the paper I have tried to deal only with purely factual matters; but I quite agree that further details could be given of what actually happened.

I agree also with the remarks made about the landing barges. Fortunately, they were not my particular job, and no one has asked me to write about them. But I think the subject is one on which a paper might well be written. The kitchen barge was the crowning glory of the whole landing craft effort; it was a magnificent-looking craft, and it supplied the food.

I am very glad that reference has been made to C.C.O. and to Mr. Sheffer. Admiralty rules do not permit the mention of names in a paper, and I did not mention names in my opening remarks because to do so would be invidious. But there is no doubt that Mr. Sheffer had a great deal to do with the inception of the landing craft programme, and I am sorry that he is not here, to hear it said.

FIG. 34.—L.C.P. (L)

FIG. 35.—L.C.P. (S)

FIG. 36.—L.C.I. (L)

201

FIG. 37.—L.C.I. (S)

FIG. 38.—M.L.C. (10)

FIG. 39.—M.L.C. L.C.M. (1)

202

Fig. 40.—L.C.M. (3)

Fig. 41.—L.C.M. (7) Thornycroft

Fig. 42.—L.C.T. (1)

203

With regard to the remarks of Major Plowden, his A and B craft were called Z craft by us, which proves that we thought they were the last word in landing craft:

I am sure everyone who heard it enjoyed Mr. Barnaby's contribution. I think he was too flattering. But I do not think he can claim the sole credit for the side buoyancy tanks which we had. If Noah had built the Ark on the floating dock principle he would probably have been here still!

The Chairman (Sir Stanley V. Goodall, K.C.B., O.B.E.): Just before the meeting I asked Mr. Woollard, who was my Assistant Director in charge of landing craft—under whom Mr. Baker worked—to speak, but with his usual

most of them were fitted with powerful oil engines aft, running at slow revolutions; those with 80 B.H.P. had a good turn of speed.

Each lighter, nicknamed "Black Beetle," carried a platoon of soldiers that could be disembarked over the hinged brow forward in less than two minutes. Some of the lighters carried ammunition, stores and so on.

These were undoubtedly the first landing craft and the prototype of many of those built in 1940, twenty-five years later.

Mr. H. J. Tabb, R.C.N.C. (Member): Mr. Baker's valuable paper has interested me very much and provides further evidence of the enormous variety of the tasks

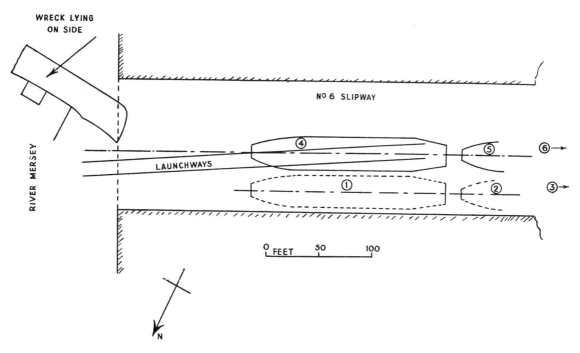

modesty he declined. The idea that landing craft should be designed on the floating dock principle came to three different people at about the same time; they were Mr. Woollard, Mr. Baker, and the German designer, because German craft were built on this same principle.

For the landing craft that served us so well we are indebted to Messrs. Thornycroft, Mr. Baker, and our American friends and allies.

I ask you to accord your hearty thanks to Mr. Baker for his paper.

Written Contributions to the Discussion

Mr. Walter Pollock (Member): The many particulars and excellent plans and photographs in this paper are really a splendid record of war craft that have done valuable work. It is a pity that the original power-driven landing craft that I designed for Lord Fisher in 1915 were not included because the Admiralty built about 240 of these X-Lighters under my supervision. They were length 105 ft. 6 in., breadth 21 ft. and depth 7 ft. 6 in.;

allotted to the Naval Construction Department during the past war. He has referred to the good work of Messrs. Cammell Laird in completing a number of L.C.T.(3) in record time, and I should like to amplify this reference with information gained whilst carrying out my duties as Principal (Ship) Overseer at Birkenhead.

Eight of these vessels were ordered on November 10, 1943 and, although two vessels were laid down early in December, no berths were available for the remainder until the launch of the light fleet carrier, H.M.S. *Venerable*, which took place on December 30th. After the launch the slipway was cleared and six vessels were laid down between January 10 and February 1, 1944, the slip being arranged with two lines of three vessels as shown in the accompanying figure. Good progress was made and, rather to the surprise of the shipbuilders, the machinery and other items supplied by the Admiralty arrived in good time. On March 20, 1944, the third vessel was launched from the north side of number 6 slip and almost immediately afterwards a coasting vessel, being towed up the river in a sinking

Fig. 43.—L.C.T. (2)

Fig. 44.—L.C.T. (3)

Fig. 45.—L.C.T. (4) UNSTIFFENED

condition, foundered off the end of the slipway and obstructed the direct line in which vessels numbered (4), (5), and (6) in the figure were to be launched. Efforts to refloat the wreck showed that it was unlikely to be removed in time for the programme of deliveries to be kept.

Launchways were already in place for vessel No. 4 and would normally have been extended to serve also for vessels numbered 5 and 6. At great speed, however, the groundways were slewed to clear the wreck and new sliding ways were fitted to the vessel, the large area of flat bottom materially assisting this operation. The port groundways were provided with a substantial ribband to guide the vessel and the port sliding ways were slightly increased in width. Vessel No. 4 was launched on the appointed day, six days after vessel 3 and the process of re-aligning the groundways for vessel 5 was begun immediately.

Fitting out these vessels was an equally noteworthy feat, and the last vessel left the yard only 7 days after launching. The following table shows the time occupied for each of the vessels:

Slip	Vessel	Laid down	Launched	Completed
4/5	1	13. 12. 43	15. 2. 44	12. 3. 44
	2	21. 12. 43	21. 2. 44	9. 3. 44
6	1	10. 1. 44	28. 2. 44	12. 3. 44
	2	16. 1. 44	6. 3. 44	16. 3. 44
	3	21. 1. 44	11. 3. 44	20. 3. 44
	4	29. 1. 44	17. 3. 44	25. 3. 44
	5	31. 1. 44	23. 3. 44	30. 3. 44
	6	1. 2. 44	29. 3. 44	5. 4. 44

Mr. E. C. Goldsworthy (Associate): The author is to be congratulated on the simple manner in which he has given us the history of the development of all forms of landing craft, and it is particularly interesting to read how the various difficulties were overcome as they arose in service. Nevertheless, the control of these shallow-draught flat-bottomed craft appears still to be unsatisfactory. Yet success or failure of any landing may depend on the ability of the craft to beach end on and hold that position, no matter what might be the direction and force of the wind or stream.

The author states that L.C.T.(1) ran from side to side as she proceeded down the Tyne at 10 knots and goes on to describe the fears of the people on board, and how they would never be likely to forget it. That was in November 1941. He mentions it again in connection with L.C.T.(R) when he speaks of the "vagaries" of the L.C.T. and the difficulty of navigating these vessels to an exact firing position.

No mention is made of their performance when in process of beaching and also in getting away from the beach, but from the reports of their behaviour under comparatively calm conditions one must assume that with a cross sea and wind the odds are against a true landing being made.

If, when beaching, the vessel cannot be held end on it would be difficult and might be impossible to get away. This latter aspect was emphasized by a participant in the Dieppe Raid (*Life*, August 31st, 1942) when considerable difficulty was encountered in getting the boat off the beach, the delay resulting in loss of life since they were under constant fire from the shore and from the air.

The author describes how the first M.L.C.s and L.C.M.s used jet propulsion, which was dropped owing to the low propulsive efficiency, and although the screw propeller used for all subsequent types gave a better speed it is regretted that the propulsive efficiency with screws was not given. It would be interesting to know whether cycloidal propulsion of the Voith-Schneider or similar type was considered, and also whether practical tests were made with any of the vessels in this country fitted with this system. With cycloidal propulsion a good propulsive efficiency, even on the shallowest draughts, could be anticipated and the vessels would have been under perfect control irrespective of wind or sea. The craft could have been landed end on to the beach and been held in that position ready for immediate action or, in the case of support flak, gun or rocket craft, steadied on a fixed position.

Mr. E. P. Paxman: The machinery for landing craft has to meet a number of requirements not usually called for in units of such power. These requirements arise from the special service which the landing craft may have to perform, as well as from the necessity to develop a very large scale production, and to accompany it by servicing arrangements throughout the world on a proportionate basis, and from the need to make the operation of the machinery so simple that only relatively inexperienced personnel can operate it.

The operating conditions of the landing craft involve special requirements in the way of a cooling system and in the arrangement to prevent a mal-alignment of the machinery.

Driving the craft on to shallow, sandy beaches involved large quantities of sand in the cooling water and necessitated the building of sand traps in the hull, and the provision of special types of sea water pumps readily deranged by the embrasive material. Even so it was found, in the Mark III and IV craft, after some period of service, that the water jackets of the engines were frequently more than half full of sand when returned for servicing; moreover the craft were frequently allowed to dry out and this, of course, involved risks of starting up the machinery with the cooling system air locked, or even connected to the open air on the suction side. These difficulties had been foreseen in the first place, but under Admiralty instruction, it was decided to omit fresh water cooling, as the original intention was that these vessels would only be used for relatively short service. However, it was subsequently found that they were employed for very long periods, and the provision of fresh water cooling was then justified. Such a system was employed in the Mark VIII craft.

Fig. 46.—L.C.T. (5)

Fig. 47.—L.C.T. (8)

Fig. 48.—L.C.S. (M) (1)

207

FIG. 49.—L.C.S. (M) (3)

FIG. 50.—L.C.S. (L) (1)

FIG. 51.—L.C.F. (1)

208

The varying deflection of the vessels, due to variation in loading and/or running on the beaches, was taken care of in the machinery by the provision of a short carden shaft with two flexible couplings between the engine and the gear-box, and as a result, troubles due to mal-alignment were virtually unknown. These provisions also greatly facilitated the ready installation of the machinery in large numbers by unskilled labour. As an added precaution against under water shock, the engines were mounted on semi-resilient strips interposed between the engines and the ceilings; damage due to underwater explosion was as a consequence, entirely eliminated.

In order to make the operation of the machinery on board as simple as possible, the engines were non-reversing, but were connected to oil-operated reverse and reduction gears; the control of the machinery was then arranged by two levers for each unit, one to control the engine speed and the other to control the head or reverse clutches of the gear-box, and the control levers for all engines were grouped in a single station with gauge boards readily visible therefrom. Starting was effected by large electric starter motors, in the same way as a motor car; consequently, no skill whatever was necessary either to start or run the engine, or to control the direction of the propeller, and so simple was the actual operation that there were many recorded instances of troops going down and operating the machinery in the engine-room, in cases where the engine-room personnel had been injured by enemy action.

To meet the need for large scale production, the design of the engine was such as to permit of sub-contracting the various component items in large quantities. Upwards of 500 firms were in fact employed on production of components for these engines, which were thereafter brought to two factories for assembly. This arrangement avoided the need for setting up special engine factories for which the necessary personnel would have been difficult to assemble in time. It also gave a very large degree of immunity against the effects of enemy action by bombing.

To insure rigid adherence to manufacturing limits of the components, Lloyd's Register arranged for inspection throughout the country of the components, and finally of the completed engines, on behalf of the Admiralty. The system of pre-fabricating components of the engines and then assembling them at specialist factories was in many ways similar to that adopted for the actual construction of the vessels themselves.

To meet the need for ease of handling and removal for service, and to make a convenient arrangement in the engine-room, the engines were of a fairly high speed type, of V form. Although the whole power unit was compact, neither the mean effective pressures nor piston speeds were very high; the engines were so arranged that the necessary plumbing could be readily attached on board, the main units of plumbing being pre-fabricated in the same way that the engine components were, and standard piping, already bent, sent off with every engine to the shipbuilders; flexible lengths were provided in all important units of the piping, to provide both for mal-alignment and expansion. Due to the compact form of the engines, the head room required for them was extremely low. An idea of the shortness of the engine, for its power, is indicated by the fact that the engines were only approximately six feet long, compared with the craft of over 180 ft.

The arrangement of having engines separated by a short carden shaft from the gear-boxes, was found to have a further convenience in that it facilitated the coupling of two engines to a single gear-box, as was done successfully in the Mark VIII's. In this case, unlike the quad units in certain of the American landing craft, in which the engines were placed as close together as possible, the engines were separated by such a distance as permitted the easy access of a man between them—a feature which was greatly appreciated by the engine-room personnel. Subsequently plans were also developed for the utilization of four engines, coupled to a single gear-box. It is interesting to note that in the British multiple units, all engines were of the same hand, and identical—a feature of the utmost importance in reducing the quantities of parts necessary for service in places overseas; this again was in contra-distinction to the American quadruple engine unit in which each of the four engines was a distinctly different type, so that four separate types of spare engines were necessary.

Due to the design of the engine, its servicing could be carried out by the substitution of complete new sub-assemblies, e.g. complete cylinder blocks, etc. In all such cases care had been taken that any one sub-assembly would fit all the sub-assemblies of the same type in an engine, e.g. one spare cylinder block, or one spare cylinder head was so designed that it would fit each of the four units of that type on the engine, without any necessity for handed parts. Attention to detail in this manner was amply repaid in the subsequent reduction in components required in base stores.

Nothing special need be said of the effect of operating conditions on the reliability of the engines, except perhaps that it was found that in the Mediterranean valve springs became effected by condensation, which could set up subsequent corrosion fatigue and cause spring breakage. Suitable treatment for the valve springs was evolved accordingly, which obviated this difficulty.

In conclusion, it is now becoming apparent that the successful employment of such relatively compact and high speed engines for craft of this size, on such a large scale, has opened up the way to their employment in comparable commercial conditions, e.g., ferries, cross-channel boats, tankers, etc., and they are being employed for these purposes by a number of owners familiar with their war-time uses.

Mr. F. C. C. Rogers, R.C.N.C. (Associate Member): The great majority, if not all, of these craft were apparently intended for cross-channel work only, and it is a tribute to their structural efficiency that a number of the vessels of the larger types were able successfully to make the voyage to India after being stiffened.

Some information regarding these vessels has already appeared in the technical press.

As regards the L.C.T.(5), considerable difficulty was experienced in loading these vessels on L.S.T.s owing to their weight. There was an extraordinary degree of variation in the weights of individual craft for which no easily-discoverable cause could be assigned. Some of the vessels, when lightened as much as possible, could barely be lifted by the 160 ton cantilever crane at Devonport. Securing the vessels on the deck of the L.S.T. in such a way that they could be launched without undue removal of temporary work presented considerable difficulties, and some cases of shifting were reported.

It may be of interest that a later version of L.C.G.(L)4 was prepared towards the end of the war, the detail drawings being prepared by Devonport Dockyard. These vessels were modified to have a ship-shape bow. Owing to the course of the war only one such vessel was completed.

The L.C.G.(M) were found to have exceedingly bad manœuvring power and in some cases could not be made to complete a circle. They had a single middle line rudder with twin screws. Some of the vessels were fitted with small auxiliary rudders in line with the screws, and this completely cured the trouble.

An error has crept into the paper at the head of column 2 of page 169. It is stated that the Gill type jet propulsion was fitted to M.L.C.1. This is not correct—the hydraulic propulsion actually fitted was of another type. The propulsive efficiency was very poor. The later vessel M.L.C.10 was fitted with Gill type propulsion. It also had an ingenious form of stern door, which, by means of a type of operating gear invented by a member of the Royal Corps of Naval Constructors, readily opened out when the door was released for beaching.

The leeboards shown were necessary for directional stability, as without them the vessel would not proceed bow first but would spin round. The disadvantage of this design was the necessity for turning before beaching, and the rather inefficient jet propulsion which also provided the steering facilities.

The weight of the vessel light was limited to 20 tons. It is considered that the reversion to screw propulsion in the L.C.M. vessels was fully justified.

The author has obviously taken a great deal of trouble to collect and condense the information given in the paper and the information will obviously be of great use to the naval historian. It is earnestly to be hoped that this will be its only use.

Mr. D. B. Kimber, M.Sc., A.C.G.I., D.I.C., R.C.N.C. (Associate Member): I was fortunate to be among those who spent several months on the range of Normandy beaches, attempting to keep as many of these varied craft in service as possible, and I should like to comment on how some of them measured up to the particularly rugged conditions they met.

The author mentions the flimsy construction of the L.C.T.(4), and a good deal was heard at the time of this particular craft being "too weak." The essential requirement of a landing craft is that it shall touch the beach, forward, with the minimum draught. Clearly this entails a very nice judgment in paring the scantlings, which in this instance was carried to the limit, but not, I think, beyond it. No troubles were experienced with craft beaching in the orthodox fashion on smooth or gently cambered beaches, nor did one hear of many structural failures at sea, though conditions in the Channel were at times very unfavourable for loaded landing craft.

What may not have been anticipated was the degree to which the beach surfaces cut up after the first few weeks, due to:

(a) runnels in the sand, both natural and caused by the propellers of L.S.T.s coming off the beach;

(b) pits in the sand, caused by dried-out coasters, which were nearly always broached-to; and

(c) the larger and smaller pieces of wreckage which gradually but steadily accumulated.

A proportion of L.C.T.(4)s beaching on such unfavourable surfaces did fail structurally, varying from slight wrinkling of the side and bottom plating to complete rupture of the ship's back. The less severe cases continued in service with a degree of permanent set, none the worse except perhaps for the fracture of the ballast tank pumping and flooding lines inside the tank deck bulwarks—always the first sign of excessive strain when drying out on the beach.

Since L.C.T.s were not officially classified as "expendable," an attempt was always made to recover the more seriously damaged craft, either in one piece or two, and at least one returned to the U.K. under its own power, towing its fore-end! Had dry-docks and labour been available for this work, it would have been a simple matter to put these craft back in service, since the zone of damage was never extensive, but as it was, the accumulation of "half-ships" and "lame ducks" became something of an embarrassment to the naval authorities on the south coast!

L.C.T.(4), strengthened as described in the paper, did not exhibit the same straining under the same adverse beaching conditions, but this was only achieved at the expense of precious inches of beaching draught.

The importance of protecting rudders cannot be overemphasized. Before the provision of rudder guards shown in Fig. 16, an L.C.T. floating dry-dock in the Arromanches Mulberry was continuously employed changing bent rudder stocks, damaged by underwater obstruction or fouled during kedging operations. A quite moderate blow would cause the stock to seize, and it always seemed to affect the master rudder of the pair, thereby rendering the craft quite unmanageable.

I imagine the aluminium alloys would be an automatic choice for this class of shipbuilding, assuming cost to be of secondary importance, were they available in sufficient quantity for this purpose in time of war. Plywood in particular has certain disadvantages as a hull material, and would hardly be used, were it not for the unskilled labour which can so be pressed into service. L.C.V.P.'s, which spent much of their lives going alongside piers and

FIG. 52.—L.C.S. (L) (2)

FIG. 53.—L.C.G. (L) (3)

FIG. 54.—L.C.G. (L) (4)

211

ships and other solid objects, presented in particular a tough repair proposition once the joints and fastenings had become thoroughly loosened and well soaked with sea water. A composite construction, employing metal framing and plywood shell, might have had advantages, in conjunction with more generous fendering. But it must be remembered that these, and many other minor landing craft, performed duties very different from those originally envisaged for them.

Finally, a plea for simplicity. Towards the end of the war, the "tropicalising" of L.C.T.(4) for the Far East and the development of the L.C.T.(8) saw equipment of all kinds going into a craft which is essentially a self-propelled box of the simplest possible nature. Such elaboration into miniature landing ships

(a) increases the beaching draught
(b) increases time and cost of building
(c) requires more material per craft
(d) makes them less and less "expendable."

However austere the scale of crew accommodation may be, it is nearly always far better than that of the assault troops ashore. In the tropics, an accommodation or mother ship for craft taken temporarily off service might be a satisfactory alternative to attempting to provide really adequate habitability in each individual craft.

Mr. J. C. Lawrence, R.C.N.C.: This paper forms a valuable record of the fine achievement of designers and builders in producing such numbers and variety of craft of unorthodox type—an achievement which, until recently, was still under the cloak of secrecy. Having spent some time both on the staff of "naval users" and in assisting in the task of repair and maintenance of landing craft during the Mediterranean campaigns, I should like to add a few remarks from these points of view. The Mediterranean landings, from Algiers to Anzio, may be regarded as the proving ground of these novel craft, and many of the later modifications and improvements mentioned in the paper arose from experience in these earlier operations.

The author has indicated that some of the major landing craft were riveted and some were welded. This is a matter, from the maintenance point of view, of some importance. It was found that riveted craft, after many successive beachings, leaked very badly owing to the opening up of seams and loosening of rivets, while welded craft, such as L.C.T.(5) and L.C.I.(L) suffered only corrugation of the bottom without much leaking. It is appreciated, however, that in the case of the British-built craft, the type of building labour used did not permit extensive use of welding, but it is interesting to note that it was introduced in the later L.C.T.(4) and in the L.C.T.(8).

Although intended for cross-channel operations L.C.T.(4)s had first to be sailed to the Mediterranean, under their own power, to take part in the Sicily landings. I took passage in one at that time and observed that although behaviour in the long swell of the Atlantic was normal, on altering course head on to the shorter, steeper seas of the approaches to the Straits of Gibraltar the craft pounded violently, and being equivalent to a flat spring with a weight at each end, assumed an alarming vibration with an amplitude amidships in the order of two or three inches. One subsequently broke completely in half, and there were many later cases of structural failure. This, in my opinion, was not entirely due to the flimsy construction and discontinuity mentioned in the paper, but also to a mal-distribution of structure. The craft were unorthodox and the orthodox strength calculations were not entirely applicable.

The normal static strength calculation indicated deflections in sagging of less than an inch. The conclusion to be drawn was that with flat-bottomed, shallow sectioned craft of this type, the stresses set up dynamically by pounding in waves are greater than those estimated by the standard strength calculation.

With regard to seaworthiness, the major landing craft usually had very high stability indeed. The later conversions, however, such as L.C.G.(L) and L.C.T.(R) which were originally only partially decked-in, caused some uneasiness over the possibility of swamping in the undecked portion at the fore end. On another passage with the original L.C.T.(R) from the U.K. to the Mediterranean, it was noticed that the drains in this space would have been inadequate to clear green seas had the weather been less favourable than it was.

In conclusion, notice should be taken of the many useful roles carried out by landing craft other than those for which they were designed. One instance which is recalled is the use which was made of L.C.G.(L) operating as gunboats attacking German coastal convoys on the west coast of Italy before the liberation of Leghorn. Their shallow draft enabled them to get inshore of the German coastal minefield, which kept out our destroyers, and surprise the convoys with their 4·7 in. guns. One L.C.T.(4) was converted into a heavy floating sheerlegs and another into a floating electric generating station and used to supply Leghorn docks area.

Author's Written Reply to the Discussion

Mr. Merrington, Mr. King, Mr. Kimber, and Mr. Lawrence refer in somewhat flattering terms to the structural weakness of the L.C.T.(4), and Mr. Merrington asks for some information concerning their structural failures. There is no doubt that the craft were flimsy; there is no doubt that this weakness was intentional as it was hoped that their use would be confined to fair weather in the English Channel. At the same time I feel that Mr. Lawrence is right when he says that orthodox strength calculations are not altogether applicable to craft of these proportions. The peculiarity of the L.C.T.(4) needs no great description—the draught and the depth were very small in relation to the length and the beam was very great. I agree with Mr. Lawrence's conclusion that the stresses set up dynamically are greater than those estimated by the standard strength calculation. Further, the experience gained with this L.C.T. in particular had led me to the belief that the whole of our present standard strength calculations, which, as is well known, are empirical, essentially only provide guidance for ships of normal type. In all ships dynamic loading is the rule and not the exception, yet we estimate our strength on purely statical theses. This method, in spite of its limitations, has proved satisfactory for a number of years. Recent investigations have tended to show that in normal ships the actual stresses so deduced are greater than those likely to be met with in practice, whereas in the L.C.T.(4) there is some little doubt that the stresses were in practice greater than would have been given by the formula. The failures of the L.C.T.(4) would seem to have some scientific value in so far as they remind us of the limitations of the accepted method. There is room for research into the possibilities of assessing dynamic effect on ships of all kinds.

Major Plowden asks for more information about the Coble. The engines used were Ford V.8 conversions similar to those fitted in the L.C.A., but only one engine was fitted per craft, giving a normal power output of about 60. The propeller worked in a tunnel; the arrangement was entirely satisfactory and I should think that the boat was, in all important respects, as good as the prototype.

The L.C.P.S. was not a very popular boat, although I always felt that its simplicity was a great potential asset. I am very grateful to Vice-Admiral Read for intervening in the discussion to point out that even this despised boat was found useful.

Mr. King has pointed out that variable pitch propellers were first fitted in the L.C.I.L.s because of difficulties over the production of gearing, and it is easy to understand that such difficulties in this country were much more acute than in America. This leads me to Mr. Goldsworthy's remarks. It may be agreed that cycloidal propulsion would have given advantages in the control of the craft, but the gearing required for such a system was certainly not in production in this country, and it would have been very difficult to have set up new facilities on the scale likely to be required. Mr. Goldsworthy and Mr. Rogers refer to jet propulsion. I agree with Mr. Rogers that Gill type jets were not fitted in M.L.C.(1). The other type to which he refers was the Hotchkiss. Mr. Rogers and Mr. Goldsworthy both seem to think that I have been too hard on jets, but the Admiralty experience with them has been entirely unfavourable. The overall propulsive coefficient of the various types of craft fitted with screw propellers, although prejudiced to some extent by the necessity for shallow draught, varied between 0·4 and 0·5 per cent. The optimum propulsive coefficient with jet-fitted craft would have been about 0·2. Further interesting figures about jets may be found n Mr. S. W. Burnaby's book, *Marine Propellers*. The maintenance of cycloidal and jet systems would undoubtedly have caused further difficulties, and in this connection it will be recalled that the Isle of Wight ferry steamer originally fitted with Voith-Schneider propulsion has recently been converted to screw.

I am grateful to Mr. Tabb for including his interesting notes on the performance of Messrs. Cammell Laird during the winter of 1943. It will be remembered that in the text of the paper reference was made to the co-operation which we received, not only from Messrs. Cammell Laird, but from many other firms.

Mr. Paxman rightly calls attention to the engine production development which was necessary to enable the L.C.T. fleet to be achieved, and his notes on the details of the engine installation will, I am sure, be appreciated by members. I should like to support Mr. Paxman's view, too, that the successful employment of such engines during the war opens up the prospect of the further employment of lightweight, fast running engines in ships of all types. It certainly seems that during the war the main difficulties over the production of reduction and reverse gearings were overcome, and it may be that in the future motor-car type engines even will be used for the propulsion of large ships. Experiments on these lines during the late war in America were not altogether successful, but this was largely because of the peculiar arrangement of drive adopted.

The remarks of Mr. Merrington, Mr. King, Mr. Kimber, and Mr. Lawrence will be read with particular interest by members of the Institution because these gentlemen spent part of the war as Constructor Officers in the fleets to which the landing craft were attached, and Mr. Lawrence, in particular, made several voyages in these craft, some of which lasted several days. These officers were therefore among the first professional critics of the craft, and the fact that they have no strongly adverse criticisms to make gives me great satisfaction.

These contributors, as well as some of the other speakers, refer to the extraordinary adaptability of landing craft of all kinds to purposes quite different from that for which they were originally intended. I feel that this must be regarded as a doubtful compliment. The last paragraph of Mr. Kimber's remarks needs to be read in conjunction with Captain Todhunter's. During the war we undoubtedly started off with the basic idea that the landing craft must be simple or we would never get them. As time went on we began to get them and we began to get all kinds of complications; nearly every complication was resisted for a time, but in the end agreed to, and I do feel that at the present time there is a danger that the virtues of simplicity will be forgotten.

In conclusion, I once again thank all those who have taken part in the discussion. I am sure that all their remarks will add to the interest of the paper, and my only fear is that their generally flattering tone may give a wrong impression. It was easy to write a paper describing what was done, but seen in true perspective the development period was one of difficulty, and the aftcr themselves could undoubtedly, all of them, be improved in some respect or another even now.

Fig. 55.—L.C.T. (R)

Fig. 56.—L.C.G. (M) (1) EARLIEST TYPE